Photo-Offset Fundamentals

Photo-Offset Fundamentals

JOHN E. COGOLI

**Former Chairman, Industrial Arts and
Vocational-Industrial Education Department
Hartford Public High School
Hartford, Connecticut**

**BENNETT &
McKNIGHT
Publishing Company
Peoria, Illinois**

Bennett & McKnight Publishing Company
809 West Detweiller Drive
Peoria, Illinois 61615

ISBN 0-02-672180-5

(Formerly ISBN 87345-235-6)

Library of Congress
Catalog Card Number: 79-88233

Printed in the United States of America

Photopress, Inc.

Preface

This book is a basic manual for the beginner in the field of photo-offset lithography — a division of the graphic arts more popularly known as offset printing. Worker, student, teacher, apprentice, buyer, sales personnel, and other interested persons will gain a fundamental working knowledge of the offset printing method by a careful study of these pages.

The wide acceptance of the first three editions of this book, especially by schools and the industry, has prompted the preparation of this fourth edition. This edition has received careful revision and updating, especially in the areas of type composition, job planning and layout, and line and halftone photography.

No attempt has been made to include *all* the various special fields of the offset method. Such an ambitious work would defeat the very purpose of this book. However, the topics which *are* included are covered by sufficient description, hints, diagrams, and illustrations so that the serious beginner (or learner) may proceed doing practical work with little assistance or direction.

Having worked for more than three and a half decades instructing beginners, the author deeply appreciates the difficulties besetting the learner. To this end, he has constantly attempted to present this material in as self-teaching a manner as possible.

The printing industry in every major country of the world, except the United States, has converted to the International System of Measurement, abbreviated SI and often referred to as the *metric system*. In the United States, the printing industry has made a start towards conversion to the metric system. Some of the major graphic arts suppliers and equipment manufacturers now are using dual entries (metric/customary) in their catalog listings, dual labels on their cartons and containers, and dual entries in their instruction manuals, and are offering metrically graduated-and-marked tools and equipment. While metric usage is common and available with imported equipment and materials, its use remains limited in the U.S. printing industry.

In this text, a dual system of measurement has been included where it does not complicate the use of customary tools and equipment with which industry and educational institutions will continue to work for some time to come.

A glossary has been intentionally omitted at the end of this book. Instead, an extensive, well cross-referenced index has been included. Terms are fully explained on the pages where they appear in the text and are often accompanied by illustrations and notes.

Manufacturers and sources of supply for much of the equipment, supplies, and materials mentioned in the text are purposely identified in captions with the illustrations, and in credit notes where applicable. These firms and individuals have a wealth of information, experience, and resources with which they are pleased to assist learners and workers in the field.

Any suggestions which will improve future revisions will be appreciated by the author.

John E. Cogoli

John E. Cogoli

Wethersfield, Connecticut

contents

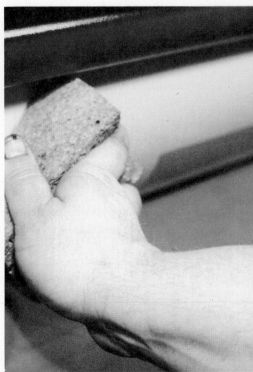

Shanebrook Graphics

HCM Corporation

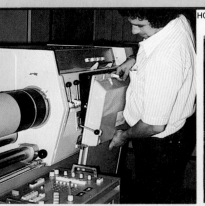

Shanebrook Gra

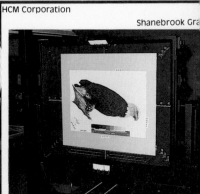

Shanebrook Graphics

Photopress, Inc.

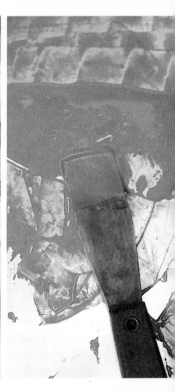

R.R. Donnelley & Sons

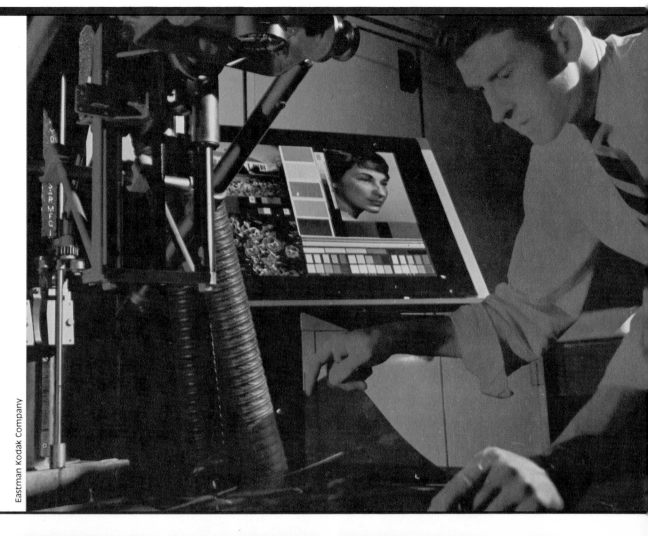

Introduction to Photo-Offset Printing

The printing industry in the United States turns out billions of dollars worth of printed products each year. In addition to paper, printing is done on wood, glass, cloth, rubber, metal, plastic and leather. Machines, methods, and processes are constantly improved. The procedures have vastly changed from the slow hand methods of early days. The printer of today is still a master of the craft and is aided by swiftly operating automatic or semiautomatic machinery.

Major Printing Processes

The printing industry must produce the needed quantities of printed products as speedily as possible at least cost. To do this, the printing industry uses a number of different printing processes. The five major processes by which most of today's printing is done are: letterpress, gravure, screen, engraving, and offset. (Note: These are not arranged in order of dollar volume.)

Letterpress

In the letterpress process of printing, raised (relief) type characters, lines, and dots of illustration plates are inked and then pressed against the paper to be printed. This transfers the ink from the typeface to the paper, Fig. 1-1. The type characters and the illustration plates for letterpress printing are always made in reverse. This is called a *mirrored image*. When printed, the typeface reads correctly from left to right. Flat forms of the original type characters may be used on the press. Also,

duplicate plates, either flat or curved, may be made from the original type matter and used on the press.

Flexography is another form of relief printing. It uses rubber or flexible plastic plates with raised characters.

Gravure

In the gravure process, original proofs of type matter and illustrations are photographed through a gravure screen. The screened negatives are placed into contact with the photographically sensitive surface of a copper gravure plate. The plate may be flat or cylindrical. After exposure of the plate, a chemical process etches the printing design *into* the

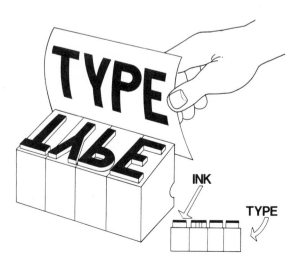

Fig. 1-1. Letterpress printing.

1

plate. The dots which are etched into the plate are tiny cup-shaped cavities below the surface of the plate.

On the gravure press, ink is applied to the plate surface, filling the cavities caused by the etching process. A scraper blade, also called a doctor blade, removes all ink from the plate except the ink in the etched cavities of the image. Pressure of the plate against the paper to be printed transfers ink from the cavities to the paper, Fig. 1-2. The result is a finished printed product.

When the printing is done from an etched cylinder instead of a flat plate, the process is called *rotogravure*. Any method which prints from below the plate surface is known as an *intaglio* (in-tal'-yo) method.

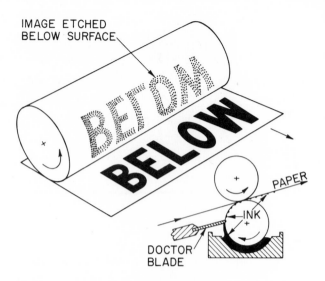

Fig. 1-2.   Gravure (rotogravure) process.

Plate Engraving

Plate engraving is another intaglio printing process. The design or lettering to be reproduced on paper must be engraved, or *cut into*, the surface of a copper or a steel plate. This engraving may be done by hand, using a tool called a *graver*, or it may be outlined by a graver and then etched with acid. In either case, the work is done in mirrored image. For very small lettering, a pantograph engraving machine may be used. This machine traces large master letters at the same time that it cuts them the desired size into the plate.

The plate on the engraving press is inked and wiped clean. The engraved lines retain ink because they are below the surrounding surface, Fig. 1-3. The plate is then forced against the printing paper, with enough pressure to cause the ink to adhere to the paper.

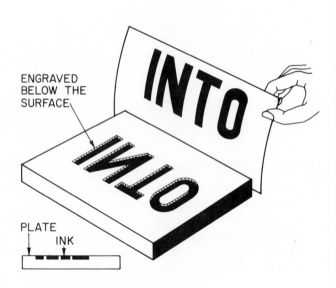

Fig. 1-3.   Printing by engraving.

Screen Process

In the screen process of printing, a finely-woven fabric is stretched tightly and fastened to a frame. A stencil bearing the desired design or printing message is adhered to the bottom side of the fabric. This stencil may be prepared photographically, or it may be prepared by cutting out the desired image or message with a knife.

After the screen stencil is prepared, paper (or any other object to be printed) is placed beneath the stencil frame. The stencil is lowered into contact with the paper, Fig. 1-4. A paint-like ink is poured into the frame. Then a rubber-blade squeegee is scraped across the stencil. This forces ink through the open areas of the stencil and onto the object beneath it.

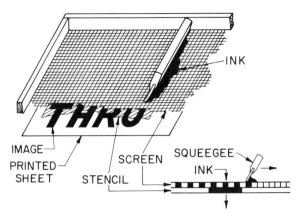

Fig. 1-4. **Screen process.**

Fig. 1-5. **Offset printing.**

Offset

In the offset process, the printing image is drawn by hand, typed, or prepared photographically on the surface of a thin, flat offset plate. This offset plate is then mounted on the plate cylinder of the offset press. During operation of the offset press, the inked image of the offset plate is printed onto the rubber-covered surface of a blanket cylinder. In turn, the blanket cylinder transfers, or *offsets,* its printed image onto the paper, Fig. 1-5. The paper is fed (under pressure) between the blan-

ket cylinder and the impression cylinder to produce the printed product.

Basic Theory of Offset Printing

In this book, study is confined to the offset process of printing. You will note that there are several other names by which the offset process is known: photo-offset, lithography, photolithography, photo-offset lithography, and offset lithography. Generally, these names refer to one and the same process. A more descriptive term, *photo-offset lithography,* is used in this book. For convenience, it is usually shortened to *offset.*

Offset printing is a *planographic method* of printing. That is, it commonly uses a *flat* printing plate on which the image, or printing area, is level with the nonprinting area. The part of the plate which does the printing is neither raised above nor cut below the surface of the plate. (See Fig. 13-7 and page 243 for information on offset plates whose image is *above* and *below* the surface.)

Offset printing can be done from a flat plate because of a basic chemical fact: *grease and water do not readily mix.*

The Plate. As purchased or prepared in the shop, the offset plate is a thin sheet of paper or metal. It has been treated chemically and mechanically so that its surface will readily hold a thin film of applied moisture.

The message to be printed, called the *image,* is placed on this plate by a photographic-chemical process. In the final steps of the process the image is developed by use of a greasy or "fatty" ink. The image may also be created directly on the plate by typing, hand lettering, or drawing. In each case, special lithographic typewriter ribbons, pencils, tusche or ink is used which will cause a greasy image on the plate. (Platemaking is discussed in more detail in Chapter 13.)

A completely prepared offset plate, then, actually contains two separate and distinct areas on its flat surface. These are the *image* (printing) area, which is composed of greasy or fatty ink, and the *clear* (nonprinting) area, Fig. 1-6.

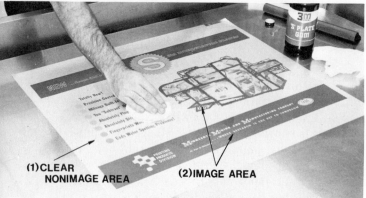

(1) CLEAR NONIMAGE AREA   (2) IMAGE AREA

Fig. 1-6.   An offset plate has two areas.

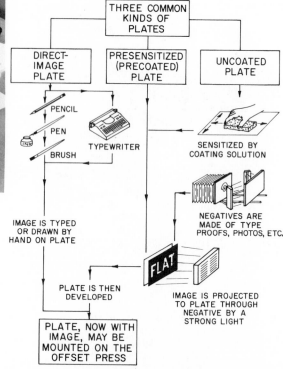

Fig. 1-7.   A printing image can be produced on the surface of three kinds of offset plates. The pencil, ink, and typewriter ribbon used for preparing the direct-image plate are especially made for lithographic purposes. To develop the presensitized and uncoated plates which are coated in the shop, a greasy lithographic developing ink is used to make the image ink-receptive. See also the photo-direct plate, Fig. 13-25.

Water Repellent and Ink Receptive. If a water-saturated cloth pad is passed over the entire surface of a completed offset plate, a thin film of moisture will adhere to the clear areas of the plate. Moisture will not adhere to the inked image area. You can actually see the moisture run off and pull away from the greasy-inked image.

If an ink roller, called a *brayer*, charged with greasy lithographic ink is passed over the entire water-dampened plate surface, a deposit of ink is added to the greasy-ink image. You can see that no ink adheres to the moisture-dampened clear areas of the plate.

These conclusions become evident:

1. The greasy-inked image is *receptive* to ink, but will *repel* water.
2. The dampened clear area of the plate is *receptive* to water, but will *repel* ink.

However, suppose an ink-charged brayer is passed over an offset plate which *has not* been moistened. The ink will adhere to the entire surface of the plate — image and clear areas alike.

Water and Ink Balance. On commercial offset presses, the water and ink are fed automatically to the offset plate. The press operator maintains and controls a careful balance between the amounts of ink and water which are allowed to reach the plate. This balance insures that only the image portions of the plate will print.

The Offset Press

A schematic drawing of an offset press is shown in Fig. 1-8. It shows only the basic parts of an offset press. Actually, offset presses have a great many more parts.

Note that the offset press has *three large cylinders:*

1. the *plate cylinder*, on which is mounted the offset plate;
2. the *blanket cylinder*, which is covered with a rubber blanket; and
3. the *impression cylinder*, which has a smooth metal surface.

Fig. 1-8. Schematic drawing of an offset press. Printing progresses from plate, to blanket, to paper.

Fig. 1-9. ATF Chief 25 offset press.

There are *two fountains*, also called reservoirs:

1. the *ink fountain*, which carries a supply of ink, and
2. the *water fountain*, which contains the plate-dampening solution.

The offset press also has *two series (trains) of rollers*. One from the ink fountain and one from the water fountain furnish ink and water to the plate.

Paper is fed automatically through the press and is stacked neatly after printing.

Inking the Plate

When the press is started in motion, the water fountain roller is brought into contact with the plate. This coats the plate with a film of moisture. The water adheres only to the clear area of the plate because the developed image repels the water.

The ink roller next contacts the dampened plate. The ink adheres to the developed image, but is repelled by the water-covered clear area. By a carefully controlled feeding of water

and ink, the offset plate is inked in only the image areas.

Printing

When the rubber-covered blanket cylinder contacts the plate cylinder, the *readable**** inked image of the plate prints onto the blanket. The image printed on the blanket is a wrong-reading or mirrored image of the plate image. See Fig. 1-8.

Finally, the paper is passed through the press between the blanket and impression cylinders. It is printed upon by the blanket — the image being mirrored again and appearing *readable* on the paper. Note that the plate does not print on the paper. Instead, the plate prints on the blanket. The blanket image is then transferred (or *offset*) to the paper, thus giving the process the term *offset printing*.

*Type matter which can be read normally from left to right is referred to as "readable," or "right reading." If type matter is reproduced so it must be read from right to left on the page, it is called "unreadable," or "wrong reading." (See also Figs. 12-10 and 12-11 for examples of right-reading and wrong-reading type matter.

Instructor's Demonstrations

A study and discussion will aid the student's understanding of the foregoing text material. In addition the student will gain deeper knowledge of the theory and practice of basic offset principles if the instructor will actually demonstrate the principles involved.

Platemaking and Presswork

The best demonstration of offset principles requires that platemaking equipment and a simple offset press, such as a duplicator, be available.

Expose and develop a presensitized paper or metal plate, using an available stripped-up flat. Explain each step and the materials used.

Mount the plate on the press which has been prepared for the printing operation. Show how the plate is dampened and how the plate image picks up a coverage of ink. Stop the press and allow the students to examine the plate.

Transfer the plate image to the blanket, and again stop the press. Point out how the blanket image is a *mirror image* of the plate image.

Take a few impressions and pass out the printed sheets to the students.

Close the demonstration by showing the students how the plate is preserved and stored for future use.

If preparations are made beforehand, the complete demonstration should cover 20 minutes or less. Allow ample time for discussion.

Plate and Proof Press

If it is neither desirable nor convenient to demonstrate with an offset duplicator or offset press, much the same principles can be demonstrated with an offset plate and a letterpress proof press.

For this demonstration, build up the proof press bed with a block of wood and several sheets of thin cardboard so that the press gives a slight *squeeze* impres-

sion. Also, ink up a hand brayer and an ink slab with offset ink.

Demonstrate the exposure and developing of an offset plate (as above) or take from storage a previously used offset plate.

Place the plate, image side up, on the built-up bed of the proof press. Wash the preservative from the plate surface with sponge and water, and roll up the image with the hand brayer. It may require several passes with the brayer to build up the image with sufficient ink. If so, sponge off the plate with water between inkings. If water accumulates on the brayer, remove it by rolling the brayer on clean newsprint.

Place a sheet of printing paper on the inked plate, and pull an impression. Additional impressions may be taken if, before each additional impression, the plate is moistened and then inked.

This demonstration will show the *grease and water theory*, and also the *mirror reversal* of the plate image when it prints on the paper.

Conclude by showing how to prepare the plate for storage. Then hold a discussion on what has been demonstrated.

Plate, Blanket and Proof Press

A third demonstration which may be made involves the same setup of offset plate and proof press. In addition, an offset-press blanket, or a portion of one, is needed.

First, as in Fig. 1-10, build up the proof press bed with a block of wood and sheets of thin cardboard. The press should give a slight squeeze impression when the offset plate and blanket pass through.

At the bench, wash off the plate with sponge and water, and roll up the plate image with a hand brayer and offset ink. Place the plate (image side up) on the proof press bed packing. Put the blanket on the plate, and pull an impression — plate image to blanket.

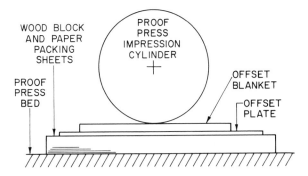

Fig. 1-10. Setup for demonstration of offset-printing theory, using letterpress proof press, offset plate, and portion of offset blanket.

Remove the printed-upon blanket. Show that its image is a mirror image of the plate image.

Now, remove the offset plate from the proof press, and place the blanket (image side up) on the built-up proof press bed.

Place a sheet of printing paper on the blanket and pull an impression. Show that the impression printed on the paper is a right-reading duplicate of the plate image.

In this demonstration, additional sheets may not be printed unless the blanket is washed between impressions. However, the inclusion of the blanket makes this a convincing demonstration.

Conclude, as before, with plate preservation and class discussion.

Questions

1. Describe the letterpress printing process.
2. Explain the term ''screen printing.''
3. Which of the major printing processes is commonly used for printing on glass bottles? Why?
4. Which two of the major printing processes employ printing plates that do their printing from lines or dots below the surface of the plate?
5. What is meant by offset printing? Why is the name ''offset'' used to describe this process?
6. What is the ''grease and water theory'' as applied to offset printing? Why is a greasy (fatty) ink used for this process?

7. With a dry offset plate on the press, which is applied first — water or ink? Why? What would happen if the other were applied first?
8. Give at least two names for that portion of the offset plate which carries no image.
9. Suppose the plate image in Fig. 1-8 were reversed, left to right. Would the resulting image appear on the paper in unreadable or readable form?
10. Define the following terms as they apply to offset printing:
    a. Water receptive
    b. Water repellent
    c. Ink receptive
    d. Ink repellent
    e. Printing area
    f. Ink fountain
    g. Water fountain
    h. Water rollers
    i. Ink rollers
    j. Impression cylinder
    k. Mirrored image

Problems and Projects

1. Examine an offset press in the shop. Locate each of the basic parts shown in the schematic drawing in Fig. 1-8.
2. Examine a used offset plate in the shop. Ask if you may rub the image with a fingertip. What can you say about the image?
3. Closely inspect two printed samples — one printed by letterpress, and the other by offset. Notice the outlines of the magnified letters of each sample. Describe and explain what you see.
4. Clip and mount on a notebook page, five samples of printed matter, each printed by a different major process. Identify and label each according to the printing process used.

New Terms

blanket cylinder	packing
brayer	planographic
characters	plate cylinder
engraving	proof press
etching	rotogravure
flat	scraper (doctor) blade
flexography	stripped-up
lithography	

CHAPTER 2 A Brief History of Photo-Offset Printing

Offset printing in its present form has been adapted in several ways from an earlier printing method called *stone lithography*. Stone slabs served as the printing plates.

The Invention of Lithography

In 1798 Alois Senefelder, a Bohemian by birth, invented the lithographic process of printing. Because he used a flat stone plate from which to print on paper, the process was called *lithography*. This term comes from two Greek words: "lithos," meaning *stone*, and "graphein," meaning to *write*. Combined, the term may be understood to mean writing from stone, or stone writing.

Senefelder made many experiments in order to perfect the lithographic process. He developed the necessary materials and methods of carrying out the process. For these reasons Senefelder is regarded as the father of lithography.

Early Attempts

During his youth in Munich, young Senefelder hoped to become an actor, as was his father before him. His father compelled him to study law, but his love for the theater won out.

However, he found more success at writing plays than in acting. He had several of his plays published. Profits were so small that Senefelder decided to try to print the plays himself and thus save part of the cost of publication. However, he lacked funds to purchase the necessary type, press and paper. He began experimenting to find a less costly printing method.

In his early attempts, Senefelder borrowed an idea from the copperplate printers of the time. He cleaned a copper plate surface and covered it with etcher's ground. On this surface he then wrote his type characters *in reverse*, cutting through the protective coating of ground and exposing the bare metal. When the copper plate was treated with acid, the exposed lines of copper were etched below the surface of the plate. The etched plates could then be printed on the engraver's press.

Senefelder had one great difficulty with his reverse writing on copper. His frequent mistakes were hard to correct. What he needed was a thin, quick-drying varnish which could be painted over his errors and would permit pen corrections to be made. For this he finally found a mixture of three parts of wax, one part of soap, some lampblack and rainwater to be satisfactory. Although he did not realize it at the time, the formula for this "correction fluid" would serve another need. It was to become the greasy or fatty lithographic ink he would use in his future work on stone.

The copper plates proved too costly for Senefelder. As a result, he turned to experimenting with a flat piece of Bavarian limestone which he had used for grinding inks. This stone cost little. Also, it was easier to grind flat than were the copper plates.

One day, after he had ground a stone plate smooth and flat for experimenting, his mother

8

asked him to write down a laundry list. Having no paper and writing ink on hand, Senefelder took some of his correction fluid and wrote the list on the stone. Later, being curious, he poured a dilute solution of aqua fortis (nitric acid) over the stone. In a few minutes, the acid etched the un-inked portion of the stone surface leaving the inked letters in slight relief (raised), much like type characters.

By carefully inking the raised letters, Senefelder obtained excellent proofs. For a time, he used this method for successful printing. After an edition was finished, the printing stones were easily ground smooth and flat again, and could be used over and over. This process proved a relatively inexpensive and easy method of printing.

Chemical Printing

While Senefelder was trying to find a way to reproduce illustrations by stone printing without redrawing the pictures on the stone, he invented his chemical process of printing. He liked to call his process "chemical printing" rather than "lithography."

Senefelder had an order to reprint a book. The original book had been illustrated with copperplate engravings. Instead of copying the illustrations onto the stone by hand, Senefelder inked an original etched copper plate with his fatty ink. Then he pulled a proof of the etching. Placing the proof carefully on a clean lithographic stone, he pulled a wood scraper across the proof with considerable pressure. Amazingly, the design on the proof was transferred to the stone!

Now, placing the stone plate in his press, he wet the entire surface of the stone with a solution of water and gum. The stone was naturally porous and retained a thin film of moisture on those parts of the surface not covered with the design. The design, being composed of fatty ink, repelled the water.

Over the entire stone plate he then passed a leather roller charged with his fatty ink. The design accepted the ink, whereas the wet portion of the stone plate remained clean. Placing a sheet of paper over the stone, he found that the resulting press impression yielded results as good or better than could be obtained from the original copper plate.

More impressions were easily made from the stone by alternately first wetting the plate with water and gum, then inking the plate. Thus, "chemical printing" was born. It is based on a basic fact of chemistry, that *grease and water do not mix.*

Senefelder's success with transferring a design, or image, from the proof paper to the stone showed him that printing could be done from stones without the labor of reverse writing. If the original work were drawn on transfer paper reading normally from left to right, it could be transferred under pressure to the stone where it would appear in reverse. This reverse image on the stone would then appear in readable form when the stone plate transferred its image to the paper in the printing process.

Naturally, if the original work were to be drawn directly on the stone, it would necessarily have to be drawn in reverse. Only a reversed image on the stone would produce a readable impression on the paper.

Lithographic Stones

The stones used for lithographic printing are a natural Bavarian limestone. When uncovered in the earth at the quarries, the stones are in

Fig. 2-1. Inking a lithographic stone before printing from it.

Metropolitan Museum of Art

the form of layers. They range from paper-thin sheets to great blocks which can be split to make thinner stones. In general, stones about 1½" to 3½" thick are strong enough to withstand impressions without cracking.

Above all, the properties of Bavarian limestone which make it ideally suited for lithography are:

1. the natural affinity of its finely grained surface to retain a thin film of applied moisture,
2. its affinity for greasy ink, and
3. the ease with which one stone may be used to grind another stone flat.

The First Lithographic Presses

The press which Senefelder used for his first stone printing was a modified etcher's press. The stone plate, with the printing paper on it, was drawn between two wooden cylinders under pressure. It was powered manually by a crank. The wetting and inking of the plate were also performed by hand.

The cumbersome operation of this cylinder press prompted Senefelder to design and construct a lithographic lever-scraper press in 1802, Fig. 2-3. The flat stone plate was placed on the press bed, wet, then inked and covered with the printing paper. Over this was placed a cloth blanket and a leather impression pad. An impression blade, suspended from above, was forced against the leather pad and scraped across it, causing the inked image to transfer to the paper. In this press, inking, wetting, and power were also applied by hand. However, since the stone plate was stationary, printing was less work and therefore faster.

Professor Mitterer, an associate of Senefelder, developed a cylinder-scraper press about 1806-1817. In this press, the stone plate was carried horizontally underneath a stationary scraper

General Printing Ink Company
Div. of Sun Chemical Corporation

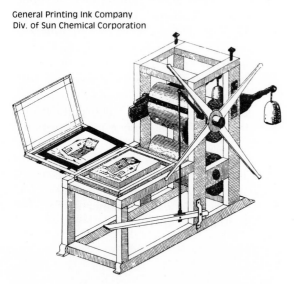

Fig. 2-2.   Copperplate cylinder press modified for lithographic printing by Senefelder about 1798.

General Printing Ink Company
Div. of Sun Chemical Corporation

Fig. 2-3.   Lever-scraper lithographic printing press invented by Senefelder in 1802.

General Printing Ink Company
Div. of Sun Chemical Corporation

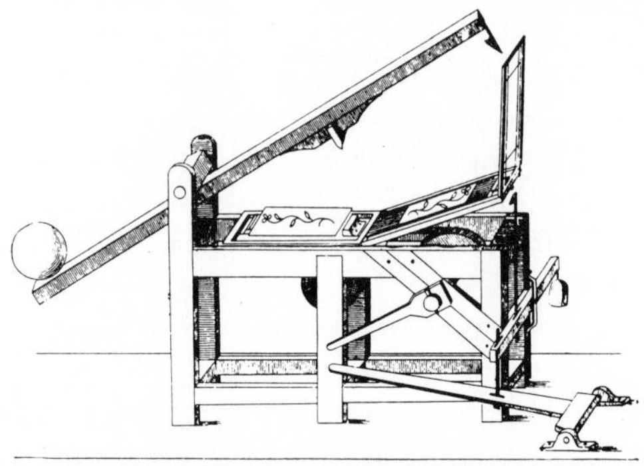

Fig. 2-4.   Cylinder-scraper lithographic press invented by Professor Mitterer about 1806-1817.

blade which pressed the paper against the inked stone. See Fig. 2-4. Inking and dampening were done by hand. Power was applied manually by a crank. This cylinder-scraper press was regarded by both Senefelder and Mitterer as an improvement over the lever-scraper press.

In 1813, Senefelder demonstrated the use of a flat *metal* plate on his lever press for lithographic printing. He also showed that cloth, paper and wood could each be coated with an artificial stone composition. Any of these materials could replace the weighty limestone slabs then in use for printing by lithography.

A few years later, in 1817, Senefelder exhibited a water-powered press. It mechanically dampened and inked the flat stone or metal plates. As yet, no curved plates were used for printing.

Applications of the Lithographic Process

Senefelder printed circulars, statistical tables, charts, prayer books, music sheets, portraits, landscapes and textbooks by the lithographic (stone-printing) process. The advantages of the new process were quickly appreciated by printers everywhere, and the process was readily adopted in the United States.

Nathaniel Currier began his apprenticeship in the lithographic trade in 1825 at 15 years of age. He was perhaps the most famous of all American lithographers. His realistic lithographic print of the sinking of the S.S. Lexington in Long Island Sound on January 13, 1840, was published three days after the tragedy. He sold so many thousands of copies that he decided to specialize exclusively in lithographic scenes depicting life in America, Fig. 2-5. Some of his editions ran to more than 70,000 copies.

James Ives, an assistant of Nathaniel Currier, became a partner in the firm in 1857. From that time on, the firm was known as Currier & Ives. More than 7,000 different Currier & Ives lithographic prints are still in existence today.

Some graphic arts supply houses today carry lithographic stones, crayons, presses and other supplies for artists who wish to use this medium. Portraits, landscapes, still life and other forms of artwork produced by crayon or

Museum of the City of New York

Fig. 2-5. "Westward the Course of Empire Takes Its Way" is a lithograph by Currier and Ives, 1868.

pen and ink on stone are referred to as *lithographic prints*. They are much prized for framing or for reproduction as illustrations in publications.

Use of Metal Plates on Cylinder Presses

Senefelder's original introduction of the flat metal plate for lithographic printing led to much experimentation and research concerning its use. It was discovered that thin sheets of aluminum were flexible enough to be wrapped around and fastened to a cylinder. This plate-covered revolving cylinder could then print onto the paper. Aluminum was light, easily formed into thin sheets, and could be grained satisfactorily to retain the film of water necessary. However, it was at that time too expensive for general use. Zinc was cheaper, and was therefore substituted for the first metal plates. Improved manufacturing methods later lowered the cost of aluminum so that both zinc and aluminum were commonly used for lithographic plates. Aluminum is now the preferred metal for lithographic plates.

It should be noted that when metal plates were first used, the plate printed *directly onto the paper*. The use of curved metal plates was an improvement over the use of the flat lithographic stones. However, printing directly from the metal plate to the paper resulted in a relatively short life for the metal plate image.

Advent of Offset

The introduction of the *offset* principle in the lithographic press is credited to the ingenuity and awareness of Ira Rubel, an American lithographic press operator. He introduced the addition of the blanket cylinder which received the inked image from the plate and, in turn, *offsetted* that image to the paper.

While Rubel was operating a lithographic press — one which printed directly from the plate — a sheet of paper failed to feed through. As a result, the plate printed its image onto the surface of the impression cylinder. When the next sheet was printed normally, it also picked up an *offset image* on its reverse side from the impression cylinder. The image was so clear,

Rubel decided to put it to use. In 1903, he built the first lithographic press, using an offset, rubber-covered cylinder. Today it is called the *blanket cylinder*. No longer did the plate touch the paper. All modern offset presses still are constructed on this same principle: plate to blanket to paper.

This *offsetting* of the image gave rise to the term *offset printing*. Since the process included the same lithographic principles as before, the new term was soon changed to *offset lithography*.

Introduction of Photography

Photography is one of the newer arts. Prior to its invention, much of our knowledge of past cultures was based on existing artwork of those periods — designs, pictures, or statues. The mediums used were pottery, tapestries, stone, bronze, stained-glass windows, tile mosaics, oil paint on canvas, and building surfaces. More recently, woodcuts, copperplate engravings and etchings, and stone lithographs were used. In most of these, the artist achieved a remarkable degree of minuteness and clarity of detail.

In spite of the excellence of these methods of hand-executed art, scientific minds reached farther. People were intrigued by such natural phenomena as reflected images in mirrors and pools of water, and by the shadows cast by the sun. All this suggested that exact images or pictures might be captured and recorded on paper.

Silhouette Pictures

The earliest attempts at photography were successful in producing only a silhouette outline of the subject. In about 1802, two Englishmen, Sir Humphry Davy and Thomas Wedgwood, used paper coated with silver chloride in their photographic experiments. The person to be photographed (or silhouetted) sat before a vertically mounted sheet of this paper. A light was used to project the sitter's shadow onto the paper. No method had yet been invented to reduce the unexposed silver chloride coating. Subsequent exposure of the paper to the sunlight therefore also darkened

Fig. 2-6. Daguerreotype camera.

Fig. 2-7. Daguerreotype portrait of President Abraham Lincoln.

the unexposed portions of the photographic paper. Thus, these early silhouette pictures were not long lasting.

Daguerreotype Pictures

The first practical process which produced lasting pictures in fine detail was the Daguerreotype process. It was known as *Daguerreotypy*. Louis Jacques Mendé Daguerre, a Frenchman, invented it in 1839.

In the Daguerreotype process, a silvercoated copper plate was placed in the camera. Then the exposure (sometimes as long as several minutes) was made. The plate was developed with mercury vapors, resulting in a positive picture of the subject. One drawback to this process was that there was no way to make additional prints or copies. The plate itself was the picture.

On one of his trips abroad, Samuel F.B. Morse, the inventor of telegraphy, met Daguerre who instructed Morse in the art of Daguerreotypy. At that time Morse was a portrait artist in New York City. He hoped that this new process would be useful in capturing poses of his subjects which he could later paint at his leisure.

In turn, Morse taught the new art to Mathew Brady who was quick to see the economic possibilities of the new process. Brady opened a Daguerreotypy studio in New York. The excellence of his work did much to make Daguerreotypes popular. In fact, at that time, which was prior to the Civil War, it was fashionable to

have one's portrait made by Daguerreotypy, especially by Brady. Many beautiful Daguerreotypes made during that era are yet in existence.

The First Negatives

In 1840, William Talbot (an Englishman) discovered the first practical process for producing photographic negatives from which any number of permanent positive prints could be made. He used a paper coated with silver iodide for the negative plate. Before exposure, the coated paper was dampened with silver nitrate and gallic acid. A camera exposure of about 30 seconds was required.

A most important point in Talbot's process was his method of developing the negative. He used a developing solution of the same silver nitrate and gallic acid. Then he immersed the negatives in a fixing bath of sodium thiosulphate (hypo) to remove the unexposed silver salts. This fixing bath preserved the negatives against fading when later exposed to light.

Talbot made permanent positive prints from his negatives by coating print paper with silver chloride, placing the negative in contact over the print paper, and then exposing the combination to light. Developing and fixing were done in a manner similar to that used for the negatives.

Despite the importance of Talbot's contributions, experimenters continued to seek improvements. When Talbot's paper negatives were projected onto the photographic print paper, the finished prints lacked clarity. This was caused by the grain structure of the paper fibers. To gain clear detail in the finished prints, Claude Felix Niepce, in 1847, substituted glass for the paper negatives. He coated his glass plates with albumin and potassium iodide. Just before exposure in the camera, the plate was wet with a solution of silver nitrate. The development and fixing of these negatives and the making of the positive prints were carried on in the same manner as for the paper negatives described earlier. The finished prints were of excellent quality. However, they required much longer exposures than did Talbot's paper negatives.

Wet-Collodion Negatives

In 1851, the wet-collodion negative was introduced by Frederick Scott Archer, an Englishman. In this process, glass plates were first treated with an albumin (egg white) solution and allowed to dry. When photographers wished to use a plate, they entered a darkroom, coated the plate with collodion and then with silver nitrate, and finally the plate was placed in a plateholder. While still wet, the plate (in its plateholder) had to be inserted into the camera, exposed for about five seconds, and then rushed back to the darkroom for developing.

In spite of the handicap and discomfort in handling the glass plates and the coating of

Fig. 2-8.   Collodion wet-plate camera for making cartes-de-visite (calling-card-size portraits).

Fig. 2-9.   Portrait of General Ulysses S. Grant, from a wet-collodion negative.

them in total darkness, the wet-collodion process required only a relatively short exposure time. It met with great success. Photographers of the day achieved great clarity of detail. Photographs made at that time are still acclaimed as masterpieces of the art.

Mathew Brady, who in 1852 was operating a Daguerroetypy studio, was quick to use the new wet-collodion process in his studio. Again, his results were excellent. At that time, to be photographed by Brady was a mark of distinction in society.

At the start of the Civil War, Brady saw the historical importance and the possibilities of photography in warfare. He set himself the task of making a photographic record of the War Between the States. This was the first time in history that photography was used in warfare. To do this, he obtained permission to go with the Union troops into battle to get his on-the-spot pictures.

Brady outfitted two horse-drawn, van-type wagons as photographic darkrooms. He became a familiar sight as he set up his cameras for his scenes, shielding the lens from the sun with his hat, and removing and replacing the lens cap to make his exposures, Fig. 2-10. Despite many problems in coating and developing his negatives in his portable darkrooms amid battle conditions, Brady achieved huge success. His thousands of photographs clearly portrayed the history of that war.

Dry Negatives

Photography, as we know it today, never would have achieved its popularity without the introduction of a "dry" plate. A dry plate was one which could be prepared well in advance of exposure. It was introduced in 1878 by Charles Bennett, an English photographer. Its emulsion (coating) consisted of gelatin and silver bromide. Bennett's dry plates required such a short length of exposure time that a snapshot was now possible.

George Eastman, an American and founder of the Eastman Kodak Company, experimented to find a substitute for the bulky and breakable glass plates. In 1884 he patented the first flexible film which was of a paper base. In 1889, he

John Hancock Mutual Life Insurance Company

Fig. 2-10. Mathew Brady shooting a war scene. Exposure was made by removing the lens cap. In the background is a wagon used as one of his photographic darkrooms.

The George Eastman House

Fig. 2-11. George Eastman.

introduced a thin, flexible cellulose-nitrate (celluloid) base for his film.

This flexible film made possible the roll-film camera which is so popular today. The ease with which a prepared roll of film can be loaded into and removed from the camera has brought photography within the reach and experience of all. Today, most of our photographs, both professional and amateur, are taken on flexible film, either in roll or sheet form.

Color

Photography took on an added impetus when color film was introduced. This film could be used to take both reflection-type pictures (color prints made from color negatives) and color transparencies (slides and movies). The popularity of color photography has led the consumer to expect and enjoy a wider use of flat and process color in printed materials, especially advertising literature.

The Halftone Screen

The first halftone screen for the reproduction of photographs was used by Henry Talbot, an Englishman, about the year 1852. He employed a loosely woven, gauze-like cloth as a screen. In 1885, an American, Frederick Ives, made the first cross-line halftone screen. He took two exposed (glass) negatives, scribed equally spaced lines on them through the emulsion, and then cemented them together, face to face, with the lines at right angles. With the halftone screen, photographs and type could now be printed on the same sheet.

Halftone screens of glass are still being manufactured and used. In manufacture, two sheets of glass, each with finely engraved horizontal lines, are cemented face to face with the lines

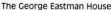
The George Eastman House

Fig. 2-12. **Early roll-film camera, Kodak No. 1.**

Roberts & Porter, Inc.

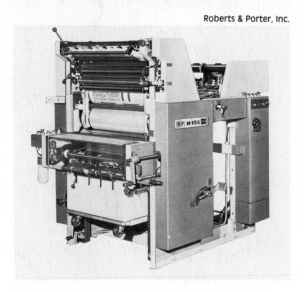

Fig. 2-13. **Harris 19″ × 25″ single-color offset press.**

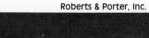
Roberts & Porter, Inc.

Fig. 2-14. **Harris 28³/₈″ × 41″ two-color, sheet-fed offset press.**

at right angles. Screens for process color work are circular. They are set in square frames arranged so that the circular screens may be rotated to the angle required for each color.

Contact halftone screens, a newer development, are made of a flexible plastic material. They are more widely used today than the glass halftone screens.

Photo-Offset Lithography

The development of photography, and along with it the halftone screen, gave offset lithography a fresh boost. With these aids, it was now possible to reproduce both line and halftone work on plates without resorting to manual artwork. The process now carried the name *photo-offset lithography*. The first metal plates which used photographically prepared negatives for their image preparation were used between 1910 and 1920.

Improvements in offset presses followed rapidly. Four-color press units and web-fed presses which printed from rolls of paper were designed and manufactured, Figs. 2-15 and 2-16. Many letterpress shops began adding offset presses or offset departments. Other plants turned wholly to offset production of magazines, newspapers, and job work.

Smaller machines, sometimes called *offset duplicators* have been developed for producing forms and sales literature in business offices, Fig. 2-17. These have been improved to the point where they do some work that, in many ways, is like that of the larger offset presses.

Today, the printing industry uses high-quality chemicals, fine plates, precision presses, and highly refined photographic processes. These enable skilled workers to produce a large volume of beautifully printed advertisements, books, packaging materials, and other products.

Harris-Intertype Corporation

Fig. 2-16. Harris-Cottrell four-over-four web-fed offset press.

AM International, Inc.

Fig. 2-17. Multilith Model 1250 offset duplicator.

Western Printing and Lithographing Company

Fig. 2-15. Four-color sheet-fed offset press.

Questions

1. Describe the nature of lithographic stone.
2. How is lithographic stone printing done?
3. Why does the applied moisture (water) adhere only to the clear portion of the stone? What helps the water to adhere to the stone?
4. Why does the ink repel the water?
5. Describe briefly the work of the inventor of lithographic printing.
6. Describe the transfer method.
7. What metal is most commonly used for lithographic plates today?
8. Describe Ira Rubel's contribution to modern offset printing. How does it differ from stone lithography?
9. Why was the rubber blanket added to the lithographic press?
10. Describe how photographers used the wet-collodion process.
11. What were Eastman's contributions to photography?
12. What contribution did the halftone screen make to the printing industry?
13. What does the term "photo-offset lithography" mean?

Problems and Projects

1. Draw an outline map of Europe, locating the areas where the principal events in this chapter took place.
2. Prepare a lithographic stone for printing. Take an impression. Make a transfer of this image to another stone, or to a paper or metal plate. Use words and a drawing in the image.
3. Obtain information on the production of aluminum. Make a display of samples of the raw materials that go into the manufacture of aluminum offset plates.
4. Try to locate and borrow an old Daguerreotype picture to show to the class. Give a report on the camera used for making Daguerreotypes, and tell how these pictures were developed.
5. Obtain information on the manufacture of rubber. Obtain samples of the raw materials used, and make a display.
6. Use a strong magnifying glass to look at a black and white picture in a newspaper and in this book. Examine the black and white cartoons and the color cartoons in the newspaper, using the same glass. Now, again with the glass, examine the full-color reproduction in Fig. 10-18 which has been printed in this book on high gloss paper. Ask your instructor to suggest some sources for information to answer the questions you have. Make a report to the class.

New Terms

cellulose	gelatin
circulars	halftone
copperplate	negatives
corrections	nitrate
dilute	process color
dry plate	silhouette
emulsion	silver chloride
exposed	sodium thiosulphate

The Offset Printing Industry

The complete, modern offset printing plant is equipped and staffed to handle all phases of the production of the printed piece from its planning and writing to the shipping of the finished product. In the smaller plants, each worker may perform a variety of operations. In the larger plants, workers tend to specialize in one operation, or even one type of work within an operation.

Divisions of Work

Work performed in a printing plant involves many workers who have many different kinds of jobs. In general, the work performed by each department or worker is as follows:

Management and Service Workers

Executives plan and direct the company operation. They plan for necessary equipment and financing. They are responsible for employment and operating policies of the plant, and supervise all employees.

The *sales staff* works with customers, determining their needs and giving information about the work to be done in the plant. To be successful in securing enough work to keep the plant active, sales people must know printing procedures. They must know what the plant can do and how much the product will cost.

Estimators analyze each piece to be printed, determine the time required for each production step, and compute the value of materials used. They give the sales department the total cost of the job to "quote" to the customer.

The *office staff* maintains correspondence and records of purchases, billings, payrolls, work performed, and taxes. These workers also do general accounting.

Maintenance workers must keep the plant clean and well-lighted. In addition, they maintain the heating and air conditioning. Sometimes they lubricate, adjust, and repair equipment and machinery.

Copywriters and advertising personnel plan sales promotional literature and campaigns. They are specially trained in sales methods and informed about production techniques.

Layout designers make the detailed layouts. These layouts actually are the "blueprints" from which the production workers do the work needed to print the finished product. On the layouts are indicated the type to be set and the artwork to be used. Both are in their respective positions and in the size and color they will appear when printed.

A staff of *photographers, retouchers, artists and drafters* provide all the original photographs, hand art, and mechanical drawings for the illustrations which will appear in the finished pieces. Sometimes the customer furnishes part, or all, of the artwork.

Composing Room

A staff of *compositors* sets type from the copy. This may be metal type, set by hand or machine. See Fig. 3-1. Sometimes phototype (photographic type) is used, Fig. 3-2.

A trial printing of the metal type is made on a proof press, Fig. 3-3. Photocopies of the phototype are made. *Proofreaders* read these copies (proofs) carefully to detect any possible errors. All mistakes found are corrected and verified for correction. The composition should be as free of errors as possible.

Proofs of the metal type composition and the actual phototype composition are then sent to the *copy preparation workers*. Figure 3-5 shows a worker preparing a page layout for the camera.

Lithographic Preparation

Camera operators make negatives of the desired size for all the type proofs, photographs, and other illustrations or hand artwork. See Figs. 3-6 and 3-7.

Fig. 3-1.   Setting (composing) metal type by hand.

Fig. 3-3.   Pulling a proof from a galley of metal type.

Fig. 3-2.   Setting phototype.

Compugraphic Corporation

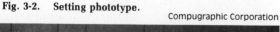

Dent-X Corporation

Fig. 3-4.   Phototype is developed (processed).

The *strippers* arrange and tape all the negatives on a sheet of goldenrod paper, according to a ruled-out layout for the plate to be made, Fig. 3-8. This stripped-up arrangement of negatives is called a *flat*. Windows are cut out of the other side of the flat so that images on the negatives can be exposed.

Platemakers clean the surface of the offset plates, prepare coating solutions, and coat the plates with the sensitizing solution. They place

Chemco Photoproducts Company

Fig. 3-7.   Page negative is ready to strip to a flat.

Fig. 3-5.   **Phototype and illustrations are pasted up for use as camera copy.**

nuArc Company, Inc.

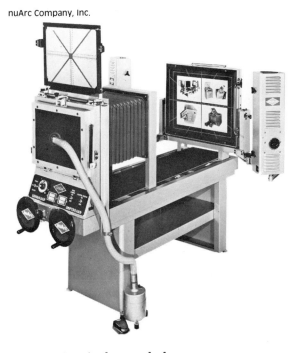

Fig. 3-6.   **Copy is photographed on a process camera.**

Chemco Photoproducts Company

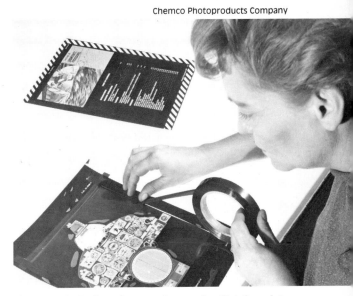

Fig. 3-8.   **Stripping the negative to the flat for plate exposure.**

nuArc Company

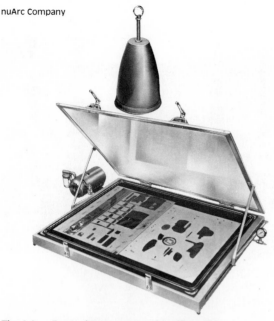

Fig. 3-9.   **Preparing to expose the offset plate.**

Western Printing and Lithographing Company

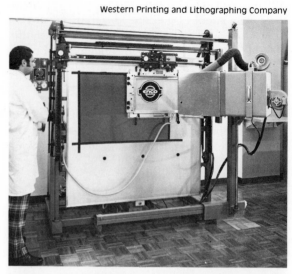

Fig. 3-11.   **Platemaking on the step-and-repeat machine.**

3M Company

Fig. 3-10.   **Developing the offset plate (by hand).**

Harris-Seybold Company

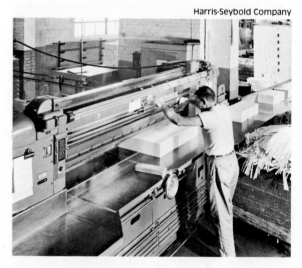

Fig. 3-12.   **Cutting paper stock to size.**

each flat over a sensitized plate, Fig. 3-9. The plate is exposed to a strong light source and then developed, Fig. 3-10. It is then sent to the pressroom.

Very often, a single-page negative for a job may be exposed many times on different parts of a large plate. This allows many copies of the job to be printed on one sheet. Then these printed sheets are cut apart into separate job-size pieces. These multiple exposures are made on a step-and-repeat machine, Fig. 3-11.

Printing and Binding

Storekeepers maintain stocks of paper, ink, and other supplies to be used in the regular run of work. Before paper is sent to the pressroom, the *papercutters* cut it to press size, Fig. 3-12. It is then *conditioned* so that the moisture con-

Fig. 3-13. View in a lithographic pressroom.

Harris-Seybold Company

Fig. 3-14. Cutting apart the printed sheets.

tent of the paper is adjusted in relation to the moisture content of the air in the pressroom. Paper stock is selected to fit the specifications for the job or is ordered specially for the job.

Press operators ready the press for operation. They attach the plate to the press, adjust the ink, water, paper feed and other mechanisms, and take trial impressions. When all is in order, the job is run. *Feeders* and *helpers* assist the head press operator on large presses.

The printed sheets are sent to the *bindery* where they may be cut, folded, punched, perforated, assembled, stitched, padded, or otherwise finished. See Figs. 3-14 and 3-15.

Shipping and Receiving

The *shipping department* wraps or packages the finished work and ships or delivers it to the customer. It also *receives* from suppliers all incoming stock and materials which are sent to the stockroom.

Special Services to the Trade

Not all the workers or facilities mentioned above are to be found in every offset shop. Some shops do only the presswork or the presswork plus some of the other operations. They may work with special service or trade shops for the other phases of production.

Challenge Machinery Company

Fig. 3-15. Sheets being folded.

Lithographic, chemical and graphic arts supply houses furnish plates, presensitized plates, films and photographic processing chemicals. They also supply platemaking and pressroom solutions and chemicals, press blankets and numerous other items for offset work.

Composition houses furnish type set to copy in either metal type or photographic type. They also supply reproduction proofs.

Special artwork for which facilities are not available is prepared by firms specializing in finished art and photography.

A layout, with the necessary proofs and photo copy, may be sent to a firm which *specializes in making a completed flat.* In some cases the firm supplies only the negatives for the job.

Some shops regularly send their flats out for *platemaking.* When shop facilities are not adequate for producing a special plate, it is made up in an outside trade shop.

The Office Offset Unit

Many small offset duplicators are found in offices, schools, and factories. These machines turn out a great deal of printed work. A small camera and platemaking unit added along with the use of the presensitized plates has made many of these units fairly complete.

Questions

1. Describe the flow of work in a complete offset shop.
2. Who sets the type for a job? What two general classes of type are used?
3. Who would take the photograph of a vacuum cleaner which is to appear in a printed job? Which worker would make the negative for the illustration of the vacuum cleaner?
4. How could a shop get along without a camera if it did not have enough camera work to justify it?
5. Study each of the divisions of work discussed. Is every one of them really necessary? State your reasons.

Problems and Projects

1. Arrange for several field trips to offset plants. Visit a small one first, then larger ones. Plan with a representative of the plant what you would like to see.
2. Arrange for the showing of one or more films on the offset process. Show the same film twice, with several days intervening, to give a chance for class discussion.
3. Invite an employee of an offset plant to talk to the class about offset printing, new techniques in offset, offset occupations or other related topics.
4. Interview one or more representative workers employed in the offset industry. Ask about advantages and disadvantages of the work, wages, hours, opportunities for training, and entrance into the occupation.
5. Secure information about training for lithographic employment and where it may be obtained, such as apprenticeship, technical schools (public and private), and colleges. Report to the class on the requirements, locations, costs, courses, and variety of training available.
6. Get facts and figures on employment in the offset industry locally, regionally and nationally, such as the number of plants, the number of workers, wages, and hours.
7. Arrange a bulletin board display of pictures of offset presses, cameras, platemaking equipment, and other tools and equipment used in offset work. Label each one.
8. Post a large world map on the board. Pinpoint locations of sources of raw materials going into the offset industry and locations of historical significance in offset work. A row of identification tags along the bottom can be connected with string to appropriate pins on the map.
9. If you are interested in a career in offset printing, try to get a job, part time or in the summer. Be willing to accept any type of work that will give you an opportunity to get acquainted with the methods, workers, and working conditions.

New Terms

compositors	mechanisms
conditioning	phototype
copywriters	platemakers
duplicators	presensitized
goldenrod	proofreaders
impressions	reproduction
layout	specifications

Job Planning and Layout

Planning must precede each printing job. It includes deciding on the size of the message, the typeface to be used, style of composition, and the placement of type and illustrations. Planning insures that the finished printed work is exactly what the customer desires.

Efficient job planning demands a knowledge of the tools, materials, and techniques used to produce the printed product. This chapter deals with some basic information.

Printer's Type

When printed, type appears as images of letters and other characters that convey the message in the printed work. Many type styles are available. A style is chosen on the basis of how well it carries the message. Indeed, type *speaks* to the reader, Fig. 4-1.

Characters in a Font of Type

A *font* is defined as a showing of all the various character images of one face and style of type. (also see the definition of a foundry type font, page 46.) The characters in a regular font usually consist of capital letters, lowercase letters, figures, and punctuation marks, Fig. 4-2. Some fonts may also contain small capitals, foreign accent marks, and special characters called pi (pi) characters. A font consisting wholly of pi characters is shown in Fig. 5-107. Pi (pi), a special character, is not usually contained in a regular font, Fig. 5-107.

Capital letters (Caps)

ABCDEFGHIJKLMN
OPQRSTUVWXYZ

Lowercase letters (l.c.)

abcdefghijklmn

opqrstuvwxyz

Figures (Figs.)

1234567890

Punctuation marks (Points)

(&.,:;!?'""''-*\$¢%/)

Figure 4-2 Characters in a font of Compugraphic's Bodoni Bold typeface. Fonts differ widely in their contents from one manufacturer to another. Check showings in type catalogs for specific typefaces.

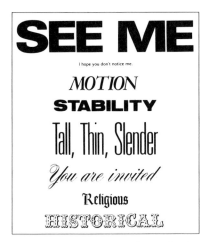

Fig. 4-1. Typeface styles often indicate the kind of message conveyed.

Typeface Image Terms

Study Fig. 4-3 to learn the names of some of the parts of the printed type character image. You will be hearing and using these terms during your studies and in your work.

Styles of Typefaces

For convenience, typeface designs may be classified into at least eight styles. Examples of these styles are shown in Fig. 4-4 and described below.

Text. This style is based on the manuscript lettering of the early scribes. It is difficult to read when set in all capitals. Using lowercase letters with initial capitals makes the typeface more easily read. The design suggests religion or antiquity.

Roman. Highly legible, the roman typeface is used widely for text or body matter in books, newspapers, and magazines. It usually has thick and thin elements, and comparatively thin serifs.

Italics. The tops of italic letters generally slant toward the right. It is available for many of the stand-upright typeface designs. Italics are used to emphasize several words or a short paragraph. It is not desirable for a whole page or book.

Sans-Serif Gothic. Sans means *without*. Sans-serif types are without serifs. Usually the

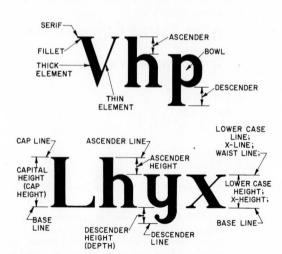

Fig. 4-3. Parts of the printed typeface image.

1. TEXT	Old English
	Engravers Text
2. ROMAN	Garamond
	Century Light
	Mallard
3. ITALIC	*Garamond Italic*
	Century Light Italic
	Mallard Italic
4. SANS-SERIF GOTHIC	Helios Light
	Lisbon
	Microstyle
5. SQUARE-SERIF GOTHIC	Stymie Light
	Stymie Bold
	Egyptian Bold Condensed
6. COPPERPLATE GOTHIC	COPPERPLATE LIGHT
	COPPERPLATE HEAVY
7. SCRIPT	*Original Script*
	Brophy Script
	Brush
8. NOVELTY	**GOLD NUGGET**
	NEON
	CALIOPE ANTIQUE

Fig. 4-4. Classification of typeface styles.

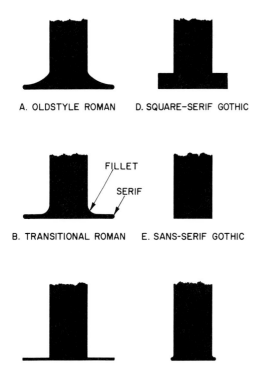

A. OLDSTYLE ROMAN   D. SQUARE-SERIF GOTHIC

B. TRANSITIONAL ROMAN   E. SANS-SERIF GOTHIC
FILLET
SERIF

C. MODERN ROMAN   F. COPPERPLATE GOTHIC

Fig. 4-5. Some styles of serifs.

Futura Light
Futura Light Italic
Futura Book
Futura Book Italic
Futura Medium
Futura Medium Italic
Futura Demibold
Futura Demibold Italic
Futura Bold
Futura Bold Italic
Futura Extrabold
Futura Extrabold Italic
Futura Extrabold Reverse
Futura Extrabold Italic Reverse
Futura Book Condensed
Futura Medium Condensed
Futura Bold Condensed
Futura Bold Condensed Italic
Futura Extrabold Condensed

Fig. 4-6. A type family is made up of several variations of the same typeface design. This is the Futura family (Compugraphic Corp.).

elements are monotone, all of one weight or thickness or a combination of thick and slightly thinner elements.

Square-Serif Gothic. This typeface is sometimes called *Egyptian*. Elements may be either all of one weight or a variety of thicknesses. Serifs are thick and block-like. See D in Fig. 4-5.

Copperplate Gothic. A monotone design in capital letters only — no lowercase letters. Square-ended elements have very tiny serifs. The style is popular for business cards, stationery, and forms. In a line, one size may be used for initial letters and a smaller size for the balance of the line. Both sizes align on the baseline of the letters.

Script. The graceful design of this type style imitates handwriting or hand lettering. It is a popular face to use for invitations and formal announcements. Because script type is generally too difficult to read in all capitals, it should be set in both capitals and lowercase.

Novelty or Decorative. This group includes the unusual faces: the grotesque, hand-brushed, shaded, antique, novelty, and so on. Some novelty faces are not as easily read as the roman types. Therefore, they should be used sparingly as either a display line or for only a few consecutive lines.

Type Family

Several variations of the same basic typeface design are known as a *type family*. Some families have a great many members. Others have only a few. Figure 4-6 shows the Futura family.

Type Series

Several sizes of the same typeface are called a *type series*. Figure 4-7 is a type series of the Ballardvale face.

Common Sizes of Type

Figure 4-7 shows the printed images for some common sizes of typeface. Today most type is produced by the phototypesetting process. Some of the phototypesetting machines use sizing lenses. With lens adjustment, the machine can produce virtually any size of type image desired. The process camera also can increase

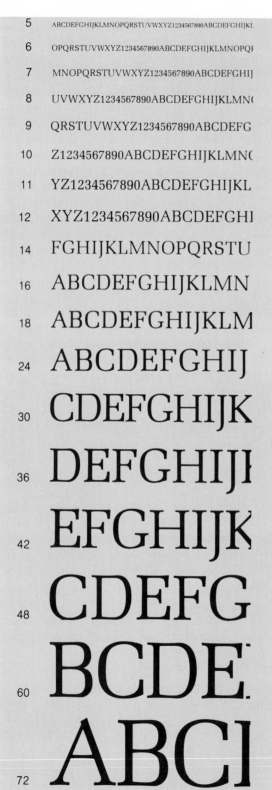

5	ABCDEFGHIJKLMNOPQRSTUVWXYZ1234567890ABCDEFGHIJKL
6	OPQRSTUVWXYZ1234567890ABCDEFGHIJKLMNOPQI
7	MNOPQRSTUVWXYZ1234567890ABCDEFGHIJ
8	UVWXYZ1234567890ABCDEFGHIJKLMN(
9	QRSTUVWXYZ1234567890ABCDEFG
10	Z1234567890ABCDEFGHIJKLMN(
11	YZ1234567890ABCDEFGHIJKL
12	XYZ1234567890ABCDEFGHI
14	FGHIJKLMNOPQRSTU
16	ABCDEFGHIJKLMN
18	ABCDEFGHIJKLM
24	ABCDEFGHIJ
30	CDEFGHIJK
36	DEFGHIJI
42	EFGHIJK
48	CDEFG
60	BCDE:
72	ABCI

Fig. 4-7. Several sizes of the same typeface design are called a "series" of type. This is the Ballardvale series (Dymo Graphic Systems).

Baskerville

12 POINT (12 set, 2 point leaded)

WHATEVER YOUR PRESENT METHOD OF composition may be, Compugraphic can put gr eater speed, capability and quality at your finge rtips for the lowest possible cost. CG offers a wide variety of typesetting equipment, all incorporat ing the latest electronic techniques for maximum reliability. In addition to a wide choice of typefa

14 POINT (9 set, 2 point leaded)

WHATEVER YOUR PRESENT METH od of composition may be, Compugraph ic can put greater speed, capability and qu ality at your fingertips for the lowest possi ble cost. CG offers a wide variety of typese tting equipment, all incorporating the lat

ABCDEFGHIJKLMNOPQRSTUVWXYZ&
abcdefghijklmnopqrstuvwxyz   1234567890

Point size	6	7	8	9	10	11	12	14	18	24
*LC alphabet length	79.8	85.9	98.2	110.6	122.9	135.0	147.2	184.0	221.2	294.4
Characters per pica	4.29	4.00	3.59	3.09	2.78	2.53	2.32	1.86	1.55	1.16

*In points

Fig. 4-8. Portion of a specimen sheet in a typeface catalog (Compugraphic Corp.).

or decrease the size of the phototype when the type is used as camera copy.

Typeface catalogs show specimen lines of type, printed in full size. Each specimen is iden- tified by its point (body) size, Fig. 4-8.

Printer's Measure

Printers use their special printer's measure system to designate and measure type sizes, length of type lines, and other measures deal- ing with type. In this system, a *point* is about

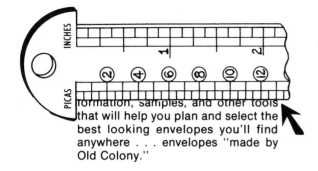

formation, samples, and other tools that will help you plan and select the best looking envelopes you'll find anywhere . . . envelopes "made by Old Colony."

Fig. 4-9. Measuring line length with a line gauge. These lines are 13 picas long.

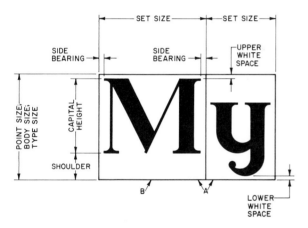

Fig. 4-10. The designer builds in some white space around each character image.
A. Design outlines of typical phototype and metal type characters.
B. A square whose set width equals its body size is called an "em."

1/72″, and 12 points equal a *pica*. Six picas equal about an inch. See Table 4-1.

Table 4-1
Printer's Measure

1 point	= 1/12 pica	= .01383″	= about 1/72″
6 points	= 1/2 pica	a nonpareil	
12 points	= 1 pica	= .16600″	= about 1/6″
72 points	= 6 picas	= .99600″	= about 1″

The *em* is another common unit of measure. The width of an em is equal to its type body size. See *B*, Fig. 4-10. Thus, when 10-point type

is used, an indention of 1 em is an indention of 10 points. In a 12-point type, an em is 1 pica (or 12 points) wide. An *en* is half the width of an em.

The term *agate* formerly denoted the 5½-point size of type. Now the term is used as a basis for pricing columnar advertising in newspapers and magazines. A single-column ad, 1″ deep, is assumed to have 14 agate lines, regardless of the actual number of lines of type in that inch. A single-column ad, 2″ deep, would be priced at 28 agate lines. A 2-column by 3″ ad would be priced at 84 agate lines — 2 × 3″ × 14.

The *length* and *width* of type forms are measured with a *line gauge*. The gauge is marked in *picas*. Laid on a line of type, the gauge may show the line as 13 picas long. Its *measure*, then, is 13 picas. See Fig. 4-9. A type form (page of type matter) may be said to be 28 × 47 picas — 28 picas wide and 47 picas deep. Always give the width first and then the depth or height.

Measuring Type Size of the Printed Image

The actual height of a printed typeface image will measure *less* than its rated type size (body size). This difference will vary among different designs of typefaces of the same type size.

In preparing a matrix design for a character, the type designer starts with a definite body size. The designer allows some white space at the top, bottom, and sides of the letter, Fig. 4-10. This white space provides a minimum automatic amount of spacing between adjacent characters. It also provides space between lines of type that are set *solid* as shown in *A* of Fig. 4-13. (Solid type has no extra space, called leading, added between lines of type. See "Leading," below.)

Type size can be estimated in several ways. Figure 4-11 shows how to estimate the body size when only a single line of printed type is available. In this method, a little white space is allowed above the cap line and below the descender line of the image. Figure 4-12 shows how to arrive at body size when at least two lines of the same size are set solid. In this method, measurement is from baseline to baseline of two successive lines. Finally, type size can be estimated by comparing a line of type with identical type in a type specimen catalog.

Leading. When space is inserted between lines, it is called leading (pronounced lĕdding). This term is derived from a practice in metal typesetting of placing thin strips of lead between successive lines of type. Now it is generally meant as the providing of vertical space

between the descenders of one line of type and the ascenders of the next line.

Examples of *leaded* and *solid* composition are shown in Fig. 4-13. Type which is set *solid* (without leading) saves space. However, leaded lines are cleaner and easier to read.

Line Spacing. Line spacing is measured from baseline to baseline of two consecutive

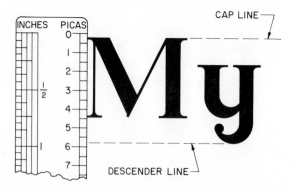

Fig. 4-11. If only one line of printed type is available, the type's body size can be estimated by measuring from cap line to descender line and allowing a little white space top and bottom. This type is probably 72 points (6 picas).

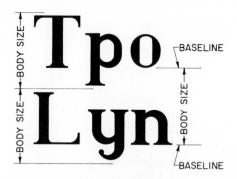

Fig. 4-12. Body size of printed type can be accurately obtained by measuring from baseline to baseline of two consecutive lines of type of the same size which are set solid.

LINE SPACING 12 pts. — **These lines of type are set "solid." That is, there is no extra space between each two lines of type. Does it seem to you that the lines are too crowded?**

A. 12-point Souvenir Bold, set solid.

LINE SPACING 14 pts. — **These lines are set with two points of space between each two lines. This is known as "leaded 2 points," or "2-point leaded." With this leading, don't you agree the type is easier to read?**

B. 12-point Souvenir Bold, leaded 2 points.

These lines are set "4-point leaded" which allows lots of air between lines. Does this much more leading improve the legibility? Line for line, this occupies more space on the page than the two examples above. — LINE SPACING 16 pts.

C. 12-point Souvenir Bold, leaded 4 points.

Fig. 4-13. Solid and leaded composition.

lines of type. It includes the body size of the type, *plus the added vertical space (leading) between the two lines*, Fig. 4-13. In phototypesetting, line spacing is the vertical distance that the phototypesetting paper (or film) is advanced for the next line of composition. This may also be referred to as film advance, line feed, or line advance. The terms "line spacing" and "leading" are sometimes confused.

Other Composition Formats

Planning the production of a printed item also requires decisions on the composition style, or *format*, to be used. This includes the paragraphs, blocks of type and pages of type matter as well as type style and leading. Various formats are shown in Figs. 4-14 through 4-26. Note the information given within each figure.

THESE LINES ARE SET IN **ALL CAPITAL** LETTERS, USUALLY REFERRED TO AS **ALL CAPS.** IT IS COMMONLY USED IN TITLES AND HEADLINES. DO NOT USE IT FOR MORE THAN A FEW LINES OF BODY TYPE.

A. All caps.

These lines are set in **capitals and lowercase letters.** This style is referred to as **caps and lowercase** and is abbreviated **caps & l.c.** or **c & l.c.** It is universally used for body type in most books, newspapers, and magazines and is the most legible of all combinations.

B. Caps and lowercase.

These Lines Show **Lowercase with Initial Caps.** It is Useful Sometimes for a Heading or Title.

C. Initial caps and lowercase.

THESE LINES ARE SET IN CAPS AND SMALL CAPS, ALSO CALLED SMALL CAPS WITH INITIAL CAPS. FULL-SIZE CAPS AND SMALL CAPS ARE AVAILABLE IN SOME TYPE FONTS. CHECK YOUR TYPE CATALOGS.

D. Caps and small caps.

Fig. 4-14. Four choices between uses of caps, small caps, and lowercase letters.

This is **hyphenated-and-justified** composition. All lines are word-spaced so that they extend the full measure. End-of-line hyphenation is used when necessary to divide a word. A short last line is ended by **quadding left.**

Fig. 4-15. Paragraph with square indention, which is really no indention. This is hyphenated-and-justified (H&J) composition.

This composition is **justified,** but not hyphenated. At times, the decision against hyphenation results in abnormally wide space between words in some lines; or **occasionally letterspacing is** used to justify a line.

Fig. 4-16. Paragraph with normal indention. Indent one em for lines up to 24 picas and 2 ems for longer lines. Very small type can take wider indentions. Lines are justified here, but hyphenation at end of lines is not used.

This is an example of a **hanging indention.** The first line hangs over into the left-hand margin. All other lines (except a short last line) are justified.

Fig. 4-17. Paragraph with hanging indention.

These lines are set **quadded left.** Another name for this format, or style, of composition is **flush left and ragged right.** In this format, all lines begin flush left except for possible paragraph indention. No justification is used. End-of-line hyphenation may or may not be used. Does this style appeal to you?

Fig. 4-18. Quadded left; or flush left and ragged right. This format might save time where hyphenation and justification involve manual operation by the phototypesetter operator.

1/8 inch	3.175 mm
1/4 inch	6.350 mm
3/8 inch	9.525 mm
1/2 inch	12.700 mm

A. Without leaders.

5/8 inch	15.875 mm
3/4 inch	19.050 mm
7/8 inch	22.225 mm
1 inch	25.400 mm

B. With leaders.

Fig. 4-21. Flush left and right, or quadded left and right.

This format is often called a **run-around.** The lines are shortened where needed to run around an illustra- tion which is less than full column width. In narrow measure, this may result sometimes in unwelcome amounts of let- terspacing in the shortened lines. Note examples of runarounds in magazines and newspapers.

Fig. 4-22. A run-around.

These lines are set **quadded right.** This is also called **flush right and ragged left.** In this format, the lines are flush at the right side, but begin randomly at the left. Hyphenation and justification are not used.

Fig. 4-19. Quadded right, or flush right and ragged left.

This style of composition
is known as
centered
or
quadded center.
It is widely used for
invitations
announcements
and
headings or titles.

Fig. 4-20. Centered lines, or quadded center. These lines are not justified or hyphenated, but have equal spacing (quadding) at both ends of each line.

THIS paragraph begins with an initial letter. This large first letter draws the eye to the starting place. This is called a **sunken initial,** since it is within the body of type matter.

A. Sunken initial letter.

ANOTHER form of initial letter is the **raised initial.** Its base line aligns with the base line of the first line of type. Its left side is flush with the col- umn. Which of the two initial letters do you prefer? Look for other ex- amples in your reading.

B. Raised initial letter.

Fig. 4-23. Two forms of the initial letter.

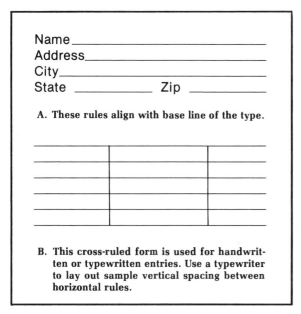

Name _____
Address _____
City _____
State _____ Zip _____

A. These rules align with base line of the type.

B. This cross-ruled form is used for handwritten or typewritten entries. Use a typewriter to lay out sample vertical spacing between horizontal rules.

Fig. 4-24. Samples of ruled forms.

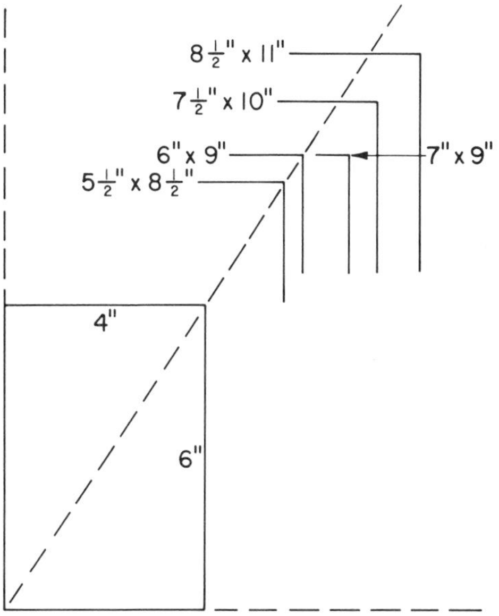

Fig. 4-27. The 4-to-6 proportion makes a pleasing page shape, and often cuts economically from stock-size sheets.

Amount of Albumin Solution

Degrees Baume	Milli- liters	U.S. Liquid Ounces
5.1	344	$11^5/_8$
5.2	336	$11^3/_8$
5.3	333	$11^1/_4$
5.4	325	11

Fig. 4-25. An example of multiple justification or tabular composition. Leaders are optional.

Amount of Albumin Solution		
Degrees Baumé	Milliliters	U.S. Liquid Ounces
5.1	344	$11^5/_8$
5.2	336	$11^3/_8$
5.3	333	$11^1/_4$
5.4	325	11

Fig. 4-26. This tabular composition has the same information as Fig. 4-25, but is set with crossrules.

Page or Sheet Proportions

Good proportion adds to the attractiveness of a printed product. A popular proportion is 4″-to-6″, Fig. 4-27. This proportion can be extended by a diagonal line to arrive at other pleasing page sizes.

For double (facing) pages, the proportions in Fig. 4-28 are pleasing. The narrower gutter margins at A and B seem to draw the type on the two pages together. Each gutter is about 1/8th the width of a whole page. To obtain the other proportions, see suggestions in Fig. 4-28.

The Layout

A full-size plan or *layout* of the product to be printed must be drawn up in detailed form before the actual production work can begin. Also, the layout must contain instructions that tell each worker exactly what is to be done. It is vitally important that the customer approve the layout before the printing process starts since the customer alone knows exactly what is desired.

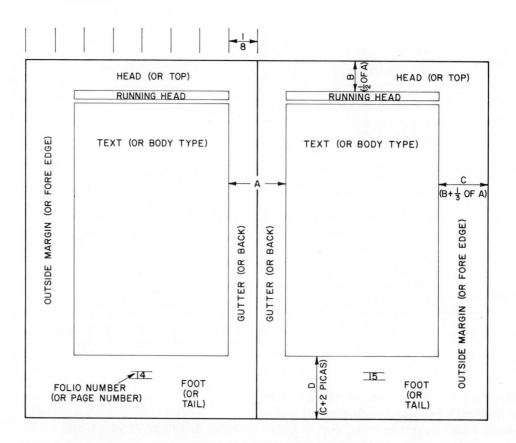

Fig. 4-28. **Proportions and anatomy of a pair of facing book pages. Page proportions are in the 4-to-6 ratio. Each gutter is 1/8 the width of the page. Both gutters combined are referred to as "A", in the above diagram. The head "B" equals 1/2 of "A". "C" equals "B" plus 1/3 "A". "D" equals "C" plus 2 picas.**

In an offset shop which employs few workers, the shop owner, supervisor, or compositor may make the layouts. In large shops, specialists in layout are employed. In some cases, customers may have their work planned and laid out by commercial advertising agencies who specialize in this work, or they may employ layout artists on their own advertising staff.

Equipment and Materials

The layout artist may work at a drafting table or artist's table. The usual equipment includes type specimen books and sheets, copyfitting tables, paper catalogs, ink charts, and drawing board. Other items used are T-square, triangles, French curves, proportional rule, scales (rulers), various grades and colors of pencils, drawing inks, drafting tools or instruments, erasers, airbrush and crayons. Also, a supply of various grades of layout paper and tracing paper should be on hand for making the layouts and for tracing large letters and illustrations.

Traditional Balanced Design

At one time it was customary to use a job or page design that balanced on a vertical center axis. In this type of design the weight of the type was at the optical center of the page, or about 3/5 from the bottom, Fig. 4-29. The choice of type was limited to one typeface, perhaps in several sizes. Sometimes a few words in a contrasting type were used. This balanced design is still used occasionally.

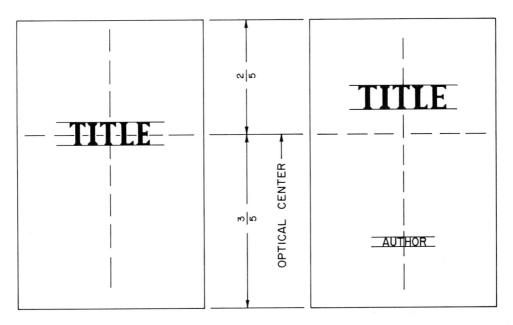

Fig. 4-29. The traditional page design was centered on a vertical axis. The weight of the type mass aimed at, or balanced, at the optical center of the page (about 3/5 from the bottom).

Today, the various styles of layouts defy classification. It is best to study current styles and adopt whatever seems attractive and legible. Formal courses in design would be most beneficial.

Thumbnail Sketches

Before a full-size layout is attempted, a number of small thumbnail sketches are made. Various arrangements can be explored until both the layout artist and the customer or account executive are pleased.

Rough Layouts

Working from the selected thumbnail sketch, the layout artist makes a rough layout. It shows how the finished job may look in full size, Fig. 4-30. The full-size rough also gives some idea of the proper sizes of type to use and the required sizes of the illustrations.

Comprehensive Layouts

When the rough layout seems promising, the artist makes a comprehensive layout. This layout will resemble, as closely as possible, the desired finished job.

The Biddle Company

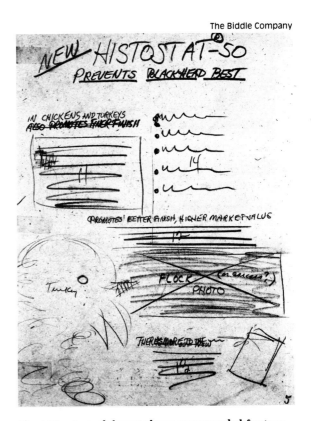

Fig. 4-30. A rough layout shows areas needed for type.

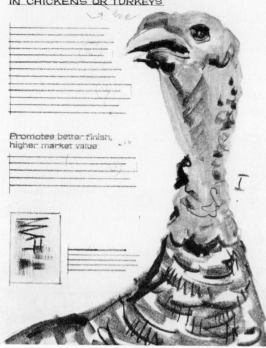

Fig. 4-31. Artist's layout provides copy space and shows art needed.

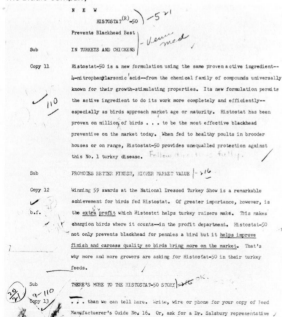

Fig. 4-32. Prepared copy marked for composition.

NEW HISTOSTAT-50

PREVENTS BLACKHEAD BEST IN TURKEYS CHICKENS AND

Histostat-50 is a new formulation using the same proven active ingredient—4-nitrophenylarsonic acid—from the chemical family of compounds universally known for their growth-stimulating properties. Its new formulation permits the active ingredient to do its work more completely and efficiently—especially as birds approach market age or maturity. Histostat has been proven on millions of birds . . . to be the most effective blackhead preventive on the market today. When fed to healthy poults in brooder houses or on range, Histostat-50 provides unequalled protection against this No. 1 turkey disease. Follow directions fully.

Promotes better finish, higher market value

Winning 59 awards at the National Dressed Turkey Show is a remarkable achievement for birds fed Histostat. Of greater importance, however, is the **extra profit** which Histostat helps turkey raisers make. This makes champion birds where it counts—in the profit department. Histostat-50 not only prevents blackhead for pennies a bird but it *helps improve finish and carcass quality so birds bring more on the market.* That's why more and more growers are asking for Histostat-50 in their turkey feeds.

There's more to the Histostat-50 story

. . . than we can tell here. Write, wire or phone for your copy of Feed Manufacturer's Guide No. 16. Or, ask for a Dr. Salsbury representative to call and personally answer your questions about using Histostat-50.

- **PALATABLE.** Birds don't back away from Histostat-50.
- **ECONOMICAL.** Even on a continuous program, Histostat-50 costs only a few cents a bird—2 turkeys saved will pay for medication for 100.
- **COMPATIBLE.** Can be used with normal feed ingredients.
- **STABLE.** Histostat-50 is a chemically stable powder—will not lose its effectiveness during handling or storage. Unaffected by pelleting or other feed ingredients.

Fig. 4-33. Etch proofs pasted in position for camera.

Fig. 4-34. Printed piece.

The layout is made on a sheet of the stock to be used for the product. The sheet is marked off to the exact finished (trimmed) size. The layout indicates the display lines of type, the body type, and any hand art and illustrations, Fig. 4-31. Spaces in which mounted proofs may be placed are left in the layout sheet for these illustrations.

Indicating Display Lines of Type

Type that is 14 points and larger is generally referred to as *display type*. It is drawn on the comprehensive layout in actual size and form. Sometimes it is traced from specimen sheets or type tracing cards and pasted in place, Fig. 4-35. The desired leading between lines also should be shown. Some representative type fonts in the various styles are shown in Fig. 4-36 to guide you in drawing these display lines.

A notation is made at the side of the layout, indicating the size and face of the type, its manufacturer, and catalog or reference number, if any. The reference should clearly identify the kind of type — hand- or machine-set metal type, phototype, or other. It should also specify length of line and the position of words in the line. For example, a sample copy notation (marking) for a display line may read: 72-point Souvenir Bold, all caps, Compugraphic, 48 picas, centered.

Indicating Text Type

Typefaces 12 points and smaller are called *text* or *body* types. These are the sizes which are used for newspaper columns, book pages, and general reading matter. Generally, the most legible body type composition consists of 10- to 12-point type. It is set in lines which are equal in length to 1½ to 2½ times the length of the lowercase alphabet of that particular typeface.

Text (or body matter) matter is generally shown on the layout by a rectangle the exact width and depth (in picas) that the type matter

Fig. 4-35. A type tracing card. Vertical lines at ends of lines show vertical space occupied by typeface plus descender (reduced).

VariTyper Corporation

A SCRIPT TYPE — ROYAL SCRIPT

A B C D E F G H I J K L M N O P Q R S T U

V W X Y Z   abcdefghijklmnopqrstuvwxyz

1234567890   .,-?!&$¢

A SCRIPT TYPE — CORONET BOLD

A B C D E F G H I J K L M N O P Q R S T U V W X Y Z

abcdefghijklmnopqrstuvwxyz

1234567890   "-?!.$¢

A SCRIPT TYPE — BRUSH

A B C D E F G H I J K L M N O P Q R S T U V W X Y Z &

abcdefghijklmnopqrstuvwxyz

1234567890   "-?!.$¢

A ROMAN TYPE — TIMES NEW ROMAN

ABCDEFGHIJKLMNOPQRSTUVWXYZ&

abcdefghijklmnopqrstuvwxyz

1234567890 ()?!.,:;-‘’*°+×=#@.,-/%£$¢

AN ITALIC TYPE — TIMES NEW ROMAN ITALIC

ABCDEFGHIJKLMNOPQRSTUVWXYZ&

abcdefghijklmnopqrstuvwxyz

1234567890 ()?!.,:;-‘’°+×=#@ -%/£$¢*

A BOLD-FACE ROMAN TYPE — BODONI BOLD

ABCDEFGHIJKLMNOPQRSTUVWXYZ&

abcdefghijklmnopqrstuvwxyz

1234567890 ‘’.,-?!$¢

Fig. 4-36. Specimen type fonts.

will occupy when set. Individual lines of text type may be indicated by parallel lines to show the height of the lowercase and capital letters.

Notations on the typewritten copy or the layout tell the compositor what face, leading, and line length are to be used. A *key* (reference) marking in the text-matter rectangle identifies the typewritten copy to set for that space.

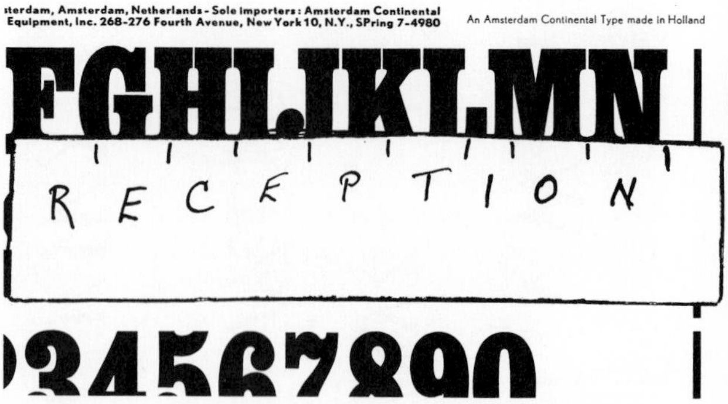

Copyfitting

It saves time and labor to know, in advance of setting the type, whether or not the type will fit in the available space. Therefore, the typewritten copy is measured to determine the number of lines of type that will result at a given width.

Display Type

Finding out how much space a word or group of words will require if set in display type requires the use of a specimen sheet for the type being used. Take a strip of paper and mark off on it the exact widths of each letter and space in the line on the specimen sheet. Then transfer the measurement to the layout. See Fig. 4-37.

• •Text Type

To find out, in advance, how many lines of text type must be set, use the following method:

1. *Number of characters in the copy.* Determine how many typewritten characters there are in the total copy.
   a. Find the number of typewriter characters in *one inch* of the typewritten copy. (Pica typewriter type is 10 characters per inch; elite typewriter type is 12 characters per inch.)
   b. Multiply the *average length* of copy lines (in inches) by the number of typewriter characters per inch. The result is the number of typewriter characters per line of copy.
   c. Multiply the number of typewriter characters per line by the number of type-written lines in the copy. The result is the

Fig. 4-37. **Using a strip of paper to copyfit a display line from type tracing card.**

number of typewriter characters on the page.

> • **Note:** In computing typewriter characters per inch, per line, and per page, *punctuation marks and spaces are included.*

d. Multiply the number of typewriter characters per page by the number of pages of copy to find the total number of typewriter characters in the job. In counting the number of pages in the copy, make allowance for partial pages of copy, and spaces left for illustrations on the copy pages.

> • **Note:** It will aid greatly if the typist types all lines the same width and an equal number of lines per page.

2. *Number of lines of type required.* Determine how many lines of type must be set for the total amount of copy. To do this, you must know the size and face of the type, the name of the manufacturer, whether it is hand or machine set, and the *length of line in picas* to which the type will be set.

   a. Measure (compare) the length of type line required, *in picas,* against an actual printed specimen of the type to be used. Count the number of *type* characters contained in this number of picas. This is the number of type characters required to set one line of type at the given length.

American Type Founders Company, Inc.

12 POINT BODONI BOOK AND ITALIC. The bod·
faces shown on this and accompanying pages are
of the famous types of printing history. They c
wide range of styles making easy the selection
correct body type for any piece of printing. The
have been made long enough to be of service in
lating copy space. All the faces of each size hav

12 POINT BODONI AND ITALIC. The body type
shown on this and accompanying pages are
of the famous types of printing history. They
a wide range of styles making easy the select
the correct body type for any piece of pri
The lines have been made long enough to
service in calculating copy space. All the fa

**12 Point Bodoni Bold and Italic. The body
faces shown on this and accompanying
are some of the famous types of printing
tory. They cover a wide range of styles m:
easy the selection of the correct body typ
any piece of printing. The lines are made
*enough to be of service in calculating copy***

12 Point Bernhard Modern Roman and Itali
body type faces shown on this and accompa
pages are some of the famous types of printin
tory. They cover a wide range of styles makin
the selection of the correct body type for any
of printing. The lines have been made long e
to be of service in calculating copy space. All th

Fig. 4-38. **Legible body types (part of a specimen sheet).**

• **Note:** It is best to check the number
of characters in several lines of the required length (or of a much longer line)
and divide by the number of lines to obtain an average number of characters
per line of type.

In counting type characters, include
punctuation marks and spaces.
b. Divide the total number of *typewritten*
characters in the job by the number of
type characters required for one line of
the desired length. The result is the *total
number of lines of type* for the required
length of line.

Type founders and manufacturers of
typecasting and slug-casting machines furnish
character counts per pica for their typefaces,
Fig. 4-8. These are preferred by some for
copyfitting.

Leading Between Lines

The amount of vertical space which will be
occupied in a column by one line of type equals
the body size of that type plus the thickness of
the leading used between lines of type in the
column. See Fig. 4-13. For example, if 12-point
type is used, and 2-point leading is used between lines, each line of type will actually account for 14 points of vertical measure in the
column. Also, if 12-point type is set with 4
points of lead between lines, each line of type
will actually account for 14 points of vertical
measure in the column.

• **Note:** There is no leading beneath the bottom
line of type in a form.

If the type is set solid, the depth of the column or page would be equal to the body size of
the type multiplied by the number of lines of
type in the column.

To determine how many lines of a certain
size type will fit in a given depth of page, find
the depth of the page in points (picas × 12);
then subtract one thickness of leading from the
depth of the page; finally, divide this result by
the size of the type plus the amount of leading
between lines. For example: How many lines of
10-point type will fit on a page 40 picas deep if
the type to be set is leaded 4 points?

a. 10-point type + 4-point leading = 14 pts.
per line
b. 40-pica depth × 12 pts. per pica = 480
pts. depth.
c. 480 pts. − 4-point leading = 476 pts.
depth. (You subtract 4 points because
there is no leading below the last line in
the type page.)
d. 476 pts. ÷ 14 = 34 lines.

Typing Line-for-Line

If there are to be several pages of typed
copy, the typist should type the copy so that
each line of typing will equal a line of type

when the type is set. Also, the typist should type each page to contain the same number of lines as there will be lines of type on the page.

Find out from the type specimen book how many type characters will be contained in a type line of the planned length. Set the typewriter carriage for this number of characters. Try to maintain this average number of typewriter characters on each line.

Typewriter paper can be preprinted with faint vertical lines showing the desired width of the lines to be typed. This will show whether the typist is overrunning the line. An overrun line can be balanced by underrunning the following line.

Illustrations

The exact space to be occupied by an illustration should be indicated on the layout. It can be shown by a rectangle of the desired size or by a profile outline. Mark each space reserved for an illustration by using a key letter, number or title that corresponds to the marking on the illustration. This will help to insure that illustrations will be correctly located in the printed product.

To improve the layout, the illustration may be sketched in the allotted space, or a proof of it may be pasted in the space. A more convincing layout is achieved if color is used to simulate the job as it will appear when printed.

The Dummy

For a printed product having a number of pages, a dummy is required. It serves as a pattern for arrangement of the elements. To prepare a dummy, secure a number of pieces of the stock to be used. Cut these to a size that, after folding once, will be the untrimmed page size of the product. Prepare a piece of cover stock of the same size (after folding).

Assemble the cover and sufficient folded sheets. Staple them once through the fold, near the top. Number the pages in the lower outside corners consecutively, beginning with "1" on the first right-hand page.

Cut a number of pieces of stock, each the final untrimmed-page size of the booklet page. These page-size pieces will serve as layout sheets for the pages of the booklet. (Page proofs may be used instead.) When laid out, these single pages will be attached to the dummy pages. The outside cover will be clipped to the outside cover of the dummy. The title page will be clipped to page 1 if it is desired there and remaining pages clipped where desired in the dummy. On each single page, indicate the actual page number it will carry when printed.

Each page should be laid out completely for the job. Ruled lines should be drawn to indicate the space to be occupied by the body type. Display type, ornaments and illustrations should be indicated in their actual size and in the exact position. Dimensions must be given for the width and depth of the printed page and the location of the page numbers and running heads. If the page has more than one column, the width of the columns and the spacing between columns must be specified. Typefaces, sizes, and length of line must be indicated.

Draw trim lines on the cover and pages to indicate the appearance after trimming head, foot and outside edge of the printed and folded booklet. Indicate all margins to show how much white space will remain at the head, gutter (next to the fold), foot, and outside margin (or fore edge).

In short, the dummy must be made to look as much like the finished work as possible. Yet, while still in the planning stage, individual pages can be shifted, added, or removed without much trouble. Once the dummy is approved, the pages can be made up and production can start.

Questions

1. The cap height of a letter extends from the cap line to what line?
2. Name two styles of typefaces that are difficult to read when set in all capitals.
3. What is a series of type?
4. How many points in a pica? How many picas in an inch?
5. A 24-point en is how many picas wide?
6. How is the size of type estimated if only one printed line is available?
7. What is meant by having type set solid? How would you measure the size of printed type that has been set solid?

8. What is leaded type?
9. Explain hyphenated and justified composition.
10. What is another name for quadded left composition?
11. What composition format is popular for invitations and formal announcements?
12. What arithmetic proportion (ratio) results in a pleasing page shape?
13. Where is the optical center of a page?
14. What are thumbnail sketches?
15. What is a comprehensive layout?
16. How is display type indicated on the comprehensive layout? How is body type indicated? How are illustrations indicated?
17. What does each item in the following copy markups indicate?
    a. 12-point Korinna Bold (Compugraphic), 2-points leaded, H&J, 24 picas, caps and l.c.
    b. 18-point Megaron Bold (Varityper), centered, 36 picas, all caps.
18. How is keying done?
19. Of what value is a dummy?
20. Tell how to copyfit display type.
21. Tell how to copyfit body type.

Problems and Projects

1. Make a list of the display type in your shop, listing the faces of the type and the body sizes of each. Repeat the procedure, this time listing the body (text) type in the shop.
2. List tools, materials, and equipment for layout work which the shop is lacking. Consult current catalogs and make out a requisition for ordering this material. Use company names, catalog numbers, catalog date, item name as used in catalog and include size, finish, color, price, and other information needed to describe specifically the items desired.
3. Make layouts — thumbnails, roughs, then comprehensives — for the following:
    a. Personal card, imprinted note paper and return envelope.
    b. Greeting card — single sheet, folded sheet, or French fold.
    c. Matched set of business card, letterhead, envelope corner, check and stub, and billhead.
    d. Menu.
    e. Four-page program (for a graduation, musicale, school play, etc.)
    f. Poster or show card.
4. Mount a collection of printed samples of one of the above-mentioned items on full-size sheets of heavy board.
5. Redesign a printed job which is used in your school shop or business. Make a comprehensive layout. Decide whether your new design will more economically utilize a stock size of paper.
6. Plan a job which will require a dummy and copyfitting of both display and text type and which, when printed, will be of practical use in the shop.

New Terms

agate	leading
ascender	lowercase
descender	nonpareil
display	phototypesetting
em	pi
face	proportions
gutter	script
initial	serif
justified	

CHAPTER 5

Type Composition for Reproduction

Any method of type composition may be used to set copy that is to be printed by photo-offset lithography. This includes long-standing methods of composition as well as the newer methods that have developed as a result of the invention of the offset process. The various means of type composition may be classified as either hot type or cold type.

Hot Type. In hot type composition (also called three-dimensional type), relief printing type characters are cast from molten metal. Examples of hot type composition methods are foundry type, Monotype, Linotype, Intertype, Ludlow (all metal types), wood type, and letterpress printing plates.

Cold Type. The cold type process (also called two-dimensional type) does not use molten metal to cast images. Rather, the composition is produced on paper or on film. Methods of cold type production include mechanical composition, impact (strike-on) composition, phototype composition, and photocopying.

In mechanical composition, the matter to be reproduced is either drawn by the artist or pasted up from preprinted sheets of commercial lettering or artwork. Artists draw their material either freehand or by using various instruments, such as compasses, stenciling devices, and special pens. Clip art and preprinted type come in prepared sheets or books and are available for immediate paste-up on the mechanical layout.

Impact composition involves typewritten material generated on standard typewriters or on special typewriter-style machines. Characters are printed by means of a typing element which strikes a ribbon, thus transferring the image onto the paper.

In phototypesetting, light projection is used to produce type characters on phototypesetting paper or film. Varieties of phototype composition are called *photodisplay type* and *phototext type*. Photodisplay type, which ranges in size from 14 points upward, is used to attract attention. Newspaper headlines and title lines are examples. Type sizes (up to 12 or 14 points) used for columns of reading matter are called *text type*.

By means of photocopying existing material, the printed work is duplicated in whole or in part.

This chapter does not attempt to explain in detail how to perform the actual operation of setting type. Rather, it describes these methods and offers concepts that apply to the several methods of type composition. For detailed instructions in the actual composition of type, the reader is advised to consult standard reference books and the operator's manuals supplied by the manufacturers of specific makes and models of equipment.

Hot Type Composition

Metal Type

Metal type is set (composed) by hand or machine to form the lines of type for the intended pages. A proof is made of the type composition and is checked for errors.

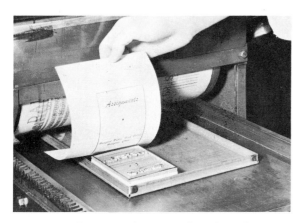

Fig. 5-1. **Pulling a proof from a galley of metal type.**

Reproduction Proofs

After proofreading and correction of errors, reproduction proofs are taken on dull, coated, white paper using black ink, Fig. 5-1. These reproduction proofs are also called *repros, etch proofs, slicks,* or *offset slicks.* The proofs, which must be clean and sharp, are then photographed, possibly being reduced or enlarged in size, to produce a film negative. Sometimes a film positive is made for platemaking. Repro proofs may also be "pulled" on cellophane or acetate. These may be used as film positives, or they also may be contact-printed photographically on film to produce film negatives.

Reproduction proofs are proofs to be photographed for platemaking. They should be pulled from newly cast type or from type reserved only for proofs. Worn and battered type may not produce clean, sharp proofs. The proof press used should be reserved only for reproduction proofs. If possible, it should be equipped with grippers and a good inking mechanism which will produce consecutive proofs with identical density of ink.

Cellophane reproduction proofs are best made on a proof press equipped with a rubber tympan sheet (blanket). The inked type is first run through the proof press with no paper over the type, thus printing directly on the blanket. Then the cellophane sheet is laid over the type, and the proof is pulled. This results in printing on both sides of the cellophane and makes the image more dense.

Current practice in the industry is to send reproduction proofs to the camera department made up in page form. Headings are in place. Necessary spacing has been placed between lines and paragraphs, and all lines are ruled in for ruled forms. In this way, the resulting negative of a complete page is ready for the stripping operation.

When enlarging or reducing type, the beauty of the original type design must not be sacrificed. Too great a reduction in size may weaken or obliterate the finer lines of the type. Conversely, too great an enlargement may coarsen or excessively darken those same fine lines.

Type Sizes

Metal type sizes are determined by the measurement (in points) of the entire body from back to belly. See Fig. 5-2. Metal types have a space beneath most characters, called the *shoulder.* This space allows for descending strokes, as "y" or "p" in Fig. 5-3, and for space between lines. This shoulder is included when measuring the body size of the type.

A printer's line gauge is used to measure the size of metal type. In Fig. 5-2, the type character measures 6 picas from back to belly. Since there are 12 points to the pica, the body

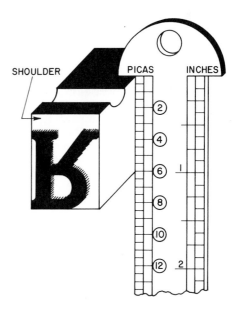

Fig. 5-2. **Measuring body size of foundry type with a line gauge. This is 72-point type. (12 points equals 1 pica.)**

American Type Founders Company, Inc.

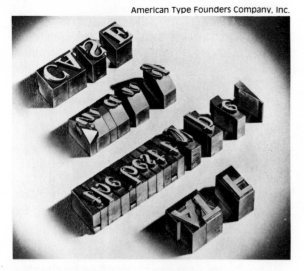

Fig. 5-3. Foundry type.

size of this type is 72 points. If a size of metal type is specified as 72/60 or 72 on 60, it indicates that the typeface is a 72-point face and the body size is 60 points. If the type size is specified as 14/16, or 14 on 16, it indicates a 14-point face on a 16-point body. The extra shoulder width eliminates the need for inserting a 2-point lead between lines. This type can be set solid, and yet appear as though leaded. This is a real time-saver.

All metal type used in the United States is cast to be .918″ high, commonly expressed as

American Type Founders Company, Inc.

AAAAAAAABBBBBBBBCCCCCCCCCCEEEEEEEEEEE″″″
BBBBBFFFFFGGGGGGHHHHHHJJJJJJJJJJJJJJJJK
KKLLLLLLMMMMMMMNNNNNNNOOOOOOOO!!PPP
PPPPPPQQQRRRRRRRSSSSSSSSSSSSSSTTTTTTTTTTTTH
HHPPPPWWWWWWWXXYYYYZZ&&ĥĥĥĥĥĥ,.,.,.:::..........---??

aaaaaaaaaaaaaaaaaaaaabbbbbbbbbbccccccccccc,......ddddddddddd
ddeeeeeeeeeeeeeeeeeeeeeeeeeeeeeffffffffffgggggggggghhhhhhhhhhh
hhhiiiiiiiiiiiiiiiiiiiiiiijjjjjjkkkkkklllllllllllll---mmmmmmmmmmmm
mmmmmmmmmmmmmmmmmmmmmmmmmnooooooooooooooooooooooo??pppp
ppppqqqqrrrrrrrrrrrrrrrrrrrrrrrssssssssssssssssssss!!tttttt
tttttttttttttttuuuuuuuuuuuuuvvvvvvvwwwwwwwwyyyyyyyyyyzzzz
xxxxfifififififffffffflflflfifififififlflflflfffffffctctcto'ro'ro'r,......,:::..........″″″

1111111112222222233333334444444555555556666666---
,....,.......777777788888888999999990000000000000$$$$$$$$

Fig. 5-4. A font of foundry type as received from the foundry. This is 18-point Engravers Old English (148), reduced.

"point nine one eight." The measurement is from the feet to the face of the type. It is referred to as *type high.*

The use of metal type is fast declining in favor of the newer photographically set type and other kinds of two-dimensional type. However, the language and the concepts applied to the newer typesetting methods are evolved from the practice of metal type composition. Several kinds of the traditionally popular metal type in use are described below.

Foundry Type

Foundry type is cast, or produced, by a type foundry in individual oblong units called *types* or *characters,* Fig. 5-3. Each has on one end a "wrong-reading" letter in relief. (Wrong-reading refers to reading from right to left.) Printers purchase foundry type in *fonts.* Fonts are complete collections or assortments of letters, figures, and punctuation marks of one size and typeface style, Fig. 5-4. The quantities of each letter in a font of foundry type are supplied according to the frequency of its normal use in printing. Blank units of various widths, called *spaces,* are used to provide the spacing between words and where needed at other points in the composition.

Foundry type is stored in typecases, Fig. 5-5. The compositor, or typesetter, picks out individual characters from the typecase and puts them in order in a composing stick which has been set to the desired length of line, Fig. 5-6. The compositor inserts spaces or quads[1] between words to make the lines of equal length (justifying). Quads and spaces are also used to provide indentions and fill out the last line of a paragraph.

Space between lines of foundry type is provided by inserting thin, 2-point strips of lead called *leads* (pronounced "leds"). Strips 6 points or more in thickness are called *slugs.*

Composed type is then placed on a traylike *galley* which is placed on the bed of a proof press. The type is inked with a brayer, covered with a clean sheet of paper, and a proof is

[1]Quads are wide spaces. The various quads used with foundry type are shown below the type case layout, in Fig. 5-5.

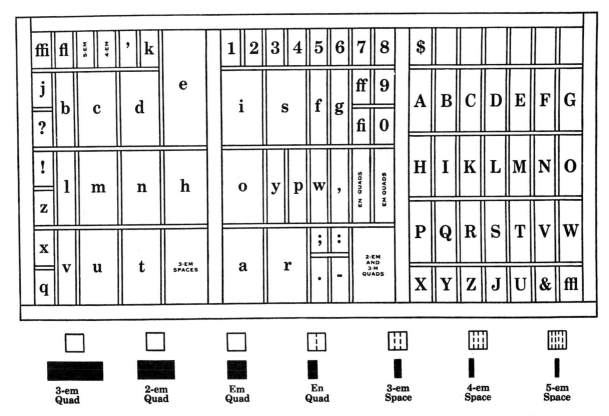

Fig. 5-5.   California Job Case layout showing usual arrangement of letters in a case for metal type. Below the case are the names and relative widths of spaces and quads. These blank pieces of type are inserted in the line for spacing.

taken as in Fig. 5-1. The galley proof is read for mistakes. Any mistakes discovered are corrected in the type form. After use, the type is cleaned of ink. It is then distributed back into the proper compartments of the type case for use when next needed. Because hand composition of type is an expensive operation, it is now largely replaced by machine methods, except sometimes for those cases where only a few lines of display are involved.

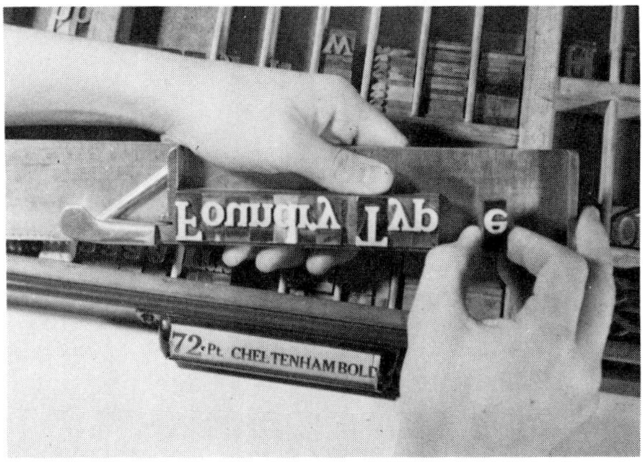

Monotype

Monotype is similar to foundry type in that it, too, is individual pieces of type. Unlike foundry type, however, Monotype is cast in the shop when needed, in complete lines of individual letters and spaces according to copy. Lines of single letters can also be cast for handsetting from type cases.

The Monotype system employs two machines: the keyboard machine and the caster, Figs. 5-7 and 5-8. An operator sits at the keyboard of the Monotype keyboard machine with the copy in

Fig. 5-6.   Setting type by hand from the case.

Monotype Corporation Limited

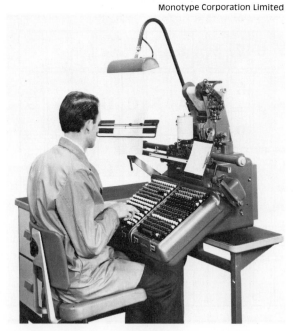

Fig. 5-7.   Monotype keyboard.

Monotype Corporation Limited

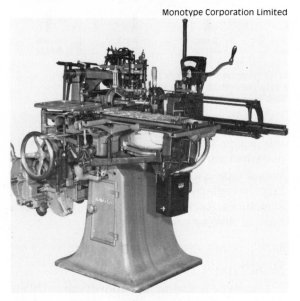

Fig. 5-8.   Monotype caster.

Lanston Monotype Company

Fig. 5-9.   Paper controller ribbon placed on Monotype caster.

Lanston Monotype Company

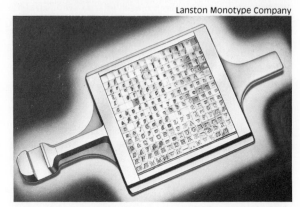

Fig. 5-10.   Monotype matrix case with 272 letter molds.

reading position. The operator manipulates the keys, selecting the desired letters and spacing combinations. In response, the machine perforates little holes in a controller ribbon (a roll of paper 4½″ wide) making a record of what is desired.

The ribbon is then removed from the keyboard machine and is placed on the Monotype caster, Fig. 5-9. On the caster machine, air is forced through the variously-placed holes in the ribbon. This causes the caster machine automatically to position the called-for matrix (mold) in place for the casting of the individual characters and spaces. See Fig. 5-10.

Complete lines of characters and spaces, as set from copy, are produced by the machine. Additional spacing between lines is provided by inserting leads and slugs.

After use, Monotype characters may be re-melted and the metal used for casting more type. Since Monotype lines are composed of individual characters, corrections may be made in a line without recasting the whole line. These individual characters make Monotype composition the preferred hot-type method of composing tabular matter, formulas, transportation timetables, run-arounds, and work requiring artistic letter-spacing.

Linotype and Intertype

The Linotype and the Intertype machines, although manufactured by different companies, are similar in appearance, operation and final product. Each machine casts solid pieces of metal (called slugs) with the characters for an entire line in relief on one narrow edge, Figs. 5-11 and 5-12. These lines of type are the required length for the job as predetermined. The proper spacing has been allowed between the words and elsewhere in the line. In the follow-

ing description of these line-casting machines, no distinction is made between the Linotype and Intertype line-casting machines.

Intertype Company

Fig. 5-12. **Intertype slug.**

Mergenthaler Linotype Company

Fig. 5-13. **Linotype Elektron II, manually operated, line-casting machine.**

Mergenthaler Linotype Company

Fig. 5-14. **Linotype keyboard.**

Mergenthaler Linotype Company

Fig. 5-11. **Linotype slugs.**

The line-casting machine carries at the top several magazines divided into channels (90 usually). Each channel holds a number of identical matrices of one character. In sizes of 14 point and less, each matrix has two molds for its character — a *regular* and an *auxiliary* position giving, for example, an italic or bold face version on the second mold. See Figs. 5-15 and 5-17.

The operator sits before the machine and manipulates the keys on the keyboard to select the letters or characters in the sequence of the copy. Each time a key is depressed, the escapement mechanism allows a corresponding matrix to drop from its channel onto a moving belt which assembles it with other matrices into a line. Between words, the operator depresses the spaceband key. This allows a two-piece wedge-shaped spaceband (Fig. 5-16) to fall into proper place between the lined-up matrices. After setting a line of matrices and spacebands, the operator sends that line on its way and commences setting another line.

Once composed, the line of *mats* (matrices) and spacebands is automatically taken over by the machine, Fig. 5-18. Upward pressure on the wedge-shaped spacebands between the words causes the line to be justified to length. The line of mats is then moved before a mold opening, molten metal is forced into the mold, resulting in a cast line of type called a *slug*. The slug is then automatically trimmed and ejected onto a galley.

The used mats are elevated to the top side of the magazine. They are then fed onto the distributor bar where the distributor screws push them along by the "ears" on the sides of the mats. On the distributor bar, the mats are

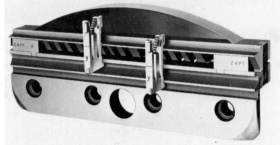

Fig. 5-17. Mold with matrices in regular and auxiliary positions.

Fig. 5-15. Linotype matrices shown in various views. Thickness "A" is known as the brass width of the characters.

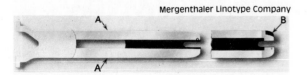

Fig. 5-16. Linotype spaceband showing the ribs at "A" and the clearance cut at "B".

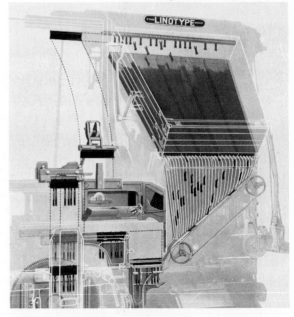

Fig. 5-18. Phantom view of linotype machine showing travel of mats and spacebands.

suspended by teeth which engage in corresponding slots in the distributor bar. The combinations of mat teeth and length of bar slots are such that, upon arriving above their respective magazine channels, each matrix is released to fall back where it originated so it may be ready for reuse.

After the slugs have been used, they are melted down. The metal then may be used for casting other slugs.

Usually, an error in a slug-cast line requires that the entire line be cast again, since it is one solid piece of metal.

Ludlow

The Ludlow machine produces a solid line of type (or slug) similar to the slug produced on the Linotype or Intertype machines, but it is hand-set, Fig. 5-20. The Ludlow method is not as fast as the Monotype, Intertype, or Linotype for straight body composition. However, it finds great use in display composition, especially for headings, advertisements, forms work, and wherever larger sizes of type are needed. It is faster than handsetting foundry type and gives the advantage of type which is always new and which needs only remelting after use.

In the Ludlow system, the compositor gathers the character matrices (molds) from the matrix case and assembles them, together with the space units, into the Ludlow matrix composing stick, Figs. 5-21 and 5-22. The matrix stick is then inserted into the Ludlow machine and locked into position for casting. Operation of the casting lever causes molten metal to be forced through the mouthpiece, against the matrices. The finished slug is then delivered on the galley at the front of the machine. By automatic recasting, any number of identical slugs can be cast from the same stickful of mats. The mats are then returned (distributed) into their case. Thus, fewer individual characters are needed than with foundry type.

Ludlow Typograph Company

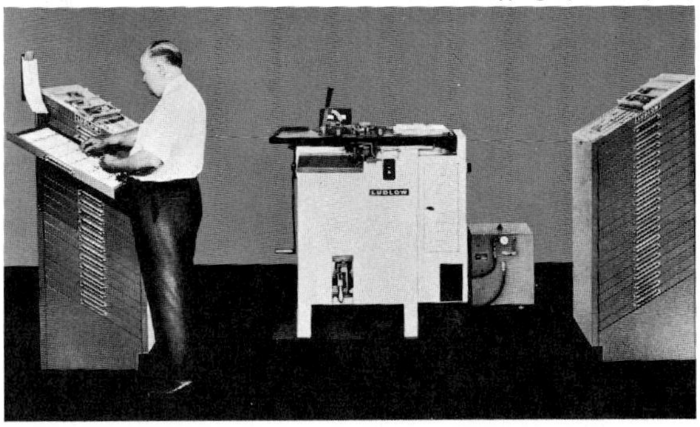

Fig. 5-19. Ludlow machine and matrix cabinets.

Ludlow Typograph Company

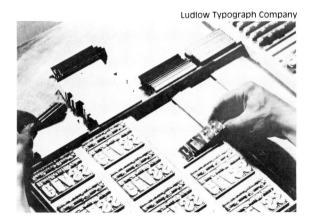

Fig. 5-20. Ludlow slugs.

Ludlow Typograph Company

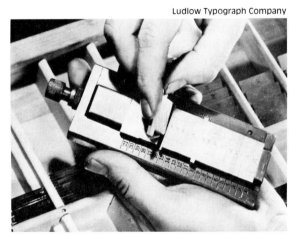

Fig. 5-21. Assembling Ludlow matrices in composing stick.

Ludlow Typograph Company

Fig. 5-22. Closeup view of Ludlow matrices in a composing stick.

Fig. 5-23. Casting Ludlow slugs.

RIG

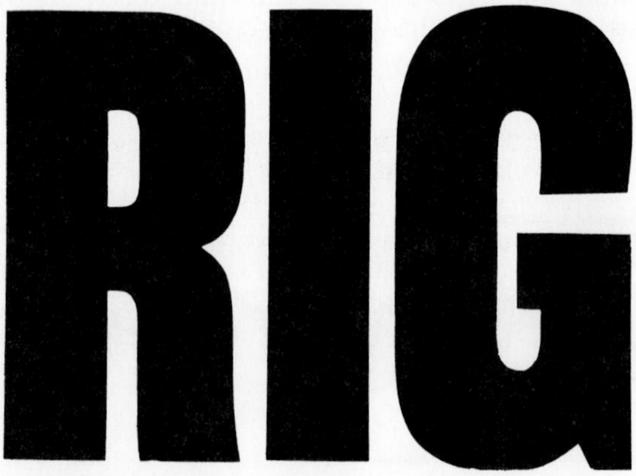

Fig. 5-24. Printed specimen of 12-line wood type.

Wood Type

Wood type is employed instead of metal type for very large sizes of type, generally in sizes 72 points and larger. Used in exactly the same manner as metal foundry type, it is set by hand, proofs are taken, and after use, it is returned to its type cases.

Wood type is generally made of end-grain maple. The faces (characters) are cut by machine and then trimmed by hand to final form. A special sealer-type impregnation on the printing face of the wood type tends to prevent checking and shrinkage, and imparts a smooth printing face to the letters.

Sizes of wood type are designated in *lines*. A line is equal to a pica, or 12 points. Thus, 12-line wood type would measure 12 picas (144 points) across the body from the belly to the back, Fig. 5-24.

Questions

1. What are repros? How are they used?
2. Of what advantage is it to the camera operator to have a reproduction proof entirely made up in page form?
3. What is the height of metal type used in the United States, in thousandths of an inch? In millimeters?
4. Describe foundry type.
5. What are line-casting machines?
6. How is justification of line achieved on the Linotype and Intertype machines?
7. What are mats? How are mats distributed on the Intertype and Linotype machines?
8. Describe the procedure for producing a slug by the Ludlow process.
9. An 18-line wood type would measure how many picas? How many inches?

Problems and Projects

1. Make a drawing of the layout of the California Job Case.
2. For your shop library, secure type specimen books from nearby printers or type composition houses.
3. Observe the action and operation of typecasting machines in your shop, or arrange for observation of these machines in other shops.
4. Secure, for permanent display, discarded matrices used on typecasting machines.
5. Arrange a display of individual types and slugs produced by the various typecasting machines.
6. Make a class report on the vocational aspects of the occupation of typecasting machine operator. Include:
   a. Where employed.
   b. Duties.
   c. Training required.
   d. Where training is available.
   e. Prerequisites for training.
   f. Wages, hours, working conditions.

New Terms

cellophane	matrices
enlargement	mechanical
galley	monotype
Intertype	quads
Linotype	slug
Ludlow	stencil
magazine	two-dimensional

Cold Type Composition — Mechanical

Much display composition is drawn either freehand or with the aid of mechanical devices. Some is pasted up from items clipped from printed sheets of letters and artwork.

Hand Lettering and Art

Special lettering, maps, cover designs, graphs, cartoons, borders, and other artwork may be produced by hand for use as camera copy. Such artwork depends on the ability of the artist. Hand lettering is especially useful for display lines or for single words in the larger sizes.

Originals prepared with pencil, airbrush, crayon, watercolors or oil paints usually contain *gradation of tone* and so must be reproduced through the halftone process. (See page 164.)

When hand art is to be incorporated into the mechanical with other items such as clip art or repro proofs, generally a pen or brush is used with India black ink on a white, semi-gloss or dull paper stock. Such artwork can be reproduced through the simpler line process. (See page 121.)

To keep the work clean, the triangles, templates and T-square should be washed occasionally with soap and water. The ink bottle should be kept in a wide-base holder *off* the drawing board. Preparatory lines should be drawn lightly (or a nonreproducing blue pencil should be used), and the ink should dry thoroughly before these pencil lines are erased. The hands should be kept clean, and all pens and brushes should be washed after use.

Errors may be cancelled by either painting over them with a white opaque or China white paint or by redrawing the copy on a separate piece of the same paper stock and pasting this over the original error. All edges of the patch then should be painted to avoid shadows on the negative when it is photographed.

Numerous special lettering pens, templates (stencils), and lettering devices are available to aid the artist in producing hand lettering of commercial quality. The reservoir pen, Fig. 5-25, with any one of several available tips, can be used to draw lines and letters of varying widths. See Fig. 5-26. Templates may be used in combination with a technical lettering (reservoir) pen for producing lettering, symbols, or even sheets of music, Fig. 5-27. Figures 5-28 and 5-29 show different lettering devices which utilize templates and lettering pens to produce attractive and accurate lettering and special effects. Speedball pens in ordinary penholders are used for freehand lettering of highly artistic design, depending upon the skill of the user. See Figs. 5-30 and 5-31.

Keuffel & Esser Company

Fig. 5-25. Rapidograph technical fountain pen.

Keuffel & Esser Company

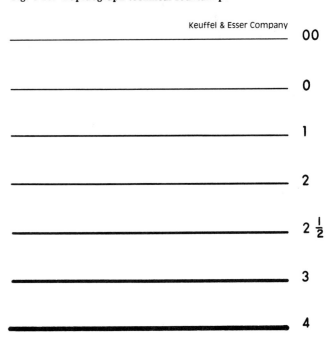

00

0

1

2

$2\frac{1}{2}$

3

4

Fig. 5-26. Rapidograph pen line widths in actual size.

Keuffel & Esser Company

MUSIC SYMBOLS

OUTLINE SHADOW

OLD ENGLISH

HEBREW

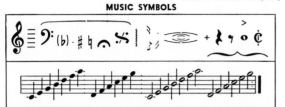

ELECTRONIC TUBE SYMBOLS

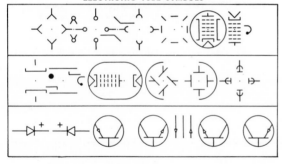

Fig. 5-27. Some typical Leroy lettering and symbol templates (reduced).

Varigraph, Inc.

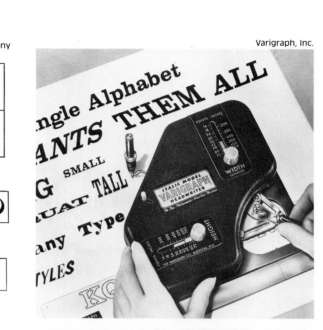

Fig. 5-28. Varigraph, italic model Headwriter.

Letterguide Company

Fig. 5-29. Letterguide scriber.

C. Howard Hunt Pen Company

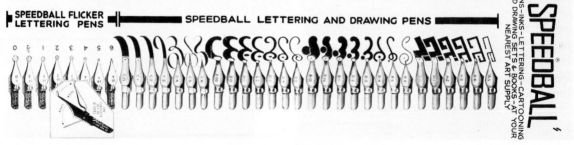

Fig. 5-30. Speedball pens.

Fig. 5-31. Hand lettering done with speedball pens.

Ruling Pen

The ruling pen is used for inking all lines other than circles. The blades, or *nibs,* of the pen should be of equal length, slightly sharp and when viewed from the front should have oval-shaped points. See Fig. 5-32F. Place ink between the points with an ordinary steel lettering pen or the quill point of the ink bottle stopper, Fig. 5-32A. Be careful not to get ink on the outside of the nibs. Fill to a height of 3/16 inch. More ink than this is likely to run too rapidly from the pen and blot on account of its weight.

Hold the pen as shown in Fig. 5-32B. The adjusting screw should be away from the body with the handle resting against the first finger. The thumb and first finger are held in such a position as to be handy for turning the adjusting screw.

When ruling lines, hold the pen in a nearly vertical position against the T-square, straightedge or triangle, Fig. 5-32C. The points of the pen should be parallel to the edge and the handle inclined slightly to the right. The pen is thus guided by the straightedge, bearing just enough

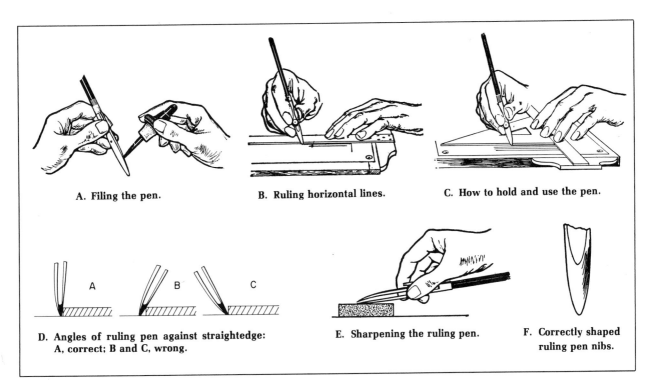

A. Filing the pen.

B. Ruling horizontal lines.

C. How to hold and use the pen.

D. Angles of ruling pen against straightedge: A, correct; B and C, wrong.

E. Sharpening the ruling pen.

F. Correctly shaped ruling pen nibs.

Fig. 5-32. The ruling pen.

against the edge to guide its direction. The line is drawn with a free arm movement, the hand resting on the tips of the third and fourth fingers and keeping the angle of inclination of the pen constant. When nearing the end of the line, hold the hand firm and draw the pen toward the end of the line with the fingers only. As the end of the line is reached, lift the pen quickly from the paper with the first and second fingers.

Both nibs of the pen should always touch the paper to obtain a clear-cut line as in view A of Fig. 5-32D. If the point of the pen is inclined out from the straightedge as in view B, only the near nib will touch, and a ragged line will result. If the pen is inclined toward the straightedge, the ink will run under the straightedge, thus making a blotted line as in view C.

Clean the pen frequently during use by inserting the point of a cloth between the nibs, rotating the pen so the cloth is wrapped once around the pen. Squeeze the nibs together lightly while drawing the cloth lightly through the nibs. Do not change the adjustment of the pen to do this.

If the ink refuses to flow from the pen because it has dried at the extreme point of the nibs, squeeze the nibs together gently and touch them to a scrap of paper. This generally will remove the dried ink.

When through using the pen, insert a cloth through the nibs, rotate the pen so the cloth is wrapped around the pen. Withdraw the pen through the roll of cloth while squeezing the nibs together gently. Repeat with the cloth slightly dampened with water. Then repeat with a dry cloth. Finally, adjust so the nibs are wide apart, thus retaining the spring.

Sharpening a Ruling Pen

If the nibs become dull and flat through use, adjust them so they touch together and sharpen them to an oval shape as shown in Figs. 5-32E and F. Use an oilstone. Hold the pen as when drawing lines, and draw the pen in a pendulum fashion. Start the stroke at about 30° to the stone and swing over until it reaches the same angle on the opposite side. When both nibs are of equal length and an oval shape is obtained, open the nibs and sharpen each to a keen edge.

Never sharpen the inside edges of the nibs. The pen should not be sharp enough to cut the paper, but it should produce fine hairlines.

Clip Art

Commercially prepared "clip art" may be purchased in sheets or books containing a variety of line and halftone illustrations, symbols, slogans, words, borders, and decorations, Fig. 5-33. Although these generally are printed in black and white, various colors are also available. Sometimes illustrations are furnished in several different sizes so that enlargements or reductions need not be made.

The purchase (or subscription) price for the clip art includes the right to reproduce any of the included pieces.

To use clip art, simply cut out the desired artwork and mount it in place on the mechanical, together with the other elements of the job for copying on the camera.

ART-PAK Clip-Art Service

Fig. 5-33. Clip art.

Preprinted Type

Preprinted type is available in several forms. They include individual letters in tab form; pressure-sensitive (self-adhesive) letters, words, symbols, borders, and decorations in sheet or roll form; and transfer type.

Tab-Type Individual Letters

Display lines may be composed by selecting and assembling printed characters. These are supplied on tabs of paper pads, as shown in Figs. 5-34 and 5-35. The letters are selected as desired, aligned in a composing stick, and fastened together with transparent tape. As the dense black reproducing print is on the reverse side, the taped line is turned over and it is mounted on the layout wherever desired. The complete page is then photographed as a unit.

Many different sizes and faces are available. These include reverse characters (black background with white letters) and transparencies (black letters on a transparent background).

Adhesive Type

Preprinted letters on clear acetate (with a self-adhesive back coating) may be cut out,

Fototype, Inc.

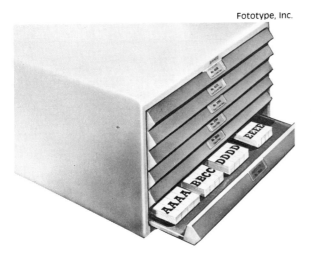

Fig. 5-34. Tab-type letters stored in cabinet.

Fototype, Inc.

Fig. 5-35. Setting tab-type letters.

Quillo Advertising Aids Company

A. Use a sharpened light blue pencil to draw a guide line with the aid of a ruler or T-square on your paper or illustration board. The light blue pencil will not reproduce in photographic reproduction.

B. Cut around selected letter and guide line with razor blade or sharp knife, cutting through acetate only. Be sure you are including the guide line under letter you are cutting out. Place the point of your knife under the edge of the cutout letter and lift away.

C. Line up guide line on the bottom of cutout letter with your blue line already drawn on paper. A slight rubbing pressure on cutout letter will hold it in place. When letters are in final position, burnish them firmly, but not the guide line. Then cut off the printed guide line. Your lettering is now ready for reproduction.

Fig. 5-36. Three steps in the application of adhesive type to a mechanical layout.

Chart-Pak, Inc.

Fig. 5-37. Some samples of preprinted, self-adhesive borders available in roll form.

Chart-Pak, Inc.

Fig. 5-38. Applying self-adhesive border (roll form) to mechanical layout.

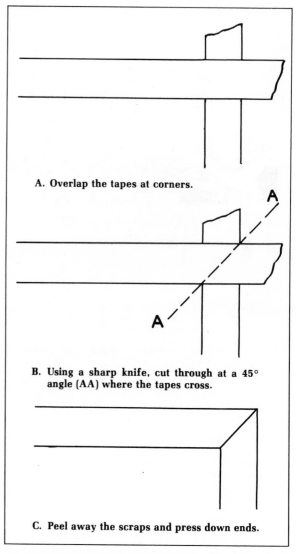

A. Overlap the tapes at corners.

B. Using a sharp knife, cut through at a 45° angle (AA) where the tapes cross.

C. Peel away the scraps and press down ends.

Fig. 5-39. Forming perfectly-joined mitered borders with self-adhesive tape.

lifted from their backing sheet, and placed on the mechanical where desired. Guide lines on the letters and on the layout aid in alignment. Figure 5-36 shows these steps.

Borders and symbols in roll or sheet form are available in a wide variety of sizes and designs, Fig. 5-37. They are simply pressed into position on the mechanical, and their self-adhesive backing holds them in place. See Fig. 5-38. Take care not to stretch the strips as you apply them; otherwise, the mechanical may curl.

Perfectly mitered corners may be formed by using self-adhesive tape as shown in Fig. 5-39.

Van Son Holland Ink Corporation of America

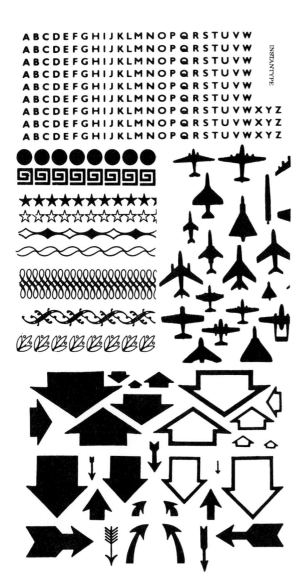

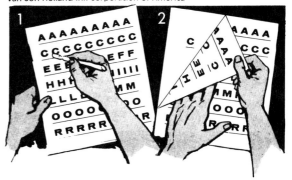

Fig. 5-41. Transferring type from sheet to artwork.

The application of transfer type is illustrated in Fig. 5-41. Guide lines are placed on the mechanical to indicate the placement of the character. The sheet of transfer type is placed over this, so that the desired character is aligned. Then, by rubbing over the surface of the sheet with a burnisher, a smooth pencil top, a ball point pen, or a similar tool, the ink on the back of the sheet is transferred to the mechanical. The sheet is then lifted and positioned for the next transfer.

To remove dry transfer lettering, cover all but the error with strips of paper. Pick off the error with masking tape or white paper tape. Experiment first to see if the tape will work well with the type used.

Copying Existing Printed Work for Reprinting

Sample copies of existing printed work are often used as camera copy. Entire pages may be used. Also, clips (parts) of an entire sheet may be pasted up on the mechanical layout with repro proofs, original art, or any form of cold type to form a page of camera copy. A page prepared in this manner may also be used as the original to make photo-direct offset plates. See page 255. For additional information on copying, see Chapter 7, "Preparing Camera Copy for Reproduction."

It is preferred that the sample of existing printed work be black on white, clean, and of good quality printing.

When copying a printed halftone dot-for-dot, an enlargement will coarsen its dot structure.

Fig. 5-40. A few of the many available stock sheets of Instantype.

Cut the overlapping pieces, peel away the scrap and burnish the joint. Folding a little bit of the roll tape onto itself after use makes it easier to unroll the tape later.

Transfer Type

Transfer type consists of plastic transparent sheets, on the back of which has been printed (in a transferable ink) letters, borders, symbols, illustrations, etc., in a wide variety of stock designs and special forms. Note Fig. 5-40.

A reduction of a printed halftone may lose the dot structure.

Any reduction of type characters or line drawings should anticipate a general sharpening of bold designs — but also a probable loss of fine detail. Enlargement usually blurs most details and may add a grainy appearance. Pre-inspection with a magnifying glass, reducing glass, or the camera's ground glass will aid in predicting the end result.

When jobs are run off on the press, some of the best copies always should be saved for possible future use as camera copy.

The "Stat." The stat is a photocopy or photostat on photoprint paper of either halftone or line work. It is used a great deal as paste-up copy on mechanicals, especially where the whole mechanical is to be reproduced as one negative. The stat is produced on a special camera that is equipped with a prism to make a rightreading photoprint in one exposure. See Fig. 5-42.

A reverse print results from using a positive print as original copy, and a positive print results from using a reverse print as original copy. However, with use of a direct-positive type of sensitized paper, a positive print can be made from original positive copy. Likewise, a reverse print can be made from original reverse print copy.

Caution: Copyrighted materials require authorization to reproduce. See Chapter 21.

Cold Type Composition — Impact, or Strike-On

A huge amount of composition for reproduction and lettering on production drawings is being done by impact (strike-on) composition. This is produced on either standard typewriters or specially designed models, with type composition as a specified use. Usually electrically operated typewriters, especially those utilizing a one-time plastic or carbon ribbon, are used to insure dense, clear, uniform letters. Typing for reproduction may be done on paper for use as repro proofs or on direct-image offset plates or masters.

General Procedures

Typing for reproduction should be done on smooth, dull white paper. Guide lines for width of columns or other positioning may be ruled with light blue, nonreproducing pencil or may be preprinted on the press with a light blue ink. This color will not be picked up by the camera.

On most standard typewriters, both letters and spaces are of equal width. However, *pro-*

Visual Graphics Corporation

Fig. 5-42. Photostat camera/processor delivers reproductions on paper or film directly from the original. The reproduction is automatically processed, dry, and ready to use with a single exposure and no film intermediary. Copy can be reproduced same size, reduced, or enlarged.

International Business Machines Corporation

ORDINARY SPACING

iiiii
ooooo
wwwww
mmmmm

As the representative c
letter should convey an
sincerity and warmth.

"EXECUTIVE" SPACING

iiiii
ooooo
wwwww
mmmmm

As the representative c
letter should convey an
sincerity and warmth.

Fig. 5-43. Typed characters of IBM Executive occupy different widths.

portional spacing is being provided on many models. This feature provides a choice of spacing widths between words and also has individual characters of varying widths as in foundry type. In Fig. 5-43 for example, typed "i" is equal to two spacing units; an "o," three units; a "w," four units; and an "m," five units. (Unit values range from 1/45″ to 1/32″.) Spaces between words may be selected to equal one, two, three, four, or five units.

To manually align the right-hand margin (that is, to justify or space each line to the desired length), it is necessary to type a first draft and mark each line with a number of spacing units needed for justification. Then type a second copy, adding the necessary spaces between words. As an aid, two sheets of paper may be placed side-by-side in a wide-carriage typewriter (or one wide sheet which is later cut in half). A line is typed on the left, the needed spacing for justification is noted, and the corrected line is typed on the right. This process is continued for the entire job. See Fig. 5-44.

Since the manual justification procedures for typewriters equipped with proportional spacing vary from one model to another, these are detailed later in this chapter as each specific model is described.

Methods of copyfitting and typing line-for-line are explained beginning on page 40.

Before a reproduction copy is made, the typewriter keys should be cleaned, and the ribbon should be tested to see that it will produce dense, black letters. A plastic, one-time carbon ribbon is a decided advantage in eliminating fabric ribbon pattern in the typed letters and in producing consistently sharp and dense letters. Typing without a ribbon through a sheet of fresh carbon paper gives a similar result.

Uniform pressure should be used in typing. However, care should be taken not to punch through the paper or the master. A thin, plastic backing sheet may be placed between the typewriter platen and the master to help avoid this. Light letters also should be avoided. An electrically operated typewriter will give uniformity to the typing stroke.

Typewritten copy can be enlarged or reduced, either in whole or in part, to vary the

A   **B**

Fig. 5-44. Manual justification of composition produced on a typewriter which has equal widths of letters and spaces.
A. Rough draft. The figures at the end of each line indicate the number of spaces (as marked with checks) which must be added to that line to bring it flush with the ruled vertical line.
B. Justified draft. The needed spacing has been inserted between the words.

type sizes, especially for headings. See Fig. 5-45. Standard typing can be dressed up by using decorative headings from other cold type methods. Also, bold typing can be achieved by several typings in the same position. Italics and distinctive headings can be obtained by using copy from typewriters having different typefaces. All the elements of a job should be pasted up and photographed as one unit.

Typing errors may be changed by using white opaque correction fluid, by erasing, or by pasting a corrected patch over the error. Also, the entire line may be retyped and pasted over the original line. Some prefer to *cut in* corrections. This is done by placing the correction over the error and making a rectangular cut through both layers. The error then is removed, and tape is placed across the back of the opening. The correction is positioned in the opening and pressed onto the tape.

Direct-Image Plates (Paper Masters)

The simplest method of duplicating typewriting (or handwork) is to type (or draw) directly onto a paper master, also called a direct-image offset plate. This is a piece of plastic or paper especially treated to receive the greasy typed image which will hold the printing ink on the press. It is also treated to hold the ink-repelling dampening solution without growing limp or tearing. The master must

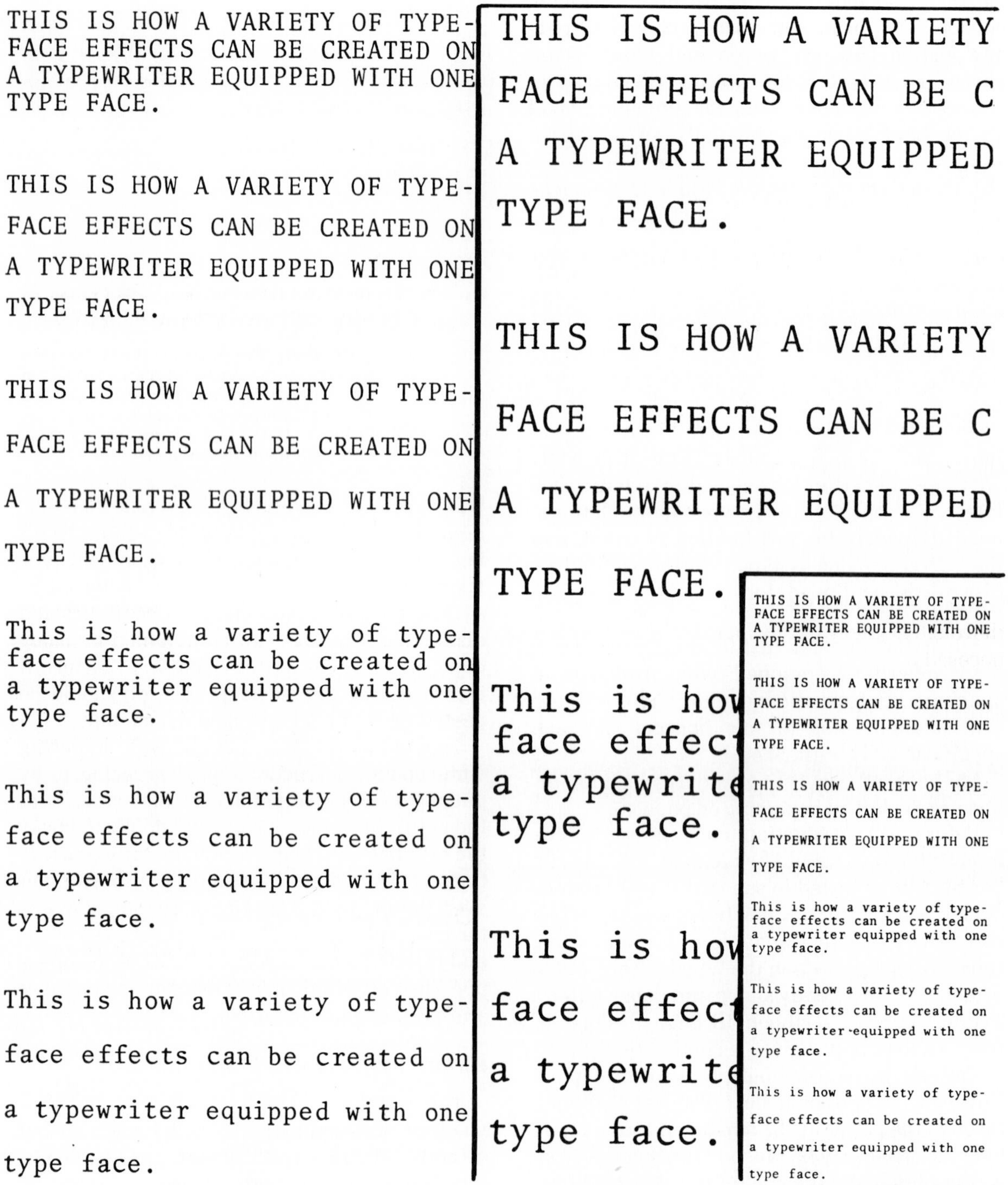

THIS IS HOW A VARIETY OF TYPE-
FACE EFFECTS CAN BE CREATED ON
A TYPEWRITER EQUIPPED WITH ONE
TYPE FACE.

THIS IS HOW A VARIETY OF TYPE-
FACE EFFECTS CAN BE CREATED ON
A TYPEWRITER EQUIPPED WITH ONE
TYPE FACE.

THIS IS HOW A VARIETY OF TYPE-
FACE EFFECTS CAN BE CREATED ON
A TYPEWRITER EQUIPPED WITH ONE
TYPE FACE.

This is how a variety of typeface effects can be created on
a typewriter equipped with one
type face.

This is how a variety of typeface effects can be created on
a typewriter equipped with one
type face.

This is how a variety of typeface effects can be created on
a typewriter equipped with one
type face.

THIS IS HOW A VARIETY
FACE EFFECTS CAN BE C
A TYPEWRITER EQUIPPED
TYPE FACE.

THIS IS HOW A VARIETY
FACE EFFECTS CAN BE C
A TYPEWRITER EQUIPPED
TYPE FACE.

This is how
face effect
a typewrite
type face.

This is how
face effect
a typewrite
type face.

THIS IS HOW A VARIETY OF TYPE-
FACE EFFECTS CAN BE CREATED ON
A TYPEWRITER EQUIPPED WITH ONE
TYPE FACE.

THIS IS HOW A VARIETY OF TYPE-
FACE EFFECTS CAN BE CREATED ON
A TYPEWRITER EQUIPPED WITH ONE
TYPE FACE.

THIS IS HOW A VARIETY OF TYPE-
FACE EFFECTS CAN BE CREATED ON
A TYPEWRITER EQUIPPED WITH ONE
TYPE FACE.

This is how a variety of typeface effects can be created on
a typewriter equipped with one
type face.

This is how a variety of typeface effects can be created on
a typewriter ·equipped with one
type face.

This is how a variety of typeface effects can be created on
a typewriter equipped with one
type face.

A. 100%   **B. 150%**   **C. 50%**

Fig. 5-45. Even though a typewriter has only one typeface and conventional spacing, the reproduced type effects can be varied considerably. A few possibilities are shown here. Use
your imagination to create others.

fit the plate cylinder of a specific press. A special waterproof typewriter ribbon is used. The procedures for preparing direct-image plates are given in Chapter 13, "Platemaking."

Typewriter Machines

Care of Machines

To keep off dust, machines should be covered when not in use. Keys should be cleaned periodically with a stiff brush and alcohol, and the excess wiped off with a clean cloth. Erasures should be done with the carriage moved all the way to the left or right, so that eraser grit will not drop into the mechanism.

Machines should be serviced periodically. On the more intricate machines, a service contract is advisable. Repairs and adjustments should be attempted only by experienced and qualified persons.

Operators should be proficient in touchtyping methods and should be taught, if possible, by a factory-sponsored instructor or someone trained in these methods. In any event, a thorough mastery of the operator's manual is a necessity.

IBM Executive Electric Typewriter

The IBM Executive electric typewriter, Fig. 5-46, is proportional spacing and may be equipped with either a fabric or carbon ribbon (or both). A typeface may be selected from the wide variety of those offered. A few are shown in Fig. 5-47.

International Business Machines Corporation

Fig. 5-46. IBM Executive electric typewriter.

International Business Machines Corporation

Newest member of the type style library, Arcadia brings beauty and simplicity to your letters.

ARCADIA TYPE

One of the most expressive IBM types Mid-Century will make your Executive letters inviting to read.

MID-CENTURY TYPE

The crisp lines of Documentary type give a businesslike dignity to this popular type style.

DOCUMENTARY TYPE

Latest addition to the Bold Face Family is Italic. It adds a personal touch to all letters.

BOLD FACE ITALIC TYPE

DEPEND ON COPPERPLATE TO WIN ATTENTION. THIS TYPE IS EXCELLENT FOR YOUR ADVERTISING MATERIAL.

COPPERPLATE GOTHIC NO.1 TYPE

Build company prestige with Modern type. This attractive face creates striking first impressions.

MODERN TYPE

Fig. 5-47. A few of the many available typefaces of the IBM Executive.

Wide carriages are available to permit the typing of two sheets side-by-side for line-by-line justification. A wide carriage also permits typing lengthwise on some direct-image plates, or typing directly on large drawings to be blueprinted.

Justifying Composition

The following procedure is recommended for manually justifying composition on the IBM Executive proportional spacing typewriter: (See Fig. 5-48.)

1. Insert the paper in the typewriter.
2. Set the desired margins for the width of the copy.
3. With the carriage positioned at the right-hand margin, insert a sharp-pointed pencil in the V notch of the justification scale, and draw a vertical line down the paper by turning the platen knob upward, Fig. 5-49.
4. Set a tab stop several markings to the right of this line.
5. Begin typing the rough draft, always using the two-unit space bar (large right-hand segment) between words. Try to end each line with a complete word or the correct word division. *Do not space after the last word.* If the line ends with a period or comma, *backspace once* before reading your scale.
6. As you type, listen for the margin bell, and try to end each line so that the pencil marking is as near the V notch as possible. It is easier to add space than to subtract space when using two units for the basic word space.
7. When the pencil line ends right on the notch, the typed line requires no change. See Fig. 5-50. Tab and type "O" (or omit any indication for justification).
8. When the pencil line rests to the right of the notch, the typed line must be increased. See Fig. 5-51. Each mark to the right of the notch means one unit. Tab and type the number of units to be added.

TYPING SHEET
PENCIL LINE
CLEAR-VIEW CARD HOLDER
"V" NOTCH
JUSTIFICATION SCALE

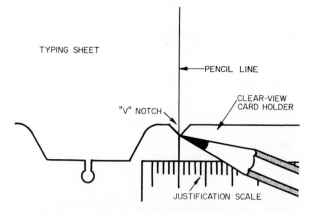

Fig. 5-49. Drawing the vertical pencil line.

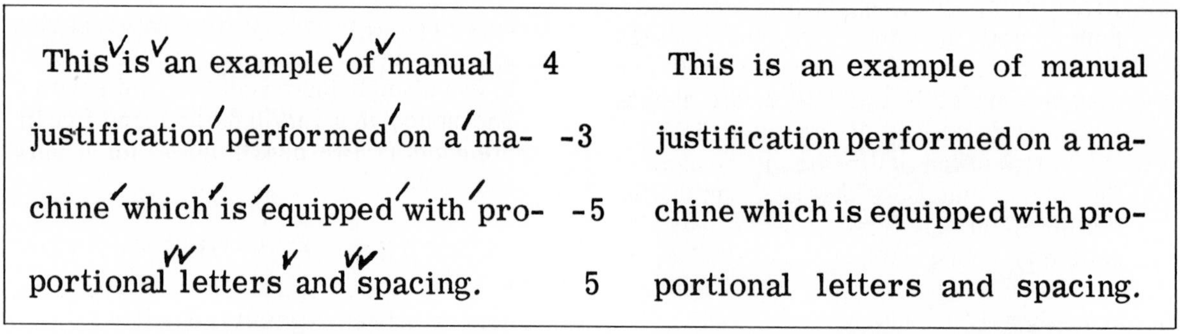

This is an example of manual 4
justification performed on a ma- -3
chine which is equipped with pro- -5
portional letters and spacing. 5
This is an example of manual
justification performed on a machine which is equipped with proportional letters and spacing.

A B

Fig. 5-48. Manual justification of composition on the IBM Executive proportional-spacing typewriter.

A. Rough draft. The figure 4 for the first line indicates that the line is four spacing increments short of reaching justification. The check marks in that line show where the additional spaces are to be added. The − 3 for the second line indicates that this line needs to be shortened by three spacing increments — at the slash marks.

B. Justified draft.

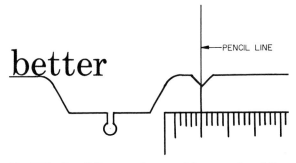

Fig. 5-50. Pencil line exactly on notch means typed line needs no change.

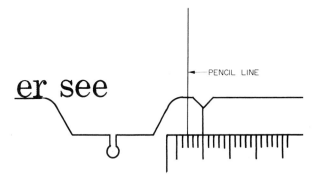

Fig. 5-52. Pencil line is three marks to left of notch. Three spacing increments must be eliminated.

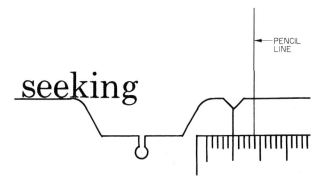

Fig. 5-51. Pencil line is four marks to right of notch. Four spacing increments must be added.

9. When the pencil line rests to the left of the notch, the typed line must be *decreased*. See Fig. 5-52. Tab and type the number of units to be omitted.

10. After typing the rough draft, remove the paper, and indicate with check marks where space units are to be increased. Use diagonal marks to indicate where spaces are to be decreased. Refer to Fig. 5-48.

11. When typing the justified copy, remember that to add one space unit between words, the three-unit space bar must be used. To omit one space unit, it is necessary to backspace once, after using the two-unit space bar.

12. When justified, the line should appear equally spaced between words. Where one word ends with a tall letter and the next begins with a tall letter (a sequence such as "tall letter"), an extra space unit is not noticeable and may even improve the appearance. Where one word ends with a

short (or round) letter and the next word begins with a short letter (such as "one wing"), a decrease of a spacing unit is hardly noticed. Space may be either added or subtracted between one word ending with a tall or short letter and the next word starting with a letter of the opposite height (such as "the letter").

The use of the two-increment space for the rough typing will produce tightly spaced composition with a minimum of ugly gaps between words (forming "lakes" and "rivers" of white space). Some operators use the three-unit space for the rough, leaving two units for shortening lines and a double two-unit space (four increments) for spacing out lines. This requires less backspacing and so may be faster, but greater care must be used to prevent loose spacing and gaps between words. It is also possible to use a single increment (two units with a backspace) in a very tight line, and five increments (a two plus a three) for a very short line.

Underwood Raphael Electric Typewriter

The Underwood Raphael electric typewriter is proportional spacing and is equipped with a polyethylene carbon ribbon. See Fig. 5-53. It is available with one of several type faces such as shown in Fig. 5-54. The relative widths of individual characters and spaces are listed in Fig. 5-55.

Justification of lines is achieved manually on the Raphael, using the *i method*, as follows:

Olivetti Underwood Corporation

Fig. 5-53. Underwood Raphael electric typewriter.

1. Establish the left margin where desired.
2. Line up the position desired for the right margin with the type guide.
3. Type a lowercase *i* on the rough-draft paper.
4. Use the penholder to draw a vertical pencil line on the entire sheet, through the *i*.
5. Type the rough draft, ending each line as close as possible to the pencil line.
6. When the typed line ends *before* the pencil line, fill in (without spacing) with *i*'s until an *i* falls on the pencil line. Count the number of *i*'s, including the one on the line, and enter that figure with a plus sign in the right margin. This is the number of half spaces which must be added to the typed line to achieve justification.
7. When the typed line ends *past* the pencil line, backspace to this line, release the Memory Line Finder and roll the platen back half a line. Type *i*'s until the last *i* is even with the right side of the last character in the line. (Restore the Memory Line Finder, and roll the platen up half a line.) Count the number of *i*'s beyond the vertical line (not including the *i* on the line), and enter that figure with a minus sign in the right margin. This is the number of half spaces which must be omitted.
8. Upon the completion of the rough draft, use a / mark to indicate where to add a half

Olivetti Underwood Corporation

Kent

The elements which make th important, impressive and comp recipient have been identified a the UNDERWOOD RAPHAEL writer.

Raphael

The elements which make the important, impressive and compl recipient have been identified a the UNDERWOOD RAPHAEL writer.

Windsor

The elements which make th important, impressive and compl recipient have been identified a the UNDERWOOD RAPHAEL writer.

Fig. 5-54. Several type styles available for the Under-wood Raphael.

Olivetti Underwood Corporation

All small letters, numbers, symbols, punctuation and space bar	= I	space
EXCEPT j i l f t '	= ½	space
w m	= I½	spaces
All capitals	= I½	spaces
EXCEPT I J	= I	space
I (Kent and Windsor only)		
	= ½	space
Backspacer	= ½	space

Fig. 5-55. Relative widths of characters and spaces on the Underwood Raphael.

space and a \ mark to indicate where to omit a half space, as shown in Fig. 5-56.

9. Now, type the justified draft or the duplicating master. To add a half space, backspace once after using the space bar *twice*. To omit a half space, backspace once after using the space bar *once*.

Olivetti Underwood Corporation

```
The\contents\of\the letter will be framed on the page    iii   -3
with/balanced/margins/on the left, right, top, andiii      +3
bottom/as carefully as though it were an expensive         +1
painting. /Any/titles/or/headings will be centerediii      +4
exactly\in\the center of the sheet. Every character  ii    -2
will appear sharp, clear, and uniform.
```

```
The contents of the letter will be framed on the page
with  balanced  margins  on the left, right, top, and
bottom  as carefully as though it were an expensive
painting.   Any titles  or headings will be centered
exactly in the center of the sheet.  Every character
will appear sharp, clear, and uniform.
```

Fig. 5-56. Manual justification on the Underwood Raphael electric typewriter.
(Above) Rough draft marked for justification.
(Below) Justified draft.

IBM Selectric Electric Typewriter

The IBM Selectric electric typewriter may be obtained with either a reusable fabric ribbon or a onetime, film-carbon ribbon. See Fig. 5-57.

Instead of the conventional type bars and moving carriage, the Selectric features a small, spherical typing element which looks like a golf ball and contains all the type characters in relief (raised). See Fig. 5-58. The printing element skims along the page, typing out the characters and storing the second of two rapidly typed characters until the first is printed. Being removable, it may be replaced by any one of a number of other elements, each with a different typeface, Fig. 5-59. By having available a number of elements, a wide variety of typefaces (each having the same spacing) can be used with the one machine.

International Business Machines Corporation

Fig. 5-57. IBM Selectric electric typewriter.

International Business Machines Corporation

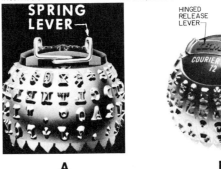

A   **B**

Fig. 5-58. IBM Selectric printing elements, or type spheres.
A. Older, spring-lever style.
B. Newer, hinged-lever style.

International Business Machines Corporation

This is 12 pitch Script type. You may use it interchangeably with all the type styles on this page. Each typing element snaps on the IBM SELI so quickly, so easily that your typi can change type without ever losing place on the typing line.

```
This is 12 pitch Adjutant type. You
may use it interchangeably with all
the type styles on this page.  Each
typing element snaps on the IBM SELI
so quickly, so easily that your typi
can change type without ever losing
place on the typing line.
```

```
This is 12 pitch Scribe type. You
may use it interchangeably with all
the type styles on this page.  Each
typing element snaps on the IBM SELI
so quickly, so easily that your typi
can change type without ever losing
place on the typing line.
```

Fig. 5-59. A few of the many typefaces available on separate printing elements for the IBM Selectric.

Changing Elements

• **Caution:** To change the element, or type sphere, turn *off* the typewriter. Be sure the typewriter is in *lowercase position* with the arrow or the triangular mark on the element facing towards the platen. Lift the front cover.

Spring-Release-Lever Style.   To remove the element, squeeze the spring levers together, and lift the element off the post, Fig. 5-60.

To replace the element, hold the element by one spring lever and slide the element down onto the post with the arrow facing the platen. Now, squeeze the two spring levers together, and gently slide the element down the post until it reaches "home" with a click.

Hinged-Release-Lever Style.   To remove, lift the element's release lever with right thumb and forefinger until it clicks into open position. Holding the element by the lever, lift it off the post.

To replace the element, first open (lift) the lever to full open position. Holding the lever with thumb and index finger, slide the element down onto the post with the triangle facing the platen. Now, close the lever gently.

International Business Machines Corporation

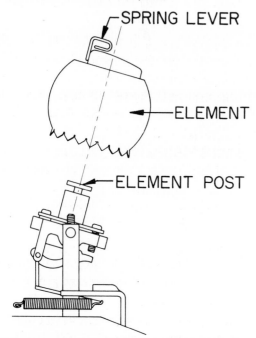

Fig. 5-60. IBM Selectric element removed from post.

International Business Machines Corporation

Fig. 5-61. IBM Selectric composer, with interchangeable typing element and proportional-spacing type.

International Business Machines Corporation

Through the innovation of a new system of type de[?] has raised the standards of direct impression typogra[?] type is designed in a nine-unit system that permits [?] ferent character widths to assure graceful proportion letter fit. Classic type faces, proven popular over t[?] have been adapted to the nine-unit system by maste[?] signers. Strict quality control is maintained throu[?] stage of design and production. The IBM Compo[?] Fonts, which are completely interchangeable with "Selectric" Composers, are assembled by skilled craf[?] assure uniform and precise reproduction. Therefore, [?] select type fonts from the wide range of type faces, weights that are offered, you can be sure of crisp an[?] production day after day, even under the most h[?]

Fig. 5-62. Sample of type set on the IBM Selectric Composer.

IBM Selectric Composer

The IBM Selectric Composer, Fig. 5-61, is keyboard operated, electrically actuated, has proportional spacing, and uses a one-time ribbon. Like the Selectric, the Composer uses a spherical typing element instead of conventional type bars. At present, more than 50 typefaces are available, ranging from 7 to 12 points in height. See Fig. 5-62 for a sample of its composition. Leading is adjustable.

Justification on the illustrated model of the Composer is semiautomatic. The operator types the first line of the rough draft, stopping short of the right-hand margin. The needed justification for that line is indicated automatically on the justification control (dial at the right of the keyboard). The operator then sets the control, aided by a color code. In a second typing, the machine automatically justifies the line.

IBM Electronic Selectric Composer

Another model, the IBM *Electronic* Selectric Composer, eliminates multiple typesetting steps. It automatically produces justified copy in one typing. In addition, many other formats can be produced automatically: centered copy, dot leaders, multiple columns, flush left (ragged right) margins, and others.

This Selectric model contains electronic modules that make up a working memory. The memory holds everything that is keyboarded — up to 8000 characters and codes. To produce automatic justification (or other format), the operator first enters the codes for that format and then types the copy. The machine automatically "plays out" the automatically justified composition.

VariTyper Composition Machine

The VariTyper composing machine is used extensively for type composition, either on paper (for photographing) or directly on offset plates. See Fig. 5-63. The VariTyper machine uses a onetime carbon ribbon and has a near-standard typewriter keyboard (arranged in three banks instead of four and with two shift positions instead of one). Some models may be obtained with differential letterspacing and automatic line justification.

On the differential-spacing models, various letters (as typed) occupy differing widths on the paper, Fig. 5-64. These variations produce

VariTyper Corporation

Fig. 5-63. VariTyper office composing machine, Model 660.

VariTyper Corporation

Fig. 5-64. Variation in widths of typed VariTyper letters.

VariTyper Corporation

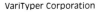

12 pt. Alexandria Medium (880-12A)

ABCDEFGHIJKLMNOPQRSTUVWXYZ& abcdefghijklmnopqrstuvwxyz abcdefghijk

10 pt. Alexandria Light (650-10B)

ABCDEFGHIJKLMNOPQRSTUVWXYZ& AB abcdefghijklmnopqrstuvwxyz abcdefghijklmn

10 pt. Bell Gothic Light (FL950-10B)

ABCDEFGHIJKLMNOPQRSTUVWXYZ& AB abcdefghijklmnopqrstuvwxyz abcdefghijklmn

10 pt. Bell Gothic Bold (FL980-10B)

ABCDEFGHIJKLMNOPQRSTUVWXYZ& ABC abcdefghijklmnopqrstuvwxyz abcdefghijklmn

10 pt. Gothic Bold Condensed (FL970-10B)

ABCDEFGHIJKLMNOPQRSTUVWXYZ& ABC abcdefghijklmnopqrstuvwxyz abcdefghijklmn

10 pt. Bodoni Book (600-10B)

ABCDEFGHIJKLMNOPQRSTUVWXYZ& ABC abcdefghijklmnopqrstuvwxyz abcdefghijklmn

10 pt. Bodoni Bold (780-10B)

ABCDEFGHIJKLMNOPQRSTUVWXYZ& ABC abcdefghijklmnopqrstuvwxyz abcdefghijklmno

10 pt. Bookman (630-10B)

ABCDEFGHIJKLMNOPQRSTUVWXYZ& ABC abcdefghijklmnopqrstuvwxyz abcdefghijklmno

10 pt. Cartoon Type (940-10A)

ABCDEFGHIJKLMNOPQRSTUVWXYZ A ABCDEFGHIJKLMNOPQRSTUVWXYZ ABCDEFGHI

10 pt. Caslon (830-10B)

ABCDEFGHIJKLMNOPQRSTUVWXYZ& ABC abcdefghijklmnopqrstuvwxyz abcdefghijklmno

8 pt. Caslon Bold (890-8C)

ABCDEFGHIJKLMNOPQRSTUVWXYZ& ABCDEF abcdefghijklmnopqrstuvwxyz abcdefghijklmnopqrst

Fig. 5-65. A few of the hundreds of instantly changeable typefaces for the VariTyper machine.

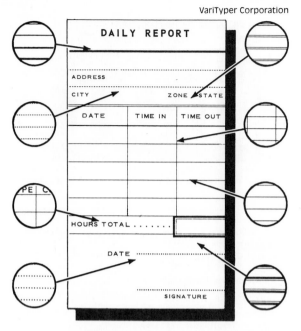

Fig. 5-66. VariTyper composition specimen involving rules and type matter.

close to a true foundry-type printed effect in the typed copy. Through the use of hundreds of instantly changeable type fonts, Fig. 5-65, the VariTyper can produce an infinite variety of composition. Special ruling attachments produce ruled forms, as shown in Fig. 5-66.

A typical type font segment is shown being installed on the VariTyper anvil in Fig. 5-67.

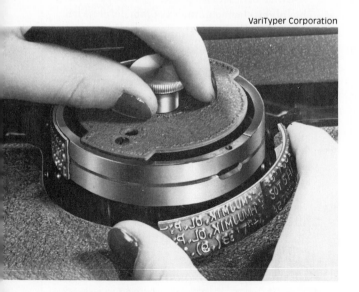

Fig. 5-67. Installing VariTyper type font on anvil. Note the second font to the left rear.

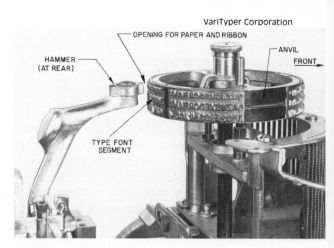

Fig. 5-68. Fundamental parts of VariTyper.

Note that the anvil accommodates *two* fonts at the same time so that, for example, a matching italic or bold face may be used interchangeably when typing. A major feature of some Vari-Typer machines is line spacing, which is adjustable by points. This allows type to be set solid or leaded 1 point, 2 points, or more, as desired.

Depressing a key on the VariTyper produces the following action:

1. The type font segment is rotated, bringing the desired type character into position before the hammer.
2. The hammer (at the rear) strikes forward, making the impression through the paper and ribbon against the type character, Fig. 5-68.
3. The paper carriage is advanced the width of the character.

The newer model VariTypers have a lightness of touch and length of keystroke similar to conventional electric typewriters. On many earlier VariTypers still in use the keys must be depressed firmly and fully (bottomed) and in a regular rhythm. Although the machine is electrically powered, each manual key bottoming stroke triggers the typing action. The power for the hammer comes from a large spring which is kept wound by an electric motor and produces a uniform impression of each character. Some practice is recommended before production of final, clean copy is attempted.

Manual justification procedure is shown in Fig. 5-69. For automatic justification (on models

VariTyper Corporation

Sample of Rough Copy for Manual Justification

llllllllll llllllllll llllllllll llllllllll llllllllll llllllllll llllllllll llllllllll llllln

Picture Writing began 5,000 years ago, and gradually developed 5
into symbols which represented words instead of objects. A fur- 4
ther development, about 1,500 years later, was the alphabet. This −1
alphabet was created by the Semites, near Egypt about the second −2
century.

Sample of Copy Justified Manually

Picture Writing began 5,000 years ago, and gradually developed
into symbols which represented words instead of objects. A further development, about 1,500 years later, was the alphabet. This
alphabet was created by the Semites, near Egypt about the second
century.

Fig. 5-69. Sample of manual justification on the VariTyper. (Reduced for illustrative purposes.)

so equipped), it is strongly recommended that the operator study the manual for the particular model. If possible the typist should be taught by a factory-trained instructor.

Briefly, automatic justification requires that the operator first set the stops for the desired widths of columns. Then, a line is typed on the left side of the sheet, using a margin dial pointer and a justifier dial pointer to guide in beginning and ending the typed line. After this, the typist tabs to the right and repeats the typing. The machine inserts the required spacing during this second typing, justifying the line automatically (if no mistakes were made in either keyboarding).

Questions

1. What kinds of ink and paper generally are used for hand-prepared art that is to be camera copied?
2. What tools and devices are available to the hand letterer?
3. What is clip art? Where is it obtained?
4. How is a heading composed from tab-type individual letters?
5. Describe the procedure in using adhesive type.
6. How is a mitered border formed with strips or a roll of adhesive border material?
7. How is transfer type applied to the mechanical?
8. What are the desirable characteristics of existing printed work which is to be used as camera copy?
9. What is a stat? How is it used?

10. In producing cold type composition for camera copy, what advantage is there in using a one-time carbon ribbon? An electric typewriter?
11. What general precautions and procedures are observed in producing typewriter composition for reproduction?
12. What is "proportional spacing" when that term is used to describe typewriter typefaces?
13. Explain how manual justification of lines is achieved on typewriters which have no means for automatic justification.
14. How is justification of line achieved on the IBM Executive electric typewriter? Explain.
15. Describe the action of the printing element (sphere) on the IBM Selectric typewriter.
16. Describe a VariTyper type font segment. How is the segment installed and removed?
17. Explain, in some detail, how the VariTyper produces its typed impressions on the paper.
18. Describe how lines are justified on a VariTyper equipped for automatic justification.

Problems and Projects

1. Arrange to have sales representatives demonstrate (in your shop) any of the typewriter composing machines you do not have.
2. Plan and execute projects which involve impact typewriter composition — justified lines, ruled forms, same-size, enlarged and reduced.
3. Under guidance of your instructor, replace one-time carbon ribbons on the typewriters your shop has. Learn to do the necessary maintenance involved in cleaning the keys and inserting and removing type fonts.
4. Arrange to take a formal course in touch typing. Ask to have such a class added to the graphic arts curriculum.
5. Start a "clip file" of printed items which you feel may be handy as clip art for projects.
6. Using cold type methods exclusively, plan and execute a calendar having a pad approximately 8½ x 11 inches.
7. Redesign and reset school forms, using cold type methods.

8. Produce wallet-size school sports schedules, using cold type methods, and reducing the type to about six points in size.
9. Plan and produce a poster, using hand lettering and clip art.
10. If the operator's manual is missing for any impact typesetting machine in the shop, write the manufacturer and request it.

New Terms

anvil	maintenance
carriage	nibs
differential	pitch
hand art	T-square
increment	template

Cold Type Composition — Phototypesetting

In phototypesetting, images of type characters are produced in desired sequence on phototypesetting paper or on film by light projection. The resulting two-dimensional type images are called *phototype,* or, simply *type,* Fig. 5-70. This phototype is then mounted on the page paste-up, in the same manner as proofs of metal type, for use as camera copy.

Phototype is most commonly produced as right-reading, *positive* (black) characters on either white phototypesetting paper base or on clear, transparent film base, Fig. 5-70 and 5-71A. Another style of phototype is the *reverse phototype* on paper in which the lettering is white (clear or open) on a black background, Fig. 5-72. A film negative, Fig. 5-71B, also produces the reverse effect.

AD CLASS is a high speed sort, merge and file management program specifically designed to provide the small and medium size newspaper with the productivity and profit enjoyed by newspapers with much larger and more expensive systems.

It stores up to 10,000 ads and can process them in approximately 10 minutes while other system operations continue.

AD CLASS features selective timing of ad repetitions by day of the week and by

Fig. 5-70. Phototype.
A. Display type (photodisplay) on paper base.
B. Display type (photodisplay) on film.
C. Text type, or body type (phototext) on paper base.

A. As a film positive.   B. As a film negative.

Fig. 5-71. Two forms of phototype composition on film base.

Fig. 5-72. Reverse phototype — on paper base, with white (open) letters and black background.

The Basic Phototypesetting Process

Phototype is produced on a wide variety of phototypesetting machines. Figure 5-73 shows an elementary schematic of the basic phototypesetting process. Exposure light source *A* sends a light beam *B* through a preselected letter image (capital letter "O") of the type font *C*. The letter image allows the light beam (now in the form of the letter "O") to pass through the shutter *D* and through the sizing lens *E*, and then, is exposed directly onto the sensitized phototypesetting paper (or on film) *F*. This process occurs as the paper or film is fed from the supply cassette *G*, past the exposure position.

After being retrieved (usually by a receiver cassette H), the exposed photopaper or film is then processed (developed) to make the phototype images visible and permanent.

• **Note:** With the ever-increasing additions of electronic principles and automated features to phototypesetting equipment, phototypesetting is sometimes also referred to as *automated type composition, computerized type composition,* and *electronic type composition.*

Processing the Phototype After Composition

At the end of the *take*[2], or job, the phototypesetting paper or film is cut off and processed in the machine's processor, if so equipped, or in a separate processor, Figs. 5-74 and 5-75. Otherwise the receiver cassette, with its exposed phototype, is removed from the phototypesetter. Processing is then carried on by the tray or tank method.

Where phototype is to be mounted same-size directly into the copy paste-up, the paper-base phototype is preferred over the film-base type.

Two of the several popular types of phototypesetting paper are resin-coated base (RC) paper and stabilization (S) paper. *Resin-coated base* paper yields long-lasting, flat-lying prints.

[2]*Take* is a portion of a job, or the whole job, assigned to a compositor.

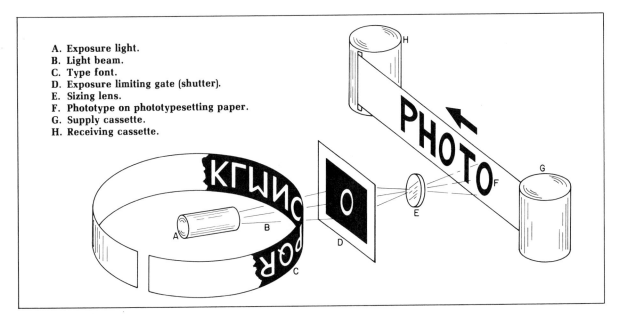

A. Exposure light.
B. Light beam.
C. Type font.
D. Exposure limiting gate (shutter).
E. Sizing lens.
F. Phototype on phototypesetting paper.
G. Supply cassette.
H. Receiving cassette.

Fig. 5-73. Simplified schematic showing how phototype is produced on a phototypesetting machine.

Fig. 5-74. Free-standing tabletop processor for RC (resin-coated) phototypesetting paper and for photo-typesetting film 35 mm to 8.2 inches wide.

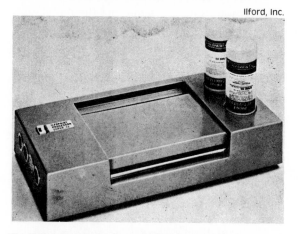

Fig. 5-75. A 12-inch photostabilization processor.

This paper is processed in the conventional manner — develop, rinse, fix, wash, and dry — using tank, tray, or mechanized processing. (See manufacturer's instructions). Characteristics of *stabilization paper* are described below.

The Stabilization Process.   In this process, phototype exposure (or other exposure) is made on a special paper which uses a developing agent in its emulsion. Stabilization paper is available in a range of contrasts, making it suitable for continuous-tone photographs as well.

The exposed phototype (or illustration) is fed into a stabilization processing unit, Fig. 5-75. Here a measured amount of *activator* fluid is applied to the exposed surface, releasing the developing agents in the emulsion of the paper. Complete development of the silver image takes but a second or two. The paper is then fed by rollers to the second chemical bath, the *stabilizer*, to set the image. The result is a stable photographic print which is delivered dry enough to paste up almost immediately.

A stabilized print has a limited keeping time. Since the stabilization print has not yet been *fixed*, its image will fade after prolonged exposure to light, heat, and humidity. To make the image permanent, fix the print in the usual hypo fixer solution, then wash and dry in the usual manner.

Display and Text

The terms *display* and *text* describe the sizes and purposes of the phototype composition.

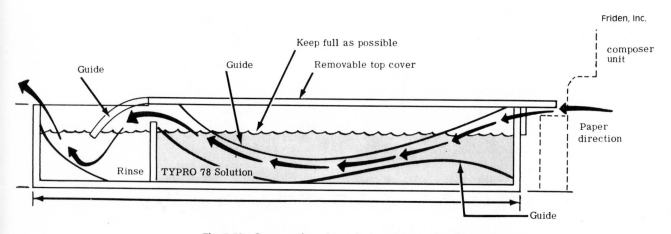

Fig. 5-76. Cross-section view of a continuous developer unit.

They also identify the phototypesetting machines which produce that type.

Display type, also called *photodisplay type* and sometimes *photolettering,* generally includes sizes from 14 points on upward to 96 points and larger. As the name *display* suggests, these larger sizes of type are used to attract attention — to display a message. Typical examples of display type include newspaper headlines, grocery ad prices, and title lines, Fig. 5-70A and B.

Text type, also called *phototext type* or *body type,* ranges in size from about 4 points (or the smallest sizes) to about 12 or 14 points. These are the sizes of type used for blocks, columns, and pages of reading matter in books, magazines, newspapers, and advertisements, Fig. 5-70C.

• **Note:** Actually, lenses on phototypesetting machines, and subsequent photo-enlarging or photo-reducing operations, can produce phototype in practically any size.

Photodisplay Typesetters

Photodisplay type is composed on machines that, in addition to setting large display sizes, sometimes are capable of setting smaller text sizes. The sizes of phototype produced may vary on individual photodisplay machines. Ranges of 10 to 84 points and 14 to 72 points are examples.

These photodisplay typesetters may be manually operated. Also, they may be automatically "commanded" by keyboard, tape, or on-line signal.

Manually Operated Photodisplay Typesetters

As shown schematically in Figs. 5-77 and 5-78, the manually operated typesetter is fitted with a selected type font. This is usually a film negative (strip, disc, or other) containing transparent images of the complete font of letters and characters, Fig. 5-79. The font is positioned between the exposure lamp and the sensitized phototypesetting paper or film. Exposure of the desired character is made through the film type font. Each succeeding desired character is then positioned and exposed. Spacing is con-

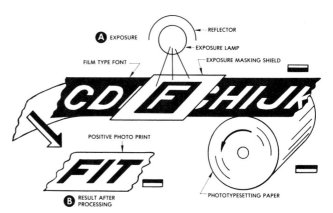

Fig. 5-77. **Schematic of how photographic display composition is manually composed by the contact printing method. Composition can also be on film to produce film positives.**

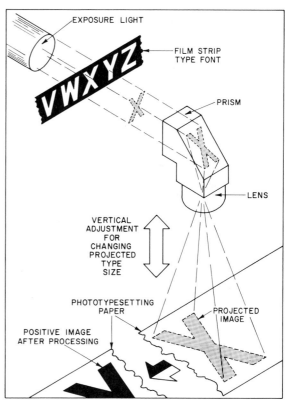

Fig. 5-78. **Schematic of how photographic display composition is manually composed by projection printing method.**

trolled by a spacing device and by reference lines on both the machine and type font.

When the desired amount of type has been composed, the paper is cut, and then

Filmotype Division of Alphatype Corporation

Fig. 5-79. Portion of a film negative (strip) style of type font.

developed, fixed, and dried. The phototype is then ready for mounting in place on the mechanical or for use in contact printing.

Photodisplay typesetters which operate on the *contact printing principle,* Fig. 5-77, usually are limited to producing same-size images of the type font characters. Photodisplay typesetters which operate on the *projection printing principle* increase the range of type sizes possible from any one type font. These machines use a built-in enlarging mechanism or lens arrangement, Fig. 5-78. Photographic enlarging or reducing of the finished phototype, after its removal from the phototypesetting machine, offers still further type size possibilities.

Several examples of manually operated photodisplay typesetters are described below.

StripPrinter

The StripPrinter is an economical contact printing phototypesetting machine for display lines on 35mm film or paper (which is 2″ wide overall), as negatives or positives, in sizes from 6 points to 96 points. See Fig. 5-80. Another model, the StripPrinter "90", sets display letters up to 2½″ high.

The StripPrinter utilizes a filmstrip font — one font for each size of type desired. In opera-

tion, the photo paper or film is loaded in the machine, and the selected type font is threaded through the exposure unit. The first letter is positioned and an exposure made. Succeeding letters are exposed by first positioning the type font and then transporting both the type font and the film or paper a preselected and indexed distance for correct spacing.

The exposed paper or film is developed, fixed, washed, and dried. It then may be mounted on the mechanical.

An additional model, the StripPrinter Supersetter, operates on the projection-printing principle. It sets various sizes of type, as desired, from a single type font.

Headliner

Several models of the VariTyper Headliner are available as table-top, contact printing photo-composing machines for composing lines of type 6 points to 84 points in size. The Model 800 delivers single lines of type, and the Model 840 composes as many as five lines of type — each machine using 35mm print paper or film. The Model 880, Fig. 5-83, page-composes on rolls of paper (8½″ wide) in finished page format. It can produce large advertisements, posters, and other material having a number of consecutive lines of larger type, with fewer sections to piece together.

StripPrinter, Inc.

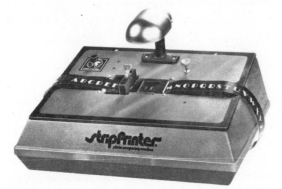

Fig. 5-80. StripPrinter.

VariTyper Corporation

Fig. 5-81. Headliner typemaster.

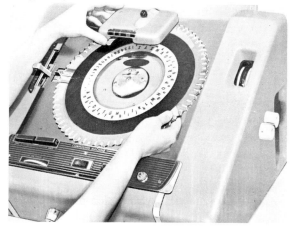

Fig. 5-82. Inserting typemaster into Model 800 Headliner.

Fig. 5-83. Turning typemaster to select a character on Model 880 Headliner.

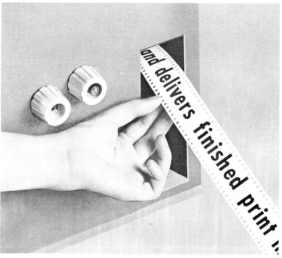

Fig. 5-84. Headliner 800 finished composition.

The Headliner employs for its type font a circular disc about the size of a phonograph record, on which are laminated the film negatives of the type characters. See Fig. 5-81. This disc, called a *Typemaster,* fits between the film exposure light and the threaded roll of either photographic print paper or film. Refer to Fig. 5-82.

Each of the many available Typemasters contains one size and style of typeface. The composed photographic type, however, may be enlarged or reduced from its original size.

Composition is done by rotating the selector knob in either direction until the desired character appears in the selector window, Fig. 5-83. The operator then depresses the print key. This automatically centers the selected character, advances the print paper or film, and makes the photographic exposure of that character on the print paper or film. This process is repeated for each successive letter. Spacing between words is provided by depressing the space key.

Separate adjustment may be made for providing desired letterspacing or for varying the spacing between words to justify the line.

When the desired amount of composition has been accomplished, the strip of paper or film is cut, and is then automatically sprocketed through the machine's developing, fixing and washing tanks. It emerges as a finished print ready for paste-up or as a developed film, Fig. 5-84.

Photo-Typositor

The Photo-Typositor is a projection-type phototypesetting machine for display typesetting, Fig. 5-85. It uses a filmstrip font, 2″ in width. The projection principle permits enlarging (to two times) and reducing (to one-fourth) type to 175 different point sizes from a single font. In addition, it will condense, expand, slant, interlock, overlap, distort, angle and letterspace, as shown in Fig. 5-86.

Visual Graphics Corporation

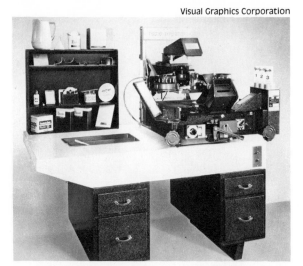

Fig. 5-85. Typical Photo-Typositor installation.

Photo-Typositor, Inc.

perspective   COMPOSE MULTIPLE LINES   BACKSLANT *ITALICS*

SWING COMPOSER   ARCS CURVES

STAGGER STAGGER   *Sets perfectly connected scripts*   ABCDEFGH

Fig. 5-86. A few of the many variations in composition with the Photo-Typositor.

Staromat

The Staromat, Fig. 5-87, is a manually oper-ated projection-style photodisplay machine. It uses a strip-style type font. By using various lenses, the Staromat can produce phototype from 1/4″ to 5-5/8″ high from each font on the font carrier. The use of a projection mirror enables the setting of images up to 39″.

The operator manually selects each letter from the type font and projects it to the phototypesetting paper. The projected image on the paper becomes visible as a tint and then darkens. This visible image allows the operator to exercise full judgment and control over the size, spacing, and arrangement of subsequent

Berthold Fototype Company

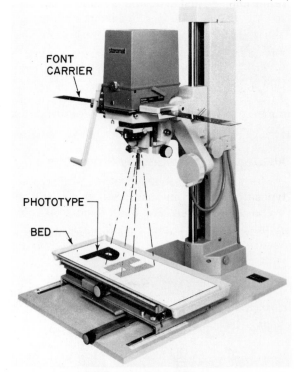

FONT CARRIER

PHOTOTYPE

BED

Fig. 5-87. Staromat is a manually operated, projection-style photo display machine. It produces type 1/4″ to 5⅝″ high by use of lenses and to 39″ high by use of a projection mirror.

Fig. 5-88. Some selected examples of photolettering on the Staromat.

letter images, just as would be done in hand lettering. Because of the freedom and control allowed the operator of a machine such as this, and because of the highly stylized and individualistic display type that can be produced, this kind of photodisplay machine is also called a *photolettering machine*. The display type produced on it is often called *photolettering*. See Fig. 5-88.

Automated Photodisplay Typesetters

Many styles of automated photodisplay typesetters are in use. Some are direct-keyboard operated, Fig. 5-89. Others are commanded by tape or other signal produced on a separate keyboard machine or signaling device, Fig. 5-115. The construction, operation, and functioning of these automated photodisplay typesetters are essentially the same as for the text phototypesetters described beginning on page 80.

Fig. 5-90. **Portion of filmstrip-negative type font.**

Fig. 5-89. **Compuwriter IV is a keyboard-operated (direct-entry) automated text-and-display phototypesetter. It is capable of producing phototype from 6 to 72 points in size.**

Type sizes produced on these machines may be strictly display sizes, as for example, from 14 through 72 points. The machine also may set both text and display sizes, as for example, from 6 through 96 points.

In addition, much photodisplay typesetting is done on composition and makeup (CAM) terminals, as shown in Fig. 5-118, and described on page 99. In newspaper shops, a CAM operator commonly performs advertising layout and makeup, as well as full news page makeup.

Questions

1. Describe the functioning of a manually operated photodisplay typesetter.
2. What makes it possible for a projection-printing photodisplay typesetter to produce many sizes of type from a single font?
3. How many sizes of type can be set from a single font on the StripPrinter?
4. Describe the Headliner Typemaster.
5. What are some of the variations in typeface style possible from a single font on the Photo-Typositor?
6. Why is the Staromat called a photolettering machine?

7. What are some typical uses for a photographic display-type composing machine?

8. Which of the display-type machines described in this section would probably cost the most and which the least? Explain why.

Problems and Projects

1. Make a type specimen book of all available typefaces on the photographic display-type composing machines in your shop.

2. Prepare copy for a large calendar, using photographic display type.

3. Prepare copy for a large poster, using photographic display type.

4. Plan a class field trip to a local type composition house and see photographic type composition being done for commercial printers.

5. What is one advantage of a photographic display-type composing machine over tab type or transfer type?

6. Request a catalog of typefaces from the manufacturer of each of the photographic display-type composing machines in your school shop. Select those you feel would be a welcome addition to your shop.

New Terms

activator	phototext
cassette	processor
command	projection
photodisplay	sizing lens
photolettering	stabilization process

Cold Type Composition — Phototext Typesetting

Phototext composition is produced on automated phototypesetting machines. These can set entire pages or galleys of fully hyphenated-and-justified text type. The type ranges in size from the smallest up to about 36 points. Some of these text machines will also set type up to 72 points in size (and larger). As a result, both the required text type and display type can be set on the one machine. Length of line may run up to 45 or more picas.

Text phototypesetters are often classified in trade literature by generation:

First generation
Second generation
  a. Direct Entry
  b. Separate Entry
Third generation
Fourth generation

First-Generation Phototext Typesetters

The first-generation phototext typesetters, introduced in the decade following 1946, were the earliest practical phototext typesetters. They were modifications of already existing hot-type (hot-metal) casting machines which were converted to set type on film or on phototypesetting paper.

These phototypesetters were almost entirely mechanical in operation. The operator manually commanded the machine directly from a keyboard, or the machine was commanded by a punched paper tape which itself was produced on a separate, manually operated keyboard machine. In either case, it was necessary for the operator to keyboard each character, each

Fig. 5-91.   Intertype Fotosetter is a typical first-generation phototext typesetter.

space or quad, and the hyphenation and justification or other end-of-line decisions much as is done on a typewriter or metal-type composing machine.

The character-generation system of one of these machines, the Intertype Fotosetter introduced in 1946, is shown in Fig. 5-93. The Fotosetter uses three-dimensional brass matrices, or mats, each fitted with a film-negative matrix of an individual type character, Fig. 5-92. In operation, the mats are assembled in a line in response to the manual operation of the keyboard. The mats are then positioned, one at a time in justified form, before a tungsten light source which projects and exposes each letter image on film or on phototypesetting paper, Fig. 5-93. The mats are then returned automatically to magazine-channel storage for re-use. The exposed film (or phototypesetting paper) is taken to the darkroom for developing and is then ready for paste-up on the mechanical for use as camera copy.

Harris Composition Systems Division, Harris Corporation

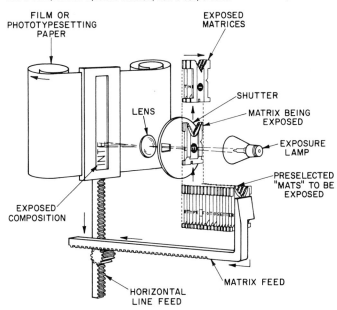

Harris Composition Systems Division, Harris Corporation

Fig. 5-93. Schematic showing the letter-by-letter exposure procedure on the Fotosetter, a first-generation phototext typesetter.

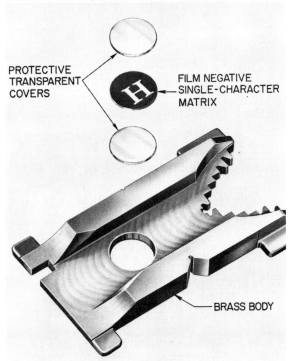

Fig. 5-92. Exploded view of a Fotomat, the single-character matrix used on the Fotosetter.

Because mechanical design and direct-keyboard operation severely limited the output speed, these first-generation machines were soon obsolete. They were replaced by the faster partially and fully automated second-, third-, and fourth-generation phototypesetters. Some of these first-generation phototext typesetters may still be in service, but they are no longer manufactured.

Second-Generation Phototext Typesetters

Second-generation phototext typesetters are electronic-photomechanical in design. A self-contained (built-in) computer interprets the phototypesetting command signals. The machine automatically directs the mechanical character-exposure system. This network generates type characters by projection of (usually) a xenon light beam through a film negative type font onto film or phototypesetting paper.

Hyphenation and justification (H & J) as well as other line-ending decisions may be performed by the keyboard operator with assistance of a built-in minicomputer. However, on the most sophisticated machines, especially the separate-entry machines, the hyphenation and justification usually is entirely performed automatically by an included computer.

These second-generation text phototypesetters may be of the *direct-keyboard-entry* style — or of the *separate-entry* style.

Direct-Keyboard-Entry Phototext Typesetters

The direct-keyboard-entry phototext typesetters, Figs. 5-94 and 5-96, are also called *direct-entry* phototypesetters. They are designed to be operated (commanded) primarily from their self-contained, or cable-connected, keyboard. See Fig. 5-95. Output speed is limited by, and depends primarily on, the speed of the keyboard operator.

Components. The direct-entry machine is a complete phototypesetting system in a single unit. Figure 5-99 shows, in schematic form, the integral units of a typical direct-entry machine. They include a standard-typewriter-style keyboard, an electronic photo-display panel (screen), a memory storage (buffer), a minicomputer, and a phototype-character-generating (optical) system.

Character-Generation (Optical) System

One example of a direct-entry character-generation (optical) system is shown schemat-

Compugraphic Corporation

Fig. 5-94. Compuwriter I direct-entry phototypesetter. Size range is from 6 point to 24 point type.

Compugraphic Corporation

CANCEL LINE	QUAD LEFT	! $	⅛ 1	¼ 2	⅜ 3	½ 4	⅝ 5	¾ 6	⅞ 7	— 8	& 9	? 0	: ;	( )	FORMAT CHANGE	REPEAT

+1U +1P	THIN SPACE	EN SPACE	Q	W	E	R	T	Y	U	I	O	P	+ −	EN LEADER	INSERT SPACE	NO LEAD MI

FILM MASTER CHANGE	EM SPACE	SHIFT LOCK	A	S	D	F	G	H	J	K	L	EM SPACE	RETURN	EM LEADER	SO FO	CALC LINE

SUPER SHIFT	FONT CHANGE	; ,	SHIFT	Z	X	C	V	B	N	M	,	.	CANCEL CHAR	SHIFT	CANCEL WORD	DISC HYPHEN

Fig. 5-95. One of the keyboard layouts as used on the Compuwriter II. Note that the letters A thru Z on the three lower banks of keys are standard typewriter layout as used on most phototypesetters.

VariTyper Division of AM International

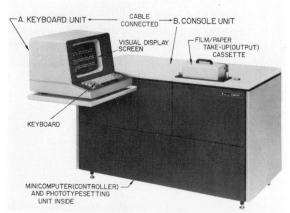

Fig. 5-96. Comp/Set direct-entry phototypesetter. Size range is from 5½ to 36 point type.

VariTyper Division of AM International

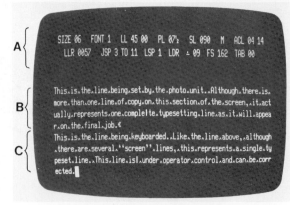

Fig. 5-97. Comp/Set visual display screen.
A. Makeready function display.
B. Line being exposed (set) by the photo unit. (The last previously keyboarded line).
C. The line being keyboarded.

ALPHANUMERIC
KEYS

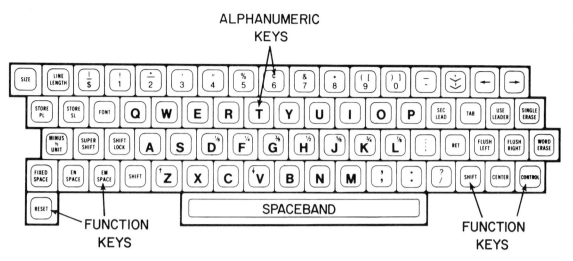

FUNCTION
KEYS

FUNCTION
KEYS

Fig. 5-98. AM Varityper Comp/Set 500 keyboard arrangement.

ically in the lower portion of Fig. 5-99. In this system, the exposure light source sends a beam of light through the selected type font character. The ray passes through the enlarger lens (for size) and then through the collimator and objective lenses. Upon reaching the mirror, the type character image is reflected onto the phototypesetting paper (or film). The mirror is part of the escapement system, which is automatically programmed to travel horizontally so as to position each type character correctly along the line of composition.

After one line of phototype has been "set", the phototypesetting paper (or film) is automatically advanced vertically a predetermined distance, and the escapement returns the mirror to the left, in position to begin exposing the next line of characters.

Advancing the phototypesetting paper (or film) vertically after each line has been exposed, is called either *leading, line spacing, line feed, line advance, paper advance,* or *film advance.* In phototext composition, this distance is equal to the body size of the type, plus the desired spacing between lines. It is measured in points, from base line to base line of successive lines of the type. See Fig. 4-13.

Figure 5-100 shows schematically another design of optical system. Here "set gears" automatically control the horizontal movement of the lens assembly so that successive type characters are spaced correctly along the line.

Makeready

Makeready is the preparation of the phototypesetter and its control settings so that the machine will produce phototype in the desired face, size, and format.

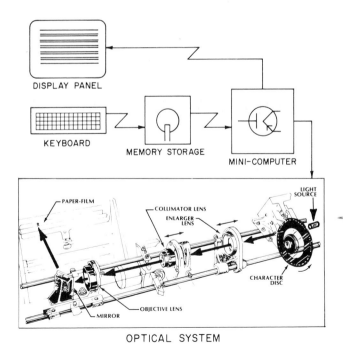

OPTICAL SYSTEM

Fig. 5-99. Schematic diagram of components of the Comp/ Set Varityper direct-keyboard-entry phototypesetter.

Compugraphic Corporation

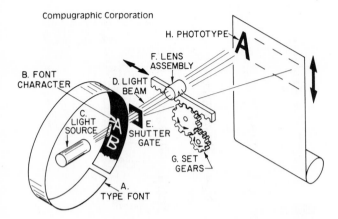

Fig. 5-100. In this optical system, set gears automatically control the horizontal movement of the lens assembly for exposure of each character.

• **Note:** Makeready must be performed on all phototypesetters, regardless of generation. The exact procedures to be followed are detailed in the operator's manual for the specific machine.

Some procedures of makeready include: installation of a supply of phototypesetting paper or film; selection or installation of the type font(s); arrangement for type (lens) size; and provision for character set (width or escapement). Certain settings must also be made. These will be for line length (measure), leading (film advance), hyphenation mode, justification range and mode, minimum and maximum spaceband ranges, letterspacing range control, and intercharacter spacing.

The type of machine used will determine the necessary steps of makeready. Operations to be performed may include installation of an item (by setting dials and switches on the machine's control panel) or the entering of *command codes* through keyboarding. Sometimes both of these steps are required.

Operation

After makeready preparation, the operator keyboards the copy in much the same manner as when operating a standard electric typewriter. As each character and symbol is keyboarded, it is automatically entered in the phototypesetter mini-computer and buffer (memory) section. These characters also appear in sequen-

tial order, in the form of lighted[3] characters, on the phototypesetter visual display panel (or screen). Also displayed is an indication of the amount of line length remaining.

The machine signals the operator when a displayed line reaches its justification zone (place of possible ending). In order to start the next line when the previous line has ended with a whole word, the operator keyboard-signals for a line-ending-and-return. If the line ending calls for a hyphen (division of word by syllable), the operator may manually keyboard that hyphen insertion, then keyboard-signal for line-ending-and-return. If the machine is capable of automatic hyphenation, then the operator may leave hyphenation decisions to the machine and simply end the line by keyboarding an end-of-line-and-return command.

After keyboarding the end-of-line-and-return signal, the operator immediately resumes keyboarding, starting on the next line of composition. Meanwhile, while this next line of composition is being keyboarded, the typesetter automatically recalls from memory, and exposes on paper or film, each of the characters of the just previously keyboarded line. The machine automatically justifies the line as needed.

After each line of phototype is exposed, the phototypesetting paper or film is automatically advanced vertically a predetermined distance (the leading) so as to accommodate the next line of type.

Usually the exposed phototypesetting paper or film is automatically fed into a light-tight receiver cassette.

When composition is complete, the operator cuts the paper or film containing the phototype composition. This paper or film is passed through a separate, or self-contained, processor for developing. The phototype is then ready for use as paste-up camera copy.

Separate-Entry Second-Generation Phototext Typesetters

Separate-entry second-generation phototext typesetters usually have no built-in keyboard, Figs. 5-101 and 5-102. They are intended to be

[3]In an LED display — Light Emitting Diodes.

Compugraphic Corporation

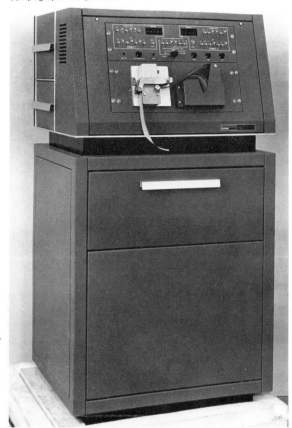

Fig. 5-101. Separate-entry, tape-operated, second generation text phototypesetter.

Mergenthaler Linotype Company

Fig. 5-102. Separate-entry, tape-driven, text and display phototypesetter — Mergenthaler's V-I-P (variable-input-phototypesetter).

Mergenthaler Linotype Company

Fig. 5-103. Video input/editing terminal (Mergenthaler MVP/2). This machine enables remote operators to prepare and edit input on magnetic (floppy) disks and thus drive a separate phototypesetter.

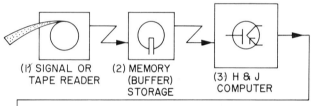

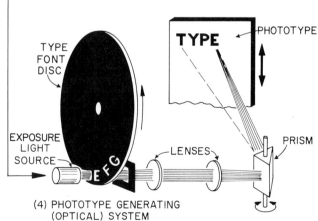

Fig. 5-104. Schematic block diagram of the components of a typical separate-entry second-generation (automated) phototypesetter. Many designs are used. This design employs a photo-negative disk-style type font carrier. Controlled rotation of the prism places each character properly along the horizontal line of composition.

part of a phototypesetting system where the machine is operated primarily from punched paper type, magnetic tape, or by electronic signal which is produced by operators on separate keyboard units. An auxiliary keyboard may be included as optional equipment for direct entry of copy. In addition, the phototypesetter may also be commanded from one or more on-line signal sources, as diagrammed in Fig. 5-113. Because it is not limited in speed by operation of a built-in keyboard, one separate-entry phototypesetter is fast enough to accept and process the tapes or output produced by operators of several or more keyboard units or other on-line signal sources.

Components. As shown in the block diagram in Fig. 5-104, a typical separate-entry second-generation phototypesetter may contain the following: (1) a *reader*, which converts incoming signal or tape into digital (on-off) electrical signal, which can be read by the computer; (2) a *memory (buffer) storage capacity* which accepts and stores the incoming signal, and then feeds it to the computer on demand; (3) a highly sophisticated computer, usually capable of accepting a raw (unjustified) copy signal and converting that signal so as to command the optical system to automatically produce hyphenated and justified lines of phototype composition; and (4) a phototype-

Mergenthaler Linotype Company

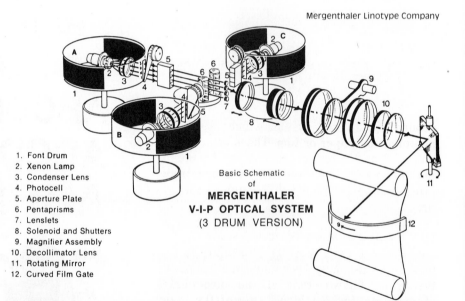

Fig. 5-105. Basic schematic of the three-drum version of the Mergenthaler V-I-P optical system. This is a separate-entry second-generation phototypesetter. Note that controlled rotation of a mirror places the phototype images horizontally along the surface of the phototypesetting paper. The paper is held in a curved plane, assuring constant focal distance from the surface of the rotating mirror to the entire line of type across the paper.

1. Font Drum
2. Xenon Lamp
3. Condenser Lens
4. Photocell
5. Aperture Plate
6. Pentaprisms
7. Lenslets
8. Solenoid and Shutters
9. Magnifier Assembly
10. Decollimator Lens
11. Rotating Mirror
12. Curved Film Gate

Basic Schematic
of
**MERGENTHALER
V-I-P OPTICAL SYSTEM**
(3 DRUM VERSION)

B-range font

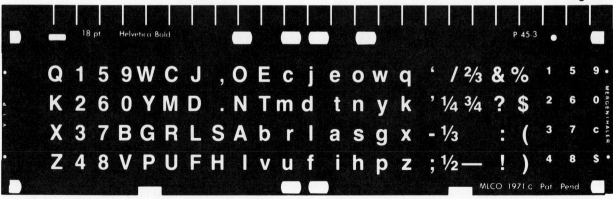

Fig. 5-106. Filmstrip style type font with one font of type.

Mergenthaler Linotype Company

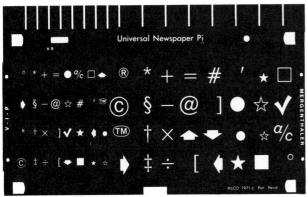

Mergenthaler Linotype Company

Universal Newspaper Pi
MERGENTHALER
V.I.P.
MLCO 1971 C Pat Pend

Pi font

Fig. 5-107. Type font with pi characters. Pi characters are those characters not found in regular fonts of type.

Fig. 5-108. A partial range of sizes of text and display phototype.

Mergenthaler Linotype Company

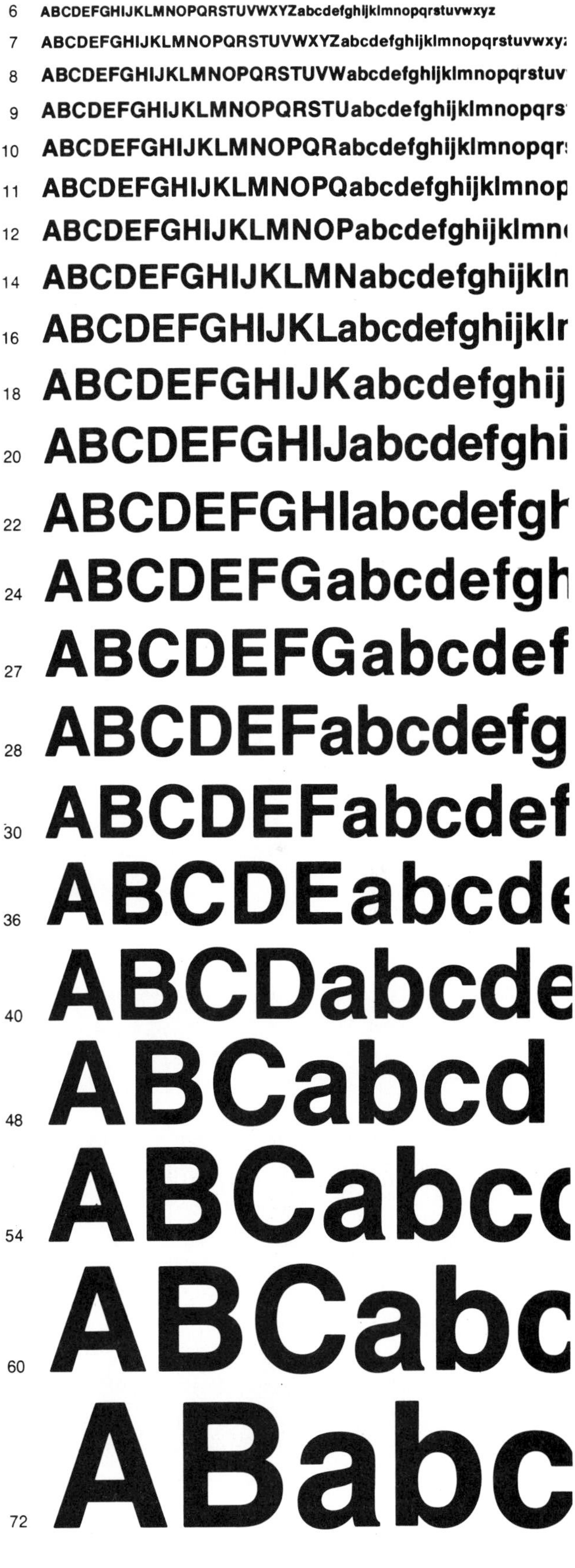

6 ABCDEFGHIJKLMNOPQRSTUVWXYZabcdefghijklmnopqrstuvwxyz
7 ABCDEFGHIJKLMNOPQRSTUVWXYZabcdefghijklmnopqrstuvwxy
8 ABCDEFGHIJKLMNOPQRSTUVWabcdefghijklmnopqrstuv
9 ABCDEFGHIJKLMNOPQRSTUabcdefghijklmnopqrs
10 ABCDEFGHIJKLMNOPQRabcdefghijklmnopqr
11 ABCDEFGHIJKLMNOPQabcdefghijklmnop
12 ABCDEFGHIJKLMNOPabcdefghijklmn
14 ABCDEFGHIJKLMNabcdefghijkln
16 ABCDEFGHIJKLabcdefghijklr
18 ABCDEFGHIJKabcdefghij
20 ABCDEFGHIJabcdefghi
22 ABCDEFGHIabcdefgh
24 ABCDEFGabcdefgh
27 ABCDEFGabcdef
28 ABCDEFabcdefg
30 ABCDEFabcdef
36 ABCDEabcde
40 ABCDabcde
48 ABCabcd
54 ABCabcc
60 ABCabc
72 ABabc

generating (optical) system which "sets" the phototype on paper or film. There may, or may not, be a built-in processing unit for developing the phototype paper or film. If not, the unprocessed phototype is run through a separate processing unit.

Character-Generating (Optical) System

In general, the character-generating system of a separate-entry second-generation phototypesetter follows that of the direct-entry phototypesetting machines. One of the many designs is shown in schematic form in Fig. 5-105. This particular design uses three filmstrip-style type fonts, Fig. 5-106. A rotating mirror places the phototype images along the line of composition. The exposure light source is a xenon lamp.

Phototype Production Sequence

Production of phototype with a separate-entry second-generation phototypesetter involves these three major procedures. They are copy signal preparation, makeready of the phototypesetter, and operation of the phototypesetter, briefly described as follows.

Copy Signal Preparation

A separate keyboard machine is generally used to prepare a punched paper tape, a magnetic tape, or a magnetic (floppy) disk according to the copy to be set in type, Figs. 5-109, 5-110, 5-111. Or, the signal may be sent on-line directly to the phototypesetter. In preparation of the tape (or other input signal), the operator keyboards the appropriate command keys for those makeready items which are not commanded by switches, dials, or other machine physical settings on the phototypesetter itself. These may be for face, size, and style of type; style of paragraph indention; and leading between lines and paragraphs. (Such items are

Compugraphic Corporation

Fig. 5-109. Punched paper tape.

Compugraphic Corporation

Fig. 5-110. Magnetic tape cassette.

sometimes referred to as *format*.) Next, the operator keyboards the alphanumeric and command keys so as to record the proper letters and word spacing according to the copy.

Most separate-entry phototypesetters use computer-controlled hyphenation and justification of lines. Therefore, the operator sets straight composition (text matter paragraphs) without entering end-of-line commands, except to indicate the opening and ending of paragraphs. The operator keyboards the copy without regard to line ending. The copy is keyboarded as one long line (sometimes referred to as "idiot" copy). Later, during typesetting, the phototypesetter's computer will automatically break the composition into equal-measure lines. The machine will automatically justify each line, hyphenate at line endings wherever necessary, and insert the proper leading between lines and between paragraphs.

Composition, now on punched paper tape, magnetic tape, or disk, is ready to be placed on the phototypesetter for "setting." The composition can be stored for repeated rerun.

Makeready

In preparing a separate-entry second-generation phototypesetter for operation, the items of makeready are performed physically by the operator. Makeready usually includes installa-

Compugraphic Corporation

Fig. 5-111. Magnetic (floppy) disk. Durable and reusable. Each disk stores the equivalent of ¹/₂ mile of paper tape.

tion of such items as a supply of phototypesetting paper or film type fonts and character-width-control devices.

Other items of makeready are usually entered as keyboarded commands on the tape or are entered as on-line signals. These commands would include, for instance, the size, face and style of type; the length of line; indention or other format; leading; and all other commands necessary for the machine to automatically set type according to the copy.

Operation

After the makeready operation is completed, the separate-entry second-generation phototypesetter is automatic in operation. If, for example, the input is tape, operation follows these general steps:

1. The input tape is installed (loaded).
2. The *Start* switch is turned on to begin the automatic typesetting process.
3. Initially, the machine reads a portion of the job tape into the phototypesetter's memory (buffer) storage.
4. On demand, or as needed, signal is recalled from the buffers and the phototype is actually phototypeset rapidly, a character at a time. The printout carriage (or optical system) moves or exposes from left to right along the line of composition. Each line of

phototype is automatically word-spaced and hyphenated and justified by decisions from the phototypesetter computer.
5. When a line is completed, the carriage or mirrors return to the left margin. The leading device moves the paper or film vertically to be in place for the next line, and more tape is then read to replenish the buffer storage.
6. Phototypesetting continues until either a command to *stop* is encountered, the tape reader runs out of tape, or the *stop* switch is turned to *off*.
7. The output phototype is then processed and is ready for paste-up.

Basic Installation

A typical basic installation of a separate-entry second-generation phototypesetter is shown in Fig. 5-112. In this system, operators of a number of separate (stand-alone) keyboard machines produce magnetic or punched-paper tape which contains the copy in coded signal form. These tapes are fed to the phototypesetter which reads the tapes, obeys the commands, and automatically composes the phototype on paper or film. After processing (developing), the phototype is ready for paste-up as camera copy.

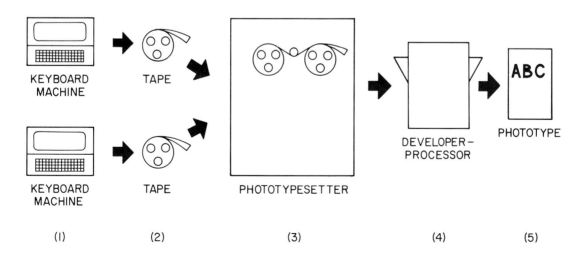

KEYBOARD MACHINE   TAPE   PHOTOTYPESETTER   DEVELOPER – PROCESSOR   PHOTOTYPE

KEYBOARD MACHINE   TAPE

(1)   (2)   (3)   (4)   (5)

Fig. 5-112. A typical basic installation of a separate-entry second-generation phototypesetter. One or more keyboard machines produce punched or magnetic tape, which is fed to the phototypesetter for typesetting. A stand-alone processor develops the phototype composition.

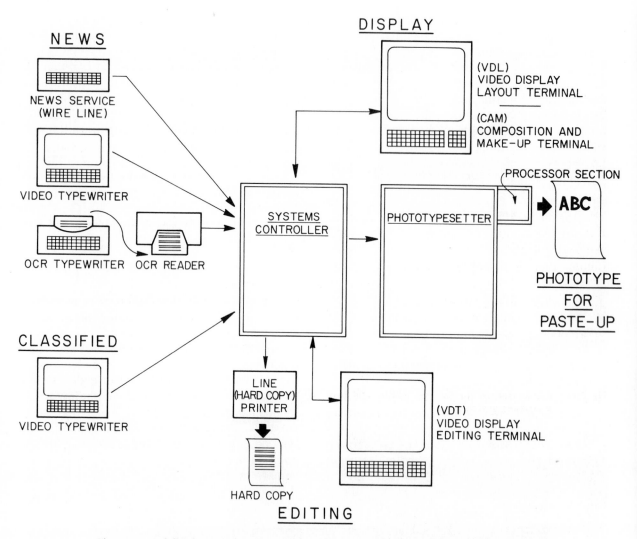

Fig. 5-113. A fully electronic (computerized) phototypesetting layout from entry of copy to photo-type output as would be used, for example, in a newspaper office. This layout is typical for separate-entry second-generation, third-generation, and fourth-generation phototypesetters.

Fully Electronic Installation

A more sophisticated and fully electronic separate-entry second-generation phototype-setter installation is shown diagrammatically in Fig. 5-113. One such as this would be used, for instance, in a newspaper office. The various separate units may or may not be cable-connected, and may be located at widely separated locations.

At the center of the system is the *controller*, a computer-controlled information storage and retrieval (IS&R) system, Fig. 5-114. News copy comes in over the news service wire lines and is entered and stored in the controller memory.

Reporters type out their news accounts on video keyboard terminals (video typewriters), Fig. 5-115. These stories are automatically entered in the controller, and can be recalled for display by the reporter (or editor) for revision, if desired.

Reporters can also enter copy on optical-character-reader (OCR) typewriters. The OCR typewriters type a *bar code* or *human-readable* characters, Fig. 5-116.

Autologic, Inc.

Taplin Business Machines

This is a sample of typewritte

Model T673A. It may be used c

without modification or specia

down to 4 lines per inch. App

are desirable. TBM Optical Pa

line-finding rules, or beginni

A. OCR bar code.

VariTyper Corporation

ABCDEFGHIJKLMNOPQRSTUVWXYZ&   1234!

?$£/%+=*   ÄÅÆÑØÖÜŸ♪♀♂| NEW HEADLI

B. OCR type font (partial), human readable.

Fig. 5-116. Copy typed on an optical-character-reader
(OCR) typewriter.

Fig. 5-114. Systems controller for text editing and text
processing systems.

Harris Corporation

Fig. 5-115. Reporters type out their stories on video keyboard terminals.

Taplin Business Machines

Fig. 5-117. OCR page reader.

Classified ads are entered by operators of
video keyboard terminals. The system checks
to be sure all information is entered, such as
starting and stopping dates. New ads are
quickly sorted and merged into the previous
day's file.

Copy for display ads may be entered in the
controller by video keyboard terminal or by

Fig. 5-118. **Electronic composition on the composition and makeup (CAM) terminal. At the** *Minneapolis Star and Tribune*, **a full-page advertisement is shown being composed on the screen of the display screen of the CAM, following the copy layout on the digitizing tablet at the compositor's right.**

Fig. 5-119. **Line printer, or hard copy printer.**

OCR units. The copy is recalled (retrieved) for display and makeup by the operator on the screen of a *composition and makeup (CAM) terminal,* Fig. 5-118, also called a *video display layout (VDL) terminal.* Here the copy appears as lines of letters of a single size.

By use of two keyboards (for characters and functions), the CAM operator follows that copy and composes the advertising in actual type sizes and positions directly on the CAM screen, exactly as they will appear in the final phototype output. In composing the ad, the operator is also aided by the advertiser's full-page layout. This is shown on the digitizing tablet at the right in Fig. 5-118. By the operator's pointing a stylus anywhere on the layout, a position cursor on the CAM screen is moved to that specific working location for operator direction or orientation.

When the operator has completed the ad composition, which may be up to a full newspaper page in size, it is sent to the controller storage. On demand, the controller releases the stored composition to the phototypesetter for automatic typesetting.

The line printer, or *hard-copy* printer, Fig. 5-119, will produce in seconds a hard copy (like a typewritten copy) of any story that has been filed in the controller. The line printer also immediately prints a copy of all new or corrected classified ads. Although the hard copy is printed in typewriter-style characters (not the actual typeface of the phototype), the hard copy is useful for proofreading and for file copies, Fig. 5-120. (See "Hard Copy Proofs from a Line Printer," page 103.)

The editor makes much use of the video display terminal (VDT), Figs. 5-121 and 6-1. The terminal may be used, for instance, to recall from controller memory any story previously filed. The story is displayed on the VDT screen and then edited. If necessary, changes are made and new copy is added. When satisfied that the information is correct, the editor signals the phototypesetter to set type.

From the phototypesetter optical unit, the exposed phototype passes through a processor unit — built-in (self-contained) or stand-alone (separate) — for developing. The finished phototype is then ready for paste-up as camera copy.

• **Note:** The installation described above is typical also for third- and fourth-generation phototypesetters.

Versatec, Inc.

IMPROVE COMPOSITION ROOM EFFICIENCY

■ The cut and paste correction proce:

    By proofing the copy on a Matri:
    with either a VDT or a correcti:
    ing it set by the phototypesett:
    cedure is no longer required. '

■ VDTs, if present, are operated onl
  mode - the correction process.

    By having the Matrix Proofer pr(
    material the proofing operation
    VDT operator. Proof reading fr(
    from hard copy and it ties up s(
    a fairly mundane task. The cor:
    very easily and quickly by a VD'
    proofed and marked-up copy will
    the errors are located and what

             This sample was

                (us

                 VERS,

Fig. 5-120. Sample printout (hard copy) from line printer.

Autologic, Inc.

Fig. 5-122. Autologic's Model APS-4 phototypesetter is a third-generation (CRT) phototypesetter with paper tape reader and magnetic tape read/write deck. This machine generates mosaic-dot phototype from font characters stored in digital form.

Third-Generation Phototext Typesetters

Third-generation phototypesetters are the cathode-ray-tube (CRT) phototypesetters. They are fully electronic and computerized, Fig. 5-122. These machines have no built-in keyboard. Instead, they are commanded by tape or electronic signal produced on separate keyboards or other input devices. All composition produced is automatically hyphenated and justified.

Dymo Graphic Systems, Inc.

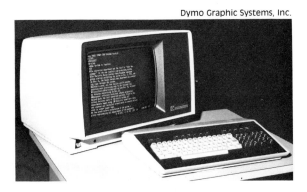

Fig. 5-121. The input/editing video terminal provides for input, manipulation of copy, and output to the phototypesetting system.

In operation, font character images are displayed on the face of a cathode-ray tube in much the same manner as the picture is formed on the screen of a home television set. These type character images are then projected (exposed) onto film or phototypesetting paper in final output size and position, Fig. 5-124. This occurs at very high speeds — 4000 or more type characters per second. This would correspond to about a speed of 1.1 seconds for setting the type for a full page of this book.

Character Generation

Two current systems of generating the phototype characters on the face of the cathode-ray tube are *dot mosaic* and *raster line*.

CRT Dot-Mosaic Character Generation

In this system, the designer's matrix drawing of each individual type character has been converted to a dot mosaic, or pattern of dots, Fig. 5-123. Each dot and row of dots is assigned a number horizontally and vertically. These numerals, which describe each type character in a

Autologic, Inc.

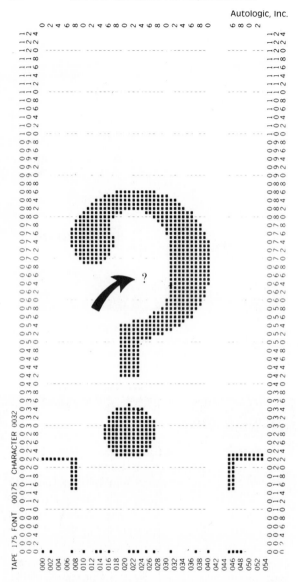

Fig. 5-123. Dot-mosaic font character. This is an actual (enlarged) digitized representation of a 9-point dot-mosaic question mark (indicated by the arrow at the center). In the 9-point size, characters have a resolution of about 720 dots per square inch. Larger sizes may have as many as 1440 dots per square inch.

master type font, are then digitally encoded on a magnetic disc or drum. Several hundred of these magnetically encoded master type fonts can be carried, or *contained*, at one time in the phototypesetter's magnetic memory storage system.

• **Note:** Digitally encoded means that the font characters are carried in magnetic memory storage in digital (off-on) signal form. These *off-on* signals will later direct the CRT beam to "paint" those type characters on the face of the tube in a mosiac pattern of closely spaced dots to form the image of each type character.

Figure 5-124 shows in schematic form how a third-generation phototypesetter produces phototype by the dot-mosaic method. Prior to typesetting, the type fonts (which are recorded on magnetic tape or discs) are loaded into the phototypesetter's font storage (4). Copy input to the phototypesetter, in the form of punched paper or magnetic tape (or by on-line signal), is interpreted by the signal reader (1) and fed into the copy-signal memory storage (2).

Upon recall from the storage by the computer (3), each character in the copy signal is assigned by the computer an appropriate digital coding according to font character storage (4). The coding directs the CRT dot beam deflection circuitry (5) to reproduce the desired dot-mosaic type character in the typesetting window on the face of the printout CRT (6), Fig. 5-125. This character is projected by the printout CRT through a lens (7) and onto the phototypesetting paper or film (8). The symbol will

Fig. 5-125. Simulated appearance of a dot-mosaic type character, generated from digital font storage, and displayed on the face of the output CRT. (A 9-point font character would have a resolution of about 720 dots per inch).

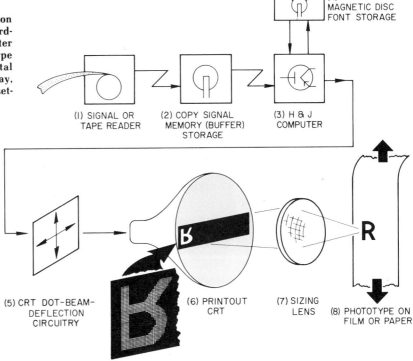

Fig. 5-124. Schematic representation showing how the third-generation phototypesetter generates dot-mosaic type characters from digital storage, to CRT display, and onto the phototypesetting paper or film.

(4) MAGNETIC DISC FONT STORAGE

(I) SIGNAL OR TAPE READER

(2) COPY SIGNAL MEMORY (BUFFER) STORAGE

(3) H & J COMPUTER

(5) CRT DOT-BEAM-DEFLECTION CIRCUITRY

(6) PRINTOUT CRT

(7) SIZING LENS

(8) PHOTOTYPE ON FILM OR PAPER

Fig. 5-126. Mergenthaler's Linotron 303, a third-generation (CRT) phototypesetter. This machine generates phototype on the raster-line principle.

Fig. 5-127. Grid-style type font for CRT raster-line character generation.

then be in proper size and position along the line of composition. After the characters for one full line have been exposed, the phototypesetting paper is advanced the proper leading, and exposure-composition of the next line begins.

Only three moving components are involved: the tape transport, the magnetic disc storage and retrieval, and the phototypesetting film or paper transport.

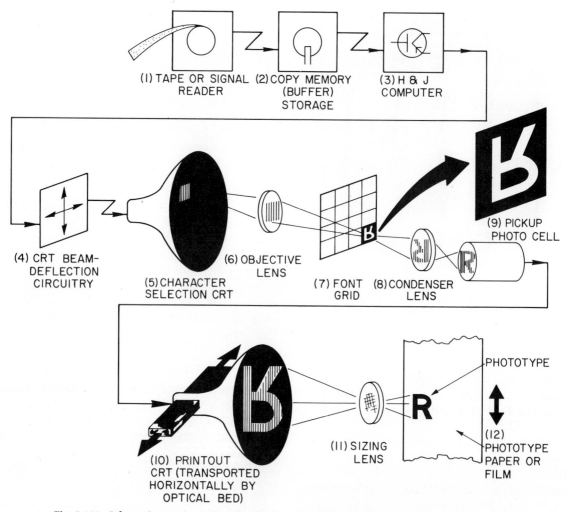

Fig. 5-128. Schematic representation showing how the CRT phototypesetter generates raster-line type characters, from photo-negative type font grid, to CRT display, and onto the phototypesetting paper or film.

CRT Raster-Line Character Generation

In the CRT raster-line system of character generation, the type font is a glass or film photo negative. This contains one or more fonts of negative photo images of individual type characters, Fig. 5-127.

Figure 5-128 shows, in schematic form, how a third-generation phototypesetter produces phototype by the raster-line method. Copy input to the phototypesetter is by paper tape, magnetic tape or disc, or by on-line digital signal. This copy-input signal comes through the signal reader (1), and is fed into, and stored in, the phototypesetter memory storage (2) until released to the computer (3).

For each desired character, the computer directs the CRT-beam-deflection circuitry (4) to generate a scanning raster. This appears on the face of the character-selection CRT (5). The scanning raster must be in the proper position (area) so that the raster will be directed by the objective lens (6) through the appropriate character in the font grid (7).

The font grid character image, now composed of scan lines, is focused by the condenser lens (8) onto the pickup photocell (9). This photocell senses the character as a succession of scan lines of various lengths and then transmits signals to the printout CRT (10). These signals switch the beam of the printout CRT on and off.

Fig. 5-129. Schematic representation showing the raster-line formation of a type character on the face of the printout CRT. In a typical character, the "painted" beam strokes are 0.001″ wide.

In this way, the printout CRT projects the raster pattern type character image through the sizing lens (11) onto the phototypesetting paper or film (12).

After exposure of each character, an optical bed transports the printout CRT horizontally to expose successive letters to form the line of composition. When a full line of characters has been exposed, the phototypesetting paper or film is automatically advanced vertically. The phototypesetter then commences to set the next line.

Each type character image produced on the paper or film is actually composed of a series of successive raster lines, much as if the character were "painted" as a series of brush strokes. See Fig. 5-129.

Advantage of Fully Electronic Character Generation

In the first- and second-generation phototypesetters described earlier, the font carriers had to be selectively and mechanically positioned for exposure. This imposed somewhat of a speed limitation on the rate of character exposure. The third-generation phototypesetters, however, eliminate the moving font carriers. They select and expose the font characters by fully electronic means, thus achieving fantastic speed in composition.

Makeready and Operation

The procedures for makeready and operation of these third-generation machines follow closely those of the separate-entry second-generation machines described earlier. The only exception is the installation of type fonts in digital storage.

Typical Installation

A typical installation of a third-generation phototypesetting system would be in a setup such as that shown in Fig. 5-113. Such a machine might be found in a newspaper office, book publishing house, trade composition house, or other large-scale user or producer of photo-type composition. Such businesses could justify the relatively higher cost of such a system since it results in greater output production.

Fourth-Generation Phototext Typesetters

The fourth-generation phototypesetters are the *laser* phototypesetters, Fig. 5-130. Like the third-generation phototypesetters, these machines are fully electronic and computerized. Input (command) is from paper or magnetic

Dymo Graphic Systems, Inc.

Fig. 5-130. The Dymo Laser Composer (DLC-1000), formerly the Photon (PTM-1000), is a fourth-generation phototypesetter.

tape, or from on-line or stored signal — all produced on separate machines or from an OCR[4] device that scans the original copy. No photographic (film negative) type fonts are used. Instead, digitally coded type fonts[5] in storage on magnetic discs, direct a precision optical laser light source. This laser light beam generates the desired phototype characters directly onto the output phototypesetting paper or film. Hyphenation and justification are fully computerized and automatic.

Laser

The word "laser" is an acronym (abbreviation) made up of the initials of the term *Light Amplification by Stimulated Emission of Radiation.* As it applies to phototypesetting, a laser might be simply described as an extremely powerful, narrow beam of visible light which is channeled so as to generate phototype character images by direct exposure on the phototypesetting paper or film.

[4]Optical character reader. See page 90.
[5]See page 259.

Fig. 5-132. Simulated appearance of a laser-beam-generated type character on the phototypesetting paper. Each character is "painted" by a series of vertical laser-beam strokes (as indicated by the strokes in the inset circle, above).

The diagram in Fig. 5-131 shows the basic functioning of the laser phototypesetter. Incoming copy signal, in the form of tape or on-line signal, is received and read by the tape or signal reader (1) and is converted into digital signal. This signal is stored in the copy memory (2) of the central processing unit (CPU) (3). The memory unit also contains the character-width tables and other typesetting instructions, such as type size and style. These may be fed in as signals, or a separate panelboard may be available for manual control of these machine settings.

Digitally coded type fonts, stored on magnetic discs, are contained in the font memory section (4). The H&J section (5) supplies the hyphenation and justification line-ending decisions.

When data information is complete for each desired character, it is passed on to the character-generation logic section (6). Here, character-shape information is converted into beam-stroke end points.

The beam modulation-and-vertical-deflection section (7) controls the laser beam (8) as it "paints" the various-length vertical lines to generate the characters on the output photopaper, Fig. 5-132. The horizontal-deflection

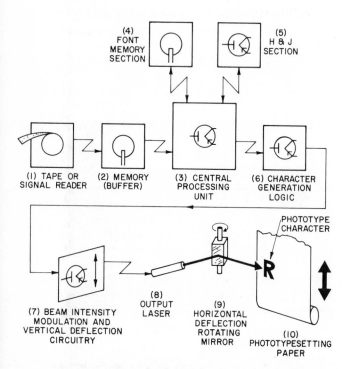

Fig. 5-131. Schematic block diagram of components of a fourth-generation (laser) phototypesetter.

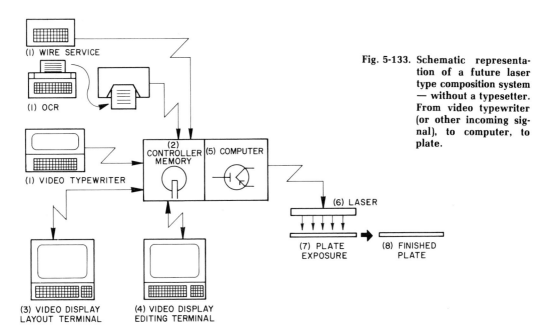

mirror (9) provides the left-to-right deflection of the laser beam along the line of composition on the phototypesetting paper. At the end of each line of composition, the photopaper is advanced vertically and composition is resumed at the left margin for the next line.

In the very near future, we may expect to see a laser typesetting system without a phototypesetter. This is diagrammed in Fig. 5-133. In such a system, the incoming signal (1) — from OCR, video typewriter, etc. — is fed to the controller memory (2). The controller causes this information to be displayed on video screens — video display layout terminal (3) and video display editing terminal (4) where it is arranged and edited in full newspaper-page format.

After arrangement (layout) and editing are satisfactory, the computer (5) is commanded to automatically transmit digital signals to the laser unit (6) which images the commanded characters directly onto the offset plate (7).[6]

Questions

1. When were the first practical phototext typesetters introduced?
2. Describe an Intertype Fotomat.

[6]See also Laser Facsimile Offset Plate system, page 259.

3. How is a direct-entry phototypesetter commanded? What determines, or limits, the machine's speed?
4. Discuss the keyboard layout of second-generation phototypesetters. Compare it with a standard typewriter keyboard.
5. On the phototypesetter, how would you define the term *leading*? How is the amount of leading measured — from where to where?
6. Name several methods of commanding (driving) a separate-entry phototypesetter.
7. Which is faster — a separate-entry or a direct-entry phototypesetter? Explain.
8. Name the component units of a typical direct-entry text phototypesetter.
9. How many of each character are on a V-I-P font?
10. What are pi characters? Name some.
11. Describe seven general steps in the operation of a separate-entry second-generation phototypesetter, assuming a punched paper tape has already been prepared.
12. Describe the work of the CAM operator.
13. How does the editor use the VDT terminal?
14. What does the hard-copy printer produce? For what purpose?
15. Describe briefly the characteristics of the third-generation phototext typesetters.
16. Give a simplified description of a laser beam as used in phototypesetting.

Problems and Projects

1. Plan a series of field trips to printing plants which use each kind of phototypesetter described in this chapter.
2. Make a bulletin board display of photographically composed pages of type matter from samples obtained on your field trip or from visits to, or correspondence with, composition houses.
3. Make a permanent (wall case) display of all the methods of type composition described in this chapter. Gather your materials from your own shop, from contributions from trade shops, and from literature supplied by the manufacturers of this equipment.
4. Plan and execute projects involving the use of hand art and cold type methods described in this chapter.
5. From catalogs and trade literature, replan your shop to include your ideas of what additional type composing equipment would be desirable. Make the drawing to scale, and write up specifications for each item of equipment, including prices.
6. The machines described are merely representative of the various models available. Check articles and advertisements in the trade journals to locate other machines. Describe their operation.

New Terms

alphanumeric	"floppy" disc
bar code	generation
buffer section	makeready
collimator lens	optical system
controller	raster lines
digital signal	

To help assure a quality printed product, proofs of all composition must be carefully read for errors. After corrections are completed, proofs are made for reproduction. Preparations for camera work and platemaking can then begin.

Since many methods of type composition are used for offset reproduction, proofs of the type matter, as received for reading, may be of several kinds.

Proofs of Metal and Wood Type Composition

Forms of metal and wood type are inked, and then a proof of the composition is pulled (printed on a proof press). Generally, to allow space for making corrections, the proof is pulled on paper that is larger than the type form.

Proofs of Phototype Composition

The final output of photographic composing (phototypesetting) machines is in the form of either negatives or positives. It may be on either film or photoprint paper, depending on the method used and the product requested.

Photocopies of the Phototype

Final proofs of the film positives and film negatives are both submitted to the proofroom as *positives*. These may be brown on Vandyke paper, blue on blueline or diazo paper, or black on photoprint or electrostatic paper. These paper proofs are used for reading and marking.

Visual Editing and Proofing Terminal

A visual editing and proofing terminal, Fig. 6-1, is used to make corrections on composition which is still on paper tape or magnetic tape, in computer storage, or being fed in (on-line) from an OCR system.

• **Note:** Other names for this terminal are CRT (cathode-ray-tube terminal) and VDT (video-display terminal).

The main components of the editing and proofing terminal are:

1. Input signal reader (tape or on-line).
2. CRT (cathode-ray-tube) display screen or panel.

Fig. 6-1. **Harris 1100 visual (CRT) editing and proofing terminal.**
Harris-Intertype Corporation

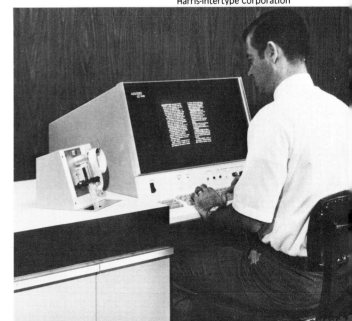

VariTyper Corporation

Fig. 6-2.   **Keyboard layout of video display terminal (VDT) for editing and proofreading.**

3. Main keyboard, similar to that of a standard electric typewriter, Fig. 6-2.
4. Auxiliary keyboard.
5. Buffer memory for temporary storage of raw input and corrected output text.
6. Minicomputer for control of all functions.
7. Output device, which delivers a new corrected tape or an on-line signal.

Operation

The incoming signal from tape or on-line from computer memory is fed into the VDT buffer memory. By operating the keyboard, the

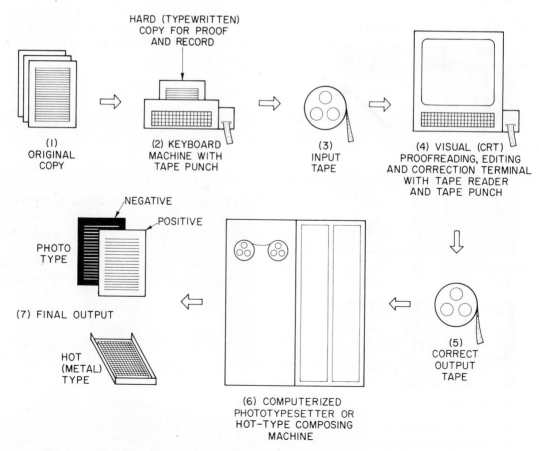

Fig. 6-4.   **Work-flow diagram showing location of visual correction terminal in computerized typesetting operation.**

A. Misspelling of the word "type" is noted in the composition on the screen of the terminal.

B. Cursor is positioned over wrong letter "e".

C. Operator keyboards correct letter "p", automatically replacing wrong letter "e".

D. Cursor is positioned over wrong letter "p".

E. Operator keyboards correct letter "e", automatically replacing the wrong letter.

F. The word "type" is now correctly spelled.

Fig. 6-3. Steps in the correction of tape composition on the visual editing and correction terminal.

operator causes a selected portion of the composition to be displayed on the face of the VDT display screen, which is similar to a home television screen. The operator reads this displayed composition, looking for errors, changes, and omissions. For instance, when finding a misspelled word, the operator by keyboard control causes a lighted cursor (lighted rectangular spot) to be positioned on the first letter of the misspelled word, Fig. 6-3. The operator then keyboards (types) the correction, which appears on the screen as it is typed. This gives the operator a visual indication of the progress of the work. As these corrections are made, they are stored in the buffer of the visual display terminal.

After all corrections are made, the operator signals the VDT to recall the corrected text from buffer storage and produce a new and fully corrected tape which can be used for phototypesetter operation — or the corrected text can be sent on-line to the phototypesetter. If desired, additional new text can be composed directly on the VDT keyboard. The final phototype output, on film or photopaper, will again be read for errors.

Hard Copy Proofs from a Line Printer

A line printer (hard-copy printer), as shown in Fig. 5-119, may be installed as a separate unit which will accept tape or may be connected on-line to the computer/controller or to the phototypesetter. This unit produces a *hard copy* of the composition *before* the phototypesetter sets the type. The hard copy is not a duplicate of the actual phototype composition. Rather, it resembles a typewritten copy of the composition, Fig. 5-120.

The hard copy will not show the actual typefaces, leading, typographic arrangement, defective characters, and density. However, the hard copy proof is extremely useful for editing and proofreading purposes such as checking continuity, sense, spelling, grammar, hyphenation, and justification. It may be kept as a file copy.

Typewritten and Pasted-Up Copy

If the camera copy is typewritten, pasted-up, or hand-lettered, great care must be taken not

Mergenthaler Linotype Company

Size and Style of Type

wf //	Wrong font (size or style of type)
	Repeat stop mark for each additional identical error in same line
lc //	Lower Case Letter
lc	Set in (LOWER CASE) or LOWER CASE
L̲	Capital letter
caps	SET IN capitals
caps + lc	Lower Case with Initial Caps *u+lc*
sm. caps	SET IN small capitals
caps + s.c.	SMALL CAPITALS WITH INITIAL CAPS
rom.	Set in (roman) (or regular) type
ital	Set in *italic (or oblique)* type
L.F.	Set in (lightface) type
bf	Set in **boldface** type
bf ital	***Bold italic***
ᵇ	Superior letter or figureᵇ
/₂\	Inferior letter or figure₂

(vertical text at right: A marginal correction of lower case matter should NOT be written in CAPITALS)

Position

⌐	Move to right	⌐	{ Ragged
⌐	⌐ Move to left		{ margin
center	⌐ Put in center of line or page ⌐ *ctr*		
⌐⌐	Lower (letters ⌐or⌐ words)		
⌐⌐	Elevate (letters ⌐or⌐ words)		
=	Straighten line (horizontally)		
fl L or //	Align type (vertically)		Square up justify — flush right and left
tr #	Transpose space (transfer)		
tr	Transpose enclosed in ring (matter)		
tr //	Transpose (order letters of or words)		
tr	Rearrange words of order numbers in ³ ² ⁴ ¹		
run over	Run over to next line. (A two-letter (di- *over* vision should be avoided)		
run back	Run back to preceding line. (This div-ision is incorrect)		
reset *up* *up* *up*	A syllable or short word stand-ing alone on a line is called a "widow"; it should be eliminat-ed		

Spacing

solid	Means "not leaded" (Pron. "ledded")
leaded	Additional space between lines
lead	Insert lead between lines
ℐ ld	Take out lead ← or) *tr lead*
⌣	Close up entirely; take out space
#⌣	Close up partly; leave some space
⌣ or ⌣	Less space between words
⅄ or *eq #*	Equalize space between words
thin #	Thin space where indicated *hair #*
l/s	LETTER-SPACE
#	Insert space (or more space)
space out	More space between words
en quad	½-em (nut) space or indention
☐	Em quad (mutton) space or indention
☐☐☐	Insert number of em quadrats shown

Insertion and Deletion

OUT *see copy*	Insert matter omitted; refer to copy (Mark copy *Out, see proof*, galley 0)
the / l	Insert margina additions
ℐ or *ℐ*	Dele — take out (delete) (Orig. δ)
ℐ	Delete and close up
stet	Let it stand — (all matter above dots)

Diacritical Marks; Signs; Symbols

ü	Diaeresis or umlaut
é	Accent acute è Accent grave
â	Circumflex accent or "doghouse"
ç	Cedilla or French c
ñ	Tilde (Spanish); til (Portuguese)
use lig ⌢	Use ligature (affix—ffi) Logotype—Qu
/	Virgule; separatrix; solidus; stop mark; shill mark
⋇	Asterisk * ⅋ Ampersand &
⁂	Asterism *₊* * Leaders . . . .
☉☐☉☐☉	Ellipsis . . . or * * * or ___
	Order of symbols: * † ‡ § ‖ ¶ #); then double seldom used

Fig. 6-5. Roundup of editors' and proofreaders' marks.

Mergenthaler Linotype Company

Paragraphing

⌐/	Begin a paragraph
no ⌐/	No paragraph.
run in	Run in or run on
2 ⌐/	Indent the number of em quads shown
flush ⌐/	No paragraph indention
hang in	Hanging indention. This style should have all lines after the first marked for the desired indention

Punctuation

⊙	Period or "full point."		
	Periods and commas ALWAYS go inside quotes		
⋏ or ,/	Comma	⊙ or :/	Colon
;/	Semicolon		
∨ or ᵛ	Apostrophe or 'single quote'		"pos"
ᵛ/ᵛ or ⁷⁷	Quotation marks	"quotes"	
?/	Question mark or "query"		
!/	Exclamation point or "bang!"		
-/ or =/	Hyphen	en or ᵉⁿ	En dash
em or ⊢⊣	One-em dash	²/em	Two-em dash
(/)	Parentheses (parens; curves; fingernails)		
[/]	Brackets (crotchets)	}	Brace

Miscellaneous

e/	Correct letter or word marked	
e/⊗ k/⊗ or X	Replace broken or imperfect type	
⊙	Reverse (upside-down type or cut)	
⊥ or ⊤	Push down space or lead that prints	
SP	Spell out (20 gr)	(Also used conversely)
G?	Question of grammar	
F?	Question of fact	
2u au: or ?	Query to author	2u ?
2u Ed	Query to editor	2u Ed
	A ring around a marginal correction indicates that it is not the typesetter's error. All queries should be ringed.	
OK ʷ/c or OK ᵃ/c	OK "with corrections" or "as corrected"	*Correct and print; no revised proof wanted*
⌐	Mark-off or break; start new line	
End	End of copy: # or 30 or *End*	

Fig. 6-5. (Continued) Roundup of editors' and proofreaders' marks.

to mar this final camera copy. For purposes of proofreading, it would be best to make a duplicate copy by photostat or other photocopy method and use this copy for proofreading and marking. Duplicate photocopies of original camera copy offer an additional advantage and safeguard, because they can be sent out of the composing room for proofreading or approval. This guards against loss of the original copy.

Proofreaders' Marks

Proofreaders' marks are really a printer's shorthand. Figure 6-5 shows the proofreaders' marks with an explanation of what each mark means, and how it is used in the margin and text.

Figure 6-6 illustrates the use of the proofreaders' marks. Normally, a good compositor would not make this many errors. Can you find any errors that have not been marked and corrected?

Reading and Marking the Proof

Correcting proofs usually involves two people. One person reads aloud from the original typewritten copy to another, who follows along on the proof, detecting and marking each error. In some instances, one person may perform the functions of both reader and marker.

The marked proof is returned, together with the original copy, to the compositor for correction of the type matter. After the compositor has corrected the errors, a *revised proof* (second proof) is taken. The proofreader and proofmarker check the revised proof against the original copy and first proof to see that no new errors have been made in correcting old ones. If necessary, a *second revised proof* is taken and read.

Reading the Proof

The reader reads the copy aloud to the proofmarker. The reader calls attention to markup instructions on the copy, spells out difficult words, and tells which letters are caps. The reader indicates whether dates and amounts are figures or words, and mentions each item of punctuation as well as special indentions and paragraphs. The marker may request that a passage be repeated.

When Johannes Gutenberg began to print in Mayence more than 500 years ago, it was his great aim to reproduce handwriting by machine. None of the beauty of handwriting was to be lost; otherwise the new art could not have established itself.

In the early days of printing there is frequent mention of the "art of writing mechanically," and in the first printed works we often read that they have been produced without the aid of a scribe's quill pen. As the scribe could only produce one book at a time, and that by long and painstaking work, an edition of 200 seemed enormous. But, once the art of printing began to spread throughout Europe, the number of readers, and thus the demand, also increased so that editions could quickly rise to 1,000 copies.

A. Original copy.

When johannes Gutenberg began to print in Mayence more than 500 years ago, it was his gerat aim to reproduce handwriting by machire. None off the beauty of handwriting was to be lost; otherwise the new art conld not have established itself. In the early days of printing there is frequent mention of the "art of writing mechanically," and in the first printed works we often read that they have been produced without the aid ofa scribe's quill pen. As the scribe could only produce one book at a time, and that by long and painstaking work an edition of 200 seemed enormous. But, once the art of printing began to spread tчrough-out Europe, the number of readers, and thous the demand, also increased, so that editions could quickly rise to 1,000 copies

B. First proof.

When johannes Gutenberg began to print in Mayence more than 500 years ago, it was his gerat aim to reproduce handwriting by machire. None off the beauty of handwriting was to be lost; otherwise the new art coнld not have es-tablished itself./In the early days of printing there is frequent mention of the "art of writing mechanically," and in the first printed works we often read that they have been produced without the aid ofa scribe's quill pen. As the scribe could only produce one book at a time, and that by long and painstaking work an edition of 200 seemed enormous. But, once the art of printing began to spread tчrough-out Europe, the number of readers, and thоus the demand, also increased, so that editions could quickly rise to 1,000 copies

C. Proof after marking.

When Johannes Gutenberg began to print in Mayence more than 500 years ago, it was his great aim to reproduce handwriting by machine. None of the beauty of handwriting was to be lost; otherwise the new art could not have es-tablished itself.

In the early days of printing there is frequent mention of the "art of writing mechanically," and in the first printed works we often read that they have been produced without the aid of a scribe's quill pen. As the scribe could only produce one book at a time, and that by long and painstaking work, an edition of 200 seemed enormous. But, once the art of printing began to spread throughout Europe, the number of read-ers, and thus the demand, also increased so that editions could quickly rise to 1,000 copies.

D. Revised proof.

Fig. 6-6. Using proofreaders' marks.

Questions

1. What is the duty of the proofreader? Of the proofmarker?
2. What might happen with one person both reading and marking?
3. What is a revised proof?
4. How should successive marks on the same side of a line be separated?
5. After all errors are corrected, why is it a wise practice to submit the proof to the customer to read and approve?
6. Is the printer totally free from blame if an obvious error in the copy escapes the customer's attention on the proof and appears in the final printing of the job?
7. Where are proofreaders' marks placed on the page?
8. Describe how composition on tape is proofread and corrected by means of the visual (CRT) proofing and editing terminal.

Problems and Projects

1. Study the proofreaders' system of marks. Memorize as many as you can.
2. Prepare a bulletin board of typographical errors found in newspapers and other printed work. Paste each clipping on a larger piece of plain paper, and mark the errors and needed corrections.
3. Assume the duty of shop proofreader, and then proofmarker, for a week each.
4. Compile a list of books on proofreading, editing, and type faces (including type face specimen books) which should be in your school and shop library.
5. Arrange for a field trip to a newspaper plant or other printing plant to see visual (CRT) proofreading and editing in action.

New Terms

cursor	positives
indentions	queries
keyboarding	virgule
margins	

Chapter 7 **Preparing Camera Copy for Reproduction**

Illustrations and type matter that are to be photographed are called *camera copy* or *copy*. Camera copy should be kept covered with a tissue overlay paper, except when being photographed. To further protect the copy, do not use paper clips on the copy. Avoid writing on the surface or on the back, as the indentations may show up in the finished work. Store flat. Very large illustrations may be rolled.

Kinds of Camera Copy

There are three kinds of camera copy: line copy, Fig. 7-1; halftone copy, Fig. 7-2; and color copy, discussed in Chapter 10.

Line Copy

Line copy includes all work that is composed entirely of lines and areas of single tones. No shadow areas or gradations of tone may be present. Examples of line copy are:

1. Proofs of printed type matter.
2. Pen-and-ink drawings, maps, and cartoons.
3. Hand-lettering with pen or brush and ink.
4. Printed photographs which have already been screened by the halftone process and are to be reproduced the same size.

Halftone Copy

Halftone copy includes all work which has gradations or variations in tone. This is often called *continuous tone* (abbreviated as C.T.). Some examples of halftone copy would be:

1. Photographs of persons, buildings, landscapes, machines, processes, etc. This includes all photographs except photographs of line copy.
2. Artistic oil paintings, such as portraits and landscapes.
3. Airbrush renderings.

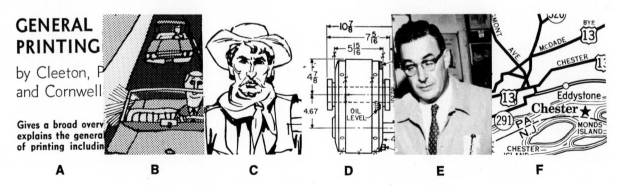

A   B   C   D   E   F

Fig. 7-1. Several of many possible examples of camera line copy: (A) type composition, (B) mechanical shading, (C) pen-and-ink line drawing, (D) pen-and-ink line drawing and template lettering, (E) halftone print, (F) pen-and-ink line drawing, transfer symbols and type matter.

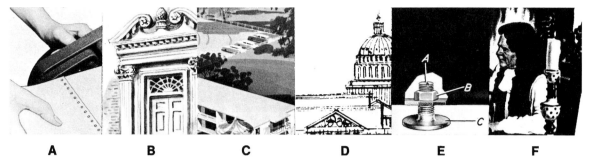

Fig. 7-2.   Some examples of halftone camera copy, each of which has gradation of tone: (A) original photograph, (B) pencil drawing, (C) wash rendering, (D) watercolor line drawing, (E) line drawing with airbrush shading, (F) opaque watercolor painting.

Scaling Reductions and Enlargements

The Diagonal-Line Method.   The resulting height and width of a desired reduction or enlargement may be figured by the diagonal line method, Fig. 7-3.

Assume that a given drawing is to be enlarged to a certain height. The resulting *width* may be figured by first drawing a rectangle the original size of the illustration. See the ABCD lines in Fig. 7-3. Then, extend lines AB, AC, and AD. Extend line AB to the desired height. At this point (E), draw a line across to the diagonal (point F), and then down to the horizontal (at G). The distance from E to F will be the width of the desired enlargment.

To figure the resulting *height* when the illustration is to be enlarged to a certain width, first mark off the width desired on the horizontal line. Extend it to the diagonal and then over to the vertical.

Reductions are figured in a similar manner.

The Percentage and Proportional Calculator (Wheel) Method.   The enlargement or reduction of an illustration may also be figured with the use of a proportional calculator, or wheel, Fig. 7-4A. It is made up of two scales. The inner scale, which rotates, is used for the original size of an illustration and the outer scale for the desired or reproduction size.

Suppose that a photo 4½ " high and 2" wide is to be reproduced at 9" high. To arrive at the new width, set 4½ " (original height) on the inner scale opposite 9" (new height) on the outer scale, as shown at A in Fig. 7-4B. Opposite 2" (original width) at B on the inner scale, read the new width measurement of 4" on the outer scale.

Figure 7-4C shows how the proportional wheel has been used to solve a proportion problem in metric measurement.

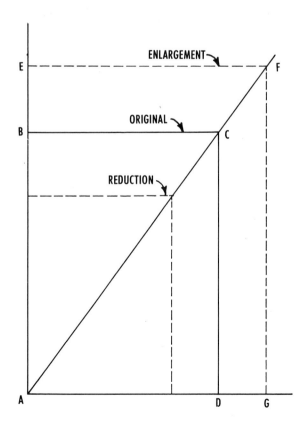

Fig. 7-3.   Figuring enlargements and reductions by the diagonal-line method.

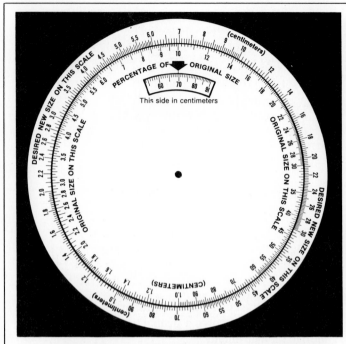

A. The calculator.

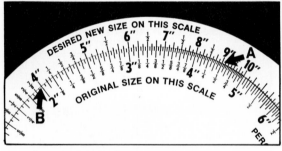

B. An original photo 4½″ high by 2″ wide, when enlarged to 9″ high, results in a new width of 4″.

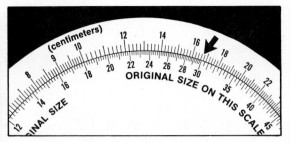

C. In a metric proportional problem, an original photo 18 cm wide and 30 cm high, when reduced to 10 cm wide results in a height of 16.6 cm (as at "A").

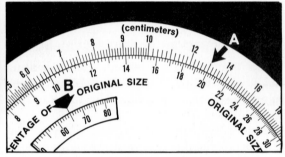

D. To find percentage, the original size of the illustration (20 cm) is set opposite the desired size (13 cm) at "A". The resulting percentage (65%) is indicated in the percentage window by the arrow "B".

Fig. 7-4.   Using a percentage and proportional calculator (wheel).

nuArc Company, Inc.

Specifying Reductions or Enlargements

The desired reproduction size should be indicated on the tissue overlay or in the margins of the original copy. This is specified as *either* the width *or* the height (not both) in inches, picas, percentage, centimeters, or a decimal. For example:

1. A map 8″ × 12″ is to be reduced to 6″ wide. The notation may read in any of these ways:
   a. Reproduce 6″ wide.
   b. Reproduce 36 picas wide.
   c. 75% reproduction (actually means 75% of the original width).
   d. Reproduce at .75.

2. A line drawing 20 picas wide is to be enlarged to 40 picas wide. The notation may read:
   a. Reproduce at 200%, or
   b. Reproduce 40 picas wide.

3. A photo 10 cm wide is to be reduced to 7 cm wide. The notation may read:
   a. Reproduce 7 cm wide, or
   b. Reproduce 70%.

Figure 7-5 shows a way to mark the desired size on the camera copy or on the artwork, thus leaving little chance for misunderstanding. The desired dimension and limiting arrows are marked directly on the artwork or on the overlay.

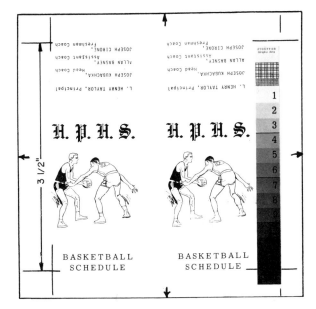

Fig. 7-5. Pasted-up copy is ready for the camera copyboard. The lines along the edges indicate the overall height and width of the copy (including the gray scale or, if the copy is small, a pertinent part of the gray scale). The arrows indicate the centers to be aligned with the centerlines on the camera copyboard. The dimension at the left and its limiting arrows indicate the desired size of the image.

Calculating the Reproduction Percentage

The reproduction percentage is determined by dividing the desired *image* size by the original *object* size, as:

$$\frac{I}{O} = R$$

in which

I = Image linear dimension (as will appear on the camera ground glass).

O = Object linear dimension (as placed on the copyboard).

R = Reproduction percentage.

The linear dimension of both I and O in the above formula must be either the height (*length*) or *width* in *both* cases. Do not use, for instance, the *height* of the image and the *width* of the object. Dimensions for both I and O should be stated in the same units — in inches, picas, millimeters, or centimeters.

In measuring width and height of artwork or proofs, *do not include the blank margins out-*

side of the type or object, unless you intentionally wish to do so.

Calculating percentage may be done in any of three ways:

1. *Using Arithmetic Calculation.* For example, an original photo measures 8″ wide. It is to be reproduced 12″ wide. What is the reproduction percentage?

   a. $\dfrac{I}{O} = R$

   b. $\dfrac{12}{8} = 1.5$, or 150% reproduction

2. *Using the Calculator (Wheel).* For example, a photo 20 cm high is to be reproduced 13 cm high. What is the reproduction percentage?

   Procedure: Set the original size of 20 cm on the inner scale opposite the desired size of 13 cm on the outer scale, Fig. 7-4D. The arrow at the percentage window indicates the answer — 65%.

3. *Using the Pocket Calculator.* This involves three steps:

   a. Convert any fractions to decimals. Use the two-place decimal values shown below:

$\frac{1}{16} = .06$	$\frac{1}{2} = .50$
$\frac{1}{8} = .12$	$\frac{9}{16} = .56$
$\frac{3}{16} = .18$	$\frac{5}{8} = .62$
$\frac{1}{4} = .25$	$\frac{11}{16} = .68$
$\frac{5}{16} = .31$	$\frac{3}{4} = .75$
$\frac{3}{8} = .37$	$\frac{13}{16} = .81$
$\frac{7}{16} = .43$	$\frac{7}{8} = .87$
	$\frac{15}{16} = .93$

   b. Divide $\dfrac{I}{O}$ on your calculator.

   c. Find the answer to three decimal places.

   Problem in Customary Measure: A drawing $6\frac{5}{8}$″ wide is to be reproduced $8\frac{3}{4}$″ wide. What is the reproduction percentage?

   a. Convert to decimals

   $8\frac{3}{4} = 8.75$

   $6\frac{5}{8} = 6.62$

   b. Divide (on the calculator)

   $$\frac{I}{O} = R$$

   $$\frac{8.75}{6.62} = 1.3217522 = 132\%$$

Problem in Metric Measure: A photo measuring 17.1 cm high is to be enlarged to 13.6 cm high. What is the reproduction percentage?

   a. No conversion to decimals needed.

   b. Divide (on the calculator):

$$\frac{I}{O} = R$$

$$\frac{13.6}{17.1} = .7953216 = 80\%$$

Preparation of Line Copy

Satisfactory photographic results can be expected from work prepared with dense, black ink on dull-finished white stock. High-gloss paper should be avoided as it may cause unwelcome reflections in the camera. Also, when mounting camera copy on backing board, use a gray or black board. These colors reduce any camera flare or unwanted reflection from the copyboard.

Line Drawings

Original drawings should be made about 1½ times the desired size. When they are reduced, the minor imperfections will be minimized.

Anticipate a proportional reduction in the width of the lines of the drawings. If lines are too thin, they may be lost completely or broken when reduced.

Reversed Printing

If it is desired to show type in reverse, that is, a solid black background with the letters white (Fig. 7-6), the line negative of the type matter is made in the usual manner. From this negative, a *film positive* is made in the darkroom by contact printing. On the film positive, the type characters or image appears black, and the background is transparent.

This film positive can be stripped into the *flat* so as to produce a solid area on the offset plate. Then, the letters will not print, but instead will show the color of the paper. This can be an eye-catching feature on a printed page. It is specified on the copy as a *reverse print.*

Ruled Forms

Ruled lines which are to appear in forms may be produced in a variety of ways. Brass or metal rule may be set with the metal type in hand composition. Rules also may be cast in machine composition along with the metal type on the same slugs or character bodies. Still another way is to set the rules along with the type characters in phototypesetting. However, when a great many lines are needed, and especially when there are cross rules, composition costs can be cut considerably by setting the type without the rules. Lines are then drawn with pen and ink on the proofs or scribed through the emulsion of the negatives after photographing the proofs.

Ruling Proofs with Pen and Ink. The type is set in the usual manner, omitting the rules. The ruled lines are then drawn on the sheet of phototype or proof sheet with a ruling pen and black India ink. (See page 55 for correct use of ruling pen.) If carefully done, with matched weights of lines, this method produces good, quick results.

Scribed lines. The desired type matter may be set up without the rules. Proofs are taken and then cemented in place on the camera copy sheet which is then laid out exactly as it will appear in the finished form. After the copy has been photographed, the stripper scribes, or scratches, the desired lines through the emulsion side of the negatives.

Preparation of Halftone Copy

Original photographs, paintings, and airbrush work have gradations in tone. Such illustrations can only be reproduced as *half-*

TAG YOUR
ROLLERS
for **W & S** *today!*

WILD & STEVENS
INCORPORATED · EST. 1859

Fig. 7-6.   **Reverse prints.**

tones and are designated as *halftone copy*, Fig. 7-7. In photographing halftone copy, a halftone *screen* is placed in front of the film in the camera. The resulting negative is an image composed of dots of varying sizes, as shown in Fig. 7-8. (The setup for halftone photography is shown in detail in Fig. 9-4.)

Sometimes an illustration which has already been printed as a halftone may be photographed for reprinting as *line copy*. This is

Photo by Robert A. McCoy

Fig. 7-7.   Landscape halftone.

Fig. 7-8.   Enlarged section of screened (halftone) negative for Fig. 7-7.

because a printed halftone is actually only a multitude of dots or checkerboard squares. Examine a printed halftone with a magnifying glass.

Reductions and Enlargements

Calculations for reductions and enlargements of halftones are the same as those described earlier in this chapter, page 111. A halftone proof or a halftone negative which is already screened may not be reduced or enlarged without destroying the gradation of screening employed in the original halftone photography.

Crop Marks

Irrelevant sections of a photograph may be eliminated in many cases to emphasize or improve the remaining portion. This is done with the use of crop marks. Select the part of the illustration which will best serve the intended purpose and crop it as shown in Fig. 7-9. Place crop marks on all four sides *on the tissue overlay*, or make lines with a grease pencil in the margins of the original if this does not mar it for further use. Do not mark across the face of the illustration.

Halftone Screen Rulings

On the tissue overlay of the illustration to be reproduced as a halftone, indicate for the camera operator which *screen ruling* is to be used.

Fig. 7-9.   Cropping improves some pictures.

Photo by Robert A. McCoy

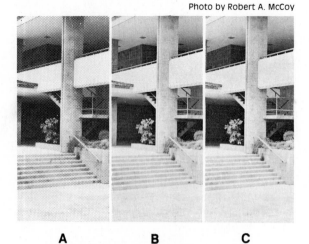

A   **B**   **C**

Fig. 7-10. Reproduction effect of screen rulings.

    A. 120 lines per inch.
    B. 133 lines per inch.
    C. 150 lines per inch.

Arthur H. Gaebel, Inc.

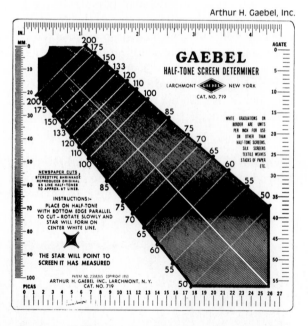

Fig. 7-11. Halftone screen determiner, for determining ruling count of a halftone print.

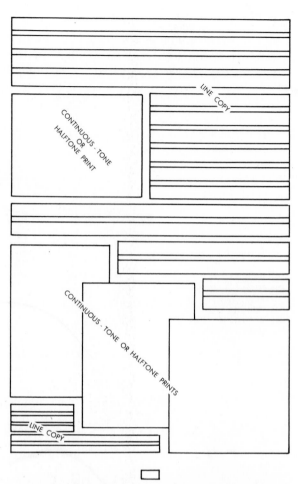

Fig. 7-12. Layout of combined line and halftone copy to be photographed on one piece of film.

Halftone screens are available in various rulings. Figure 7-10 shows effects of several screen rulings commonly used for offset printing. A listing of available screen rulings is given in Table 9-1, page 148. A halftone screen determiner, Fig. 7-11, can be used to determine the ruling count of a printed halftone illustration. The closer the lines of the halftone screen, the smaller will be the dots which comprise the halftone reproduction and, on the proper paper, the finer the picture printed.

Halftone and Linework
on the Same Sheet of Film

If halftones and linework are to appear on the same plate (to print on the same sheet in one pass through the press), it is best to prepare the camera copy so that one negative will carry both. On the layout sheet, paste up the line copy in the exact position it will occupy. Next, make positive velox prints of each of the halftone negatives. Paste these prints in exact position on the layout. Now, placing this combined paste-up in the camera copyboard, shoot it as line copy. See Fig. 7-12.

This method enables type matter to be placed very close to illustrations. It is also an easy way to arrange photos in almost any position or combination desired.

If continuous-tone prints are available in the desired sizes, they can be pasted up, along with the proofs of the type matter. The resulting page paste-up can be photographed on one sheet of Autoscreen film. The resulting negative will show the photos as halftone negatives and the linework as line negatives on the one sheet of film. (See "Autoscreen Film," page 175.)

Halftone Windows on Line Negatives

Where a halftone negative is later to be stripped into a page of linework on the flat, a clear window can be produced on the linework negative to receive this halftone negative. On the paste-up layout, paste up all the linework. Cut a rectangle of black paper the same size as the final halftone. Paste this rectangle in the exact space to be occupied by the halftone illustration. See Fig. 7-13.

After the layout is photographed and the film developed, this pasted rectangle will appear on the negative as a clear area. Then, the stripper can either mount the halftone on this area with tape or thinned rubber cement, or cut out the window and splice in the halftone negative.

Fig. 7-13. Black rectangle pasted to layout to provide window in line negative for mounting a halftone negative.

Combinations

A printed halftone picture on which lettering as well as linework appear is known as a *combination print*, Fig. 7-14. This combination may take several forms:

1. Normal (black) lettering or type matter superimposed on the halftone picture (surprinting).
2. Open lettering or type matter shown as white letters on the halftone picture (reverse print).
3. A black rectangle or open area in a halftone picture, for later imprinting of type matter or insertion of type matter.
4. Lines and arrowheads indicating names of parts, such as those on a picture of a machine.

This lettering, lines, and line drawing additions are usually not placed on the original photograph since the halftone screen would cause

Photo by Robert A. McCoy

Fig. 7-14. Combinations of type and photograph.

the additions to reproduce as halftone dots. Also, the photograph would then be unsuitable for other use.

> • **Note:** It is possible to capture both line and halftone copy on the same piece of film by using Autoscreen film. However, there are limitations on screen ruling and pattern. (See pages 172-175.)

For the combination print, it is necessary to make a transparent acetate or cellophane overlay. It is advantageous to first reduce or enlarge the photo to exact reproduction size. The overlay, bearing the desired size lettering and line additions, should then be registered to the print in exact position.

Screen Tints

A screen tint can be introduced by placing a portion of a commercial screen tint sheet, Fig. 7-15, between the negative and the offset plate during exposure of the plate. A screen tint may also be produced by *double-burning* the plate. This means that one exposure is made on the plate through the screen tint and a second exposure through the negative for the job.

The darkness of the printed tint can be varied by using a choice of a wide number of screen tint values. Figure 7-15 shows values of commercial screen tint sheets. The screens with the coarser dots (such as 65 or 85 lines per inch) are used mostly in newspapers printed by letterpress. Commercial offset printing typically uses 133-lines per inch screens, though 110 or 120 lines per inch may be used on rough papers or for easier press runs. The 150-lines per inch screen should be used only on smooth, coated paper and requires more skillful reproduction.

The percentage values of gray (white is 0% and black is 100%) shown across the top of each shade (Fig. 7-15) are only approximate, depending on ink coverage, the reflection ability of the paper, and usual production tolerances. The white and black letters on each tint area show legibility of type on various tones.

To obtain a screened (or tinted) effect in linework, a portion of a commercial screen tint sheet is simply taped beneath that part of the flat containing the portion of the negative to be screened. One exposure during platemaking will suffice. In the exposure, the emulsion side of the screen tint is toward the plate.

In Fig. 7-16, the screened (tinted) bands were introduced into the job by making two exposures on the plate. For the first exposure, a

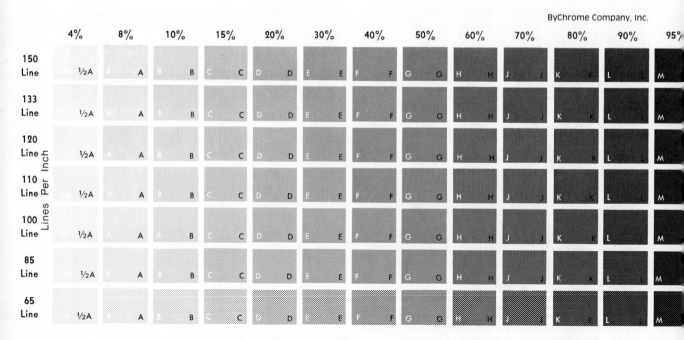

Fig. 7-15. Commercial screen tints available in sheets (developed film) of a single value.

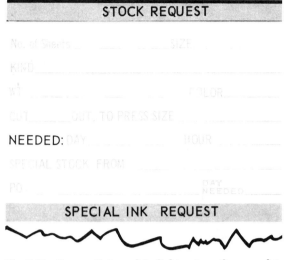

ByChrome Company, Inc.

STOCK REQUEST

No. of Sheets _____ SIZE _____

KIND _____

WT _____ COLOR _____

CUT _____ CUT. TO PRESS SIZE _____

NEEDED: DAY _____ HOUR _____

SPECIAL STOCK FROM _____

PO _____ DAY NEEDED _____

SPECIAL INK REQUEST

Fig. 7-16. Screen tint used to lighten type form, and to add gray bands behind headings.

Fig. 7-18. Samples of patterns of adhesive-type shading sheets available for art work.

flat containing the two tint bands was exposed to the plate. Then, for the second exposure, the flat containing the negative of the type matter (with a screen under most of the form) was exposed.

Although printed from one plate, in one pass through the press, the printed image in Fig. 7-16 has two tones. (If each exposure were made on a separate plate, the job could then be run in two colors.)

For a highlighted effect as in Fig. 7-17, the line negative was first burned into the plate. The second exposure was made through a screen tint sheet over which was positioned an acetate overlay sheet carrying a mask to block

out the arms and face of the press operator in the illustration. Another way is to opaque the screen in these areas.

Figure 7-18 shows some of the many patterns of adhesive-type shading sheets. These are printed on clear plastic and have an adhesive coating for sticking directly to artwork. A knife is used to outline the area needed so that it can be removed from the rest of the sheet.

Additional information on screen tints is given in Chapter 10, Color Reproduction, beginning on page 178.

Copy Paste-up

Before paste-up, all type composition (or proofs) and illustrations should be checked to be sure they are all of comparable density. None should be too light or too dark.

When possible, all the camera copy that is to appear on the offset plate should be pasted up on one sheet so it will photograph as a single film negative (or film positive). For a book, the

ByChrome Company, Inc.

Fig. 7-17. Screen tint added to a line drawing.

Fig. 7-19. Full-page paste-up (mechanical) being prepared for the camera department.

Fig. 7-20. Wax coater.

sheet contains a signature which is a predetermined number of pages. This paste-up or assembly is known also as a mechanical, Fig. 7-19. If the entire offset plate content cannot be photographed as a unit, then perhaps at least an entire book page or magazine page can be pasted up and "shot" as a unit.

Each page of this book was pasted up with the type composition in exact position. The exact position for each sized illustration on the page was indicated by a rubylith window made of a nonphotographic material. The page was then shot at same size. After the illustrations were enlarged or reduced to fit the windows,

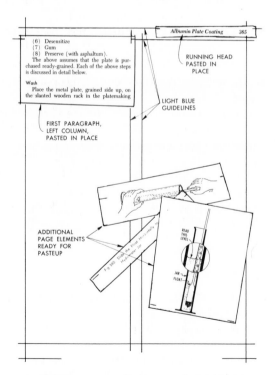

A. Elements of page being pasted up on layout sheet.

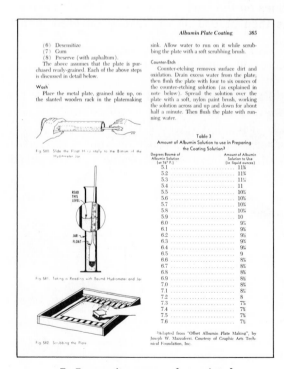

B. Page as it appears when printed.

Fig. 7-21. Page paste-up.

they were *tipped* into the windows (mounted in position on the page negative).

The page paste-up is done on a sheet of dull-finish white stock. Guidelines are drawn on this paste-up sheet in light blue pencil. (Blue pencil marks will not be picked up by the camera when the copy is photographed.) Hand-drawn additions to be reproduced may be made with India black ink. Lines and borders may be drawn with ruling pen or technical drafting pen. White opaque can be used to paint out or delete small areas or imperfections in the camera copy.

The separate elements (parts) of the page are first marked with short index or *register marks,* which aid in lining up the element to the layout. The elements are then fastened in position on the layout with rubber cement, wax, paste, or transparent adhesive tape.

If using a waxing machine, Fig. 7-20, run the copy through the waxer so that stripes of wax are applied to the back. Then, if possible, run the copy through a second time at right angles, producing a waffle-like grid pattern of wax lines on the back of the copy. The composition is then placed on the layout, covered with a protective overlay sheet, and is then burnished (rubbed briskly) with a bone folder, a hard flat

wallpaper roller, or a rubber photo-print roller. In this way, the copy is adhered firmly and evenly to the layout.

Figure 7-21 shows a book page in process of being pasted up on a layout sheet and the same page as it appears when printed.

When a page that is to appear in more than one color is pasted up, copy for the first color (with register marks) is pasted up on the main paste-up sheet. Copy for additonal colors is pasted up on transparent overlay sheets. Register marks on the overlay must coincide with those on the main sheet, Fig. 10-22, page 190.

Questions

1. What is line copy? Halftone copy?
2. What factor decides whether an illustration is to be reproduced as halftone copy?
3. What is the effect if a type proof is photographed as halftone copy?
4. What factors should be remembered when preparing line drawings for reproduction?
5. Use the diagonal-line method to determine the resulting width if a 6″ × 10″ illustration is increased in height to 12″.
6. How is camera copy protected from injury and dirt when it is not actually being photographed?
7. What is a proportional wheel? How is it used?
8. Suppose a 5″ × 7″ photograph carries the notation "75% reproduction." What will be the resulting dimensions?
9. What effect would reduction in size have in the reproduction of proofs of typefaces which have very fine lines?
10. What is a film positive? Describe the printed-on-paper effect of a film positive.
11. Discuss two methods of producing ruled lines on a negative without setting them in type.
12. How are crop marks used?
13. What halftone screen rulings are generally available?
14. Describe the printed effect of a combination negative.
15. What is the letter of a screen tint that would be a middle gray?
16. Would it be better to use black or white lettering over a 15% gray tint? Why?

Chemco Photoproducts Company

Fig. 7-22. **Pages for one side of a signature being pasted up in imposition for camera work. Note pagination dummy.**

Problems and Projects

1. Prepare a bulletin board display of halftone copy examples and one of line copy samples.
2. Compute the following by formula, and then by the diagonal-line method:
   a. 6″ × 10″, reduced to 4″ in width.
   b. 10″ × 12″, enlarged 200%.
   c. Four picas wide, and 3″ high, enlarged to 400%.
   d. 6″ × 9″, reduced to .75.
   e. 90 mm × 200 mm, reduced to 80 mm high.
3. Make a bulletin board display of film positives and the negatives from which they were made.
4. Make up (prepare) the camera copy for a ruled form, with hand-set type headings. Rule the lines with a ruling pen.
5. Prepare camera copy for a ruled form. The headings are to be hand-set foundry type. The ruled lines are to be scribed later on the negative.
6. On a tissue overlay, show how you would specify the desired cropping of a photograph.
7. Make up a display of printed samples of halftone and line combinations.

New Terms

acetate overlay	reflections
airbrush	register marks
burnish	renderings
combination negative	rubylith window
emulsion side	shading sheet
gradations	surprinting
mask	tip
opaqued screen	

Line Photography Chapter 8

In line photography, original camera copy which is composed of a single color or tone is copied on film. There are no continuous tones (gradations of tone). Examples of line copy are proofs of type matter, pen-and-ink drawings, and cartoons. (See again Fig. 7-1 as contrasted with Fig. 7-2 which shows copy with gradations of tone.) The film negatives produced by line photography are called *line negatives.*

Line photography is produced on a process camera. One of the popular styles of process camera is shown in Fig. 8-13. Other styles are shown in Figs. 8-8 and 8-10. Usually, line copy is prepared with black ink on white paper. For this reason, line photography is sometimes called simply black-and-white photography or single-color photography.

Theory of Photography

The copy usually is positioned upside-down on the camera copyboard. When the camera lights are turned on, light rays are reflected from the white areas of the copy. These reflected rays pass through the camera lens and are projected onto the ground glass of the camera back. From the operator's side of the ground glass, the image of the copy appears as right-side up and *readable*, Fig. 8-1. At the lens side of the ground glass from inside the camera, the image as projected would appear right-side up, but reversed, reading from right to left, Fig. 8-2.

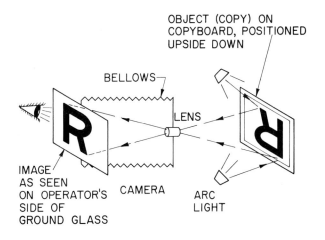

Fig. 8-1.   An upside-down object on the copyboard appears as a right-reading positive image on the operator's side of the ground glass.

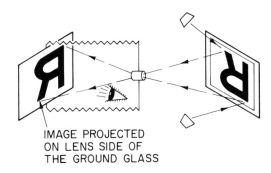

Fig. 8-2.   On the lens side of the ground glass, the image appears as a wrong-reading positive.

When an exposure is made (a picture taken) to make a line negative, the film is placed in the camera back with the emulsion (sensitized or coated) side facing the camera lens, Fig. 8-3. During the exposure, the light rays reflected from the white areas of the copy pass through the lens, striking the film emulsion. This causes a chemical change in the silver particles of the film emulsion, thus creating a *latent image*. A latent image is an invisible image which becomes visible during the developing of the film negative. See Fig. 8-4.

When this exposed film is developed, the result is a black-and-white film line negative — or, more correctly, a black-and-*transparent* film line negative, Fig. 8-5. Those areas of the film which were struck by (exposed to) reflected light rays from the white areas of the copy are intensified in the developing process and show as dense, black, opaque areas on the negative — *emulsion areas*. Those areas of the film which received no reflected light from the

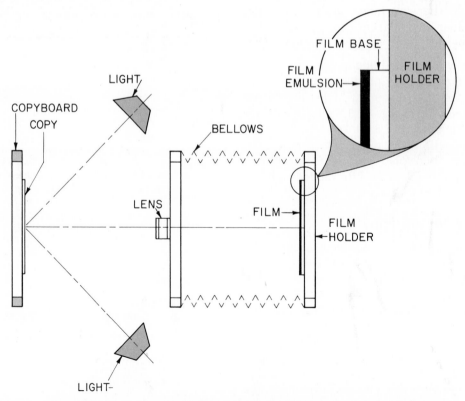

Fig. 8-3. Process camera basic setup for line photography. Film is base side toward the vacuum back. Emulsion side of film faces the lens. During exposure, light rays from the copyboard lights are reflected from the copy, through the lens, and onto the film emulsion.

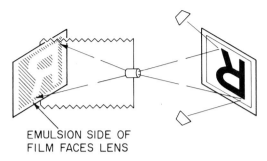

Fig. 8-4. Exposure of film in the camera will produce, on the emulsion of the film, a latent image of the object.

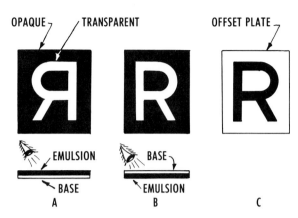

Fig. 8-5. Black-and-white film line negative.
   A. After developing, the film appears as a wrong-reading negative when viewed from the emulsion side.
   B. With the emulsion side down, the film appears as a right-reading negative.
   C. A right-reading negative, when exposed over an offset plate, will develop into a right-reading positive image on the offest plate.

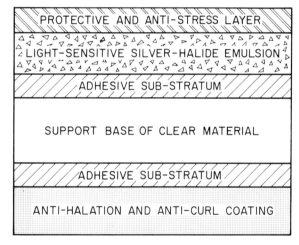

Fig. 8-6. Schematic cross section of a graphic arts film before exposure and processing.

black areas of the copy are washed away during the film developing and appear as clear, transparent areas on the negative — the *image areas*. This simple description of how the image is formed on the film will suffice for purposes here.

When a well-made line negative is placed over a sensitized offset plate in the platemaker and the exposure light is turned on, the opaque areas of the negative prevent light from passing through where no image is desired. However, the clear, transparent image areas of the negative permit light to pass through. This creates exposed areas on the plate coating which will develop as a strong, firm plate image for satisfactory offset printing.

Usually, negatives used for offset plate-making should be right-reading (reading normally from left to right) when viewed from the base side (emulsion side down) on a lighted stripping table.

The emulsion side of a negative is the duller of the two sides. For simple identification of the emulsion side, place the negative on a lighted stripping table and make a small scratch on it with a needle or knife, *outside* the image area. If the light shines through, you have scratched the emulsion side; if not, you have scratched the base side.

The Film

Most graphic arts film for line work is a relatively thin sheet of flexible-base plastic about .003″ to .008″ thick. The plastic material usually is acetate, which is economical and suitable for most uses. For precision work where maximum stability of the image size is needed, other plastics may be used, such as polyester (Estar) or polystyrene. This base material is coated on one surface with a light-sensitive emulsion of minute particles of silver salts suspended in gelatin, Fig. 8-6. This side is called the *emulsion side.* The emulsion is covered with a thin protective anti-stress layer.

The opposite surface, called the *base side,* is coated with an *anti-halation* material. This

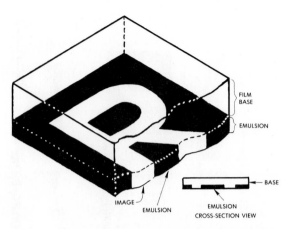

Fig. 8-7. Schematic broken-out section view of a right-reading image on a developed film negative. A cross-section view of this film is shown at lower right.

Consolidated International Equipment and Graphic Supply Company

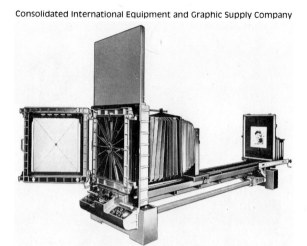

Fig. 8-8. A 31″ darkroom camera.

material absorbs the light rays which penetrate the film base during the exposure; otherwise, these might reflect back to the emulsion, spreading the image. Also, it tends to offset, or minimize, the curling, distortion or dimensional changes caused by the gelatin emulsion when it absorbs moisture.

During processing (developing, fixing, and so on), the film negative loses its outer protective layers, leaving it with a clear base side and an emulsion side which contains the image. See Fig. 8-7.

• **Note:** For film which is to be exposed with the base side towards the lens for image-reversal procedures, it is recommended that *thin-base film* be used. This type has a *thin* and *clear* anti-halation coating which causes little loss of image detail.

For most of the line photography procedures discussed in this book, a film such as Kodalith Ortho Type 3 Film is recommended. Both the regular base and the thin base film may be used. It will produce sharp line negatives of extreme contrast and will allow for considerable latitude (or variation) in exposure and processing.

• **Note:** Also consult film offerings of firms listed on page 214.

For work where dimensional stability must be absolutely maintained (such as maps and

Robertson Photo-Mechanix, Inc.

Fig. 8-9. Robertson Comet II 24″ × 31″ darkroom camera.

color reproductions), glass plates, which were previously used, have been replaced by polyester-base film.

Additional information on films will be found in Chapter 9.

Process Cameras

Process cameras used for offset photography are designed and equipped to render true images of a flat surface (at reductions, same size, and enlargements), from corner to corner, over

Fig. 8-10. The 14″ × 18″ process camera can be placed and used entirely within the darkroom.

Fig. 8-11. Inserting copy in a vertical camera.

the entire copyboard. Basically, they are built as either horizontal or vertical cameras.

Even the most modest of these cameras is costly. Also, process cameras *must be marvels of precision.* Therefore, the utmost care is essential in the operation and handling of the camera and its component parts.

Horizontal Cameras

Most large process cameras are *horizontal* ones, as shown in Figs. 8-8 and 8-9. The sliding copyboard is near one end on horizontal rails. The film holder is at the other end. The lensboard (with its lens) can be adjusted for position between the two ends.

Horizontal cameras are made in various sizes designated by the largest sheet of film which can be accommodated. These cameras range in size up to 48″ × 48″ or larger.

Vertical Cameras

Vertical process cameras, Fig. 8-11, are popular in sizes up to about 18″ × 24″. This type stands the traditional horizontal camera on end. That is, the rails are vertical, the

copyboard is low to the floor, and the film holder and ground glass positions are at the top of the camera. The operator looks downward toward the ground glass image.

Vertical cameras have certain advantages. They take much less floor area than horizontal cameras of similar capacity. Also, they are convenient to use, as walking and waste motions are minimized. However, vertical cameras cannot be built for large sizes of film without becoming too high, although special short-focus, wide-field lenses have made the height more convenient for larger vertical cameras.

Darkroom and Gallery Installations

Process cameras can be installed and used in two ways — as darkroom cameras and as gallery cameras. *Darkroom cameras* may be installed in a light-tight room. The preferred way, however, is to have the back built into the wall of a light-tight room, with the lens, lights and copyboard outside the room. In this way, the film can be positioned and removed in the dark. *Gallery cameras* are installed completely in a

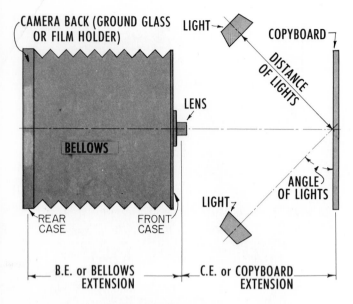

Fig. 8-12. Basic parts of the camera.

lighted room and require that a light-tight holder be loaded in a darkroom and then taken to the camera.

The *built-in, horizontal, darkroom camera* (as shown in the darkroom plans in Fig. 11-1, page 197) has the advantage of separating the brightly lighted copyboard from the back of the camera. This makes focusing on the ground glass easier. It also reduces the danger of fogging film in the darkroom, especially when more than one person is working there. In operation, the camera operator mounts the copy and adjusts the lights before entering the darkroom. The rear case with the film holder and the controls for focusing and exposing are located in the darkroom, so that most of the rest of the work can be done from this position. Film processing can proceed in the same room as the camera back, even when the camera lights are on. Such horizontal cameras sometimes are

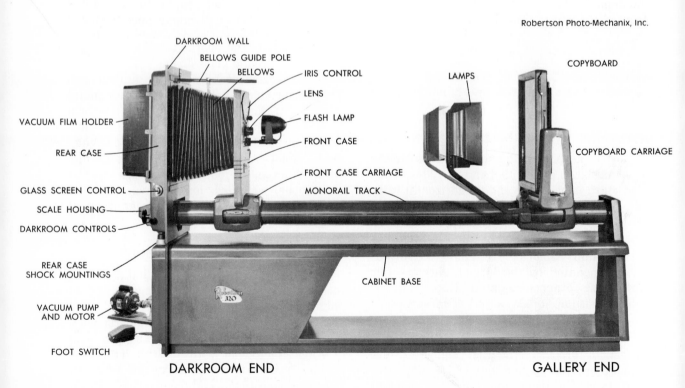

Robertson Photo-Mechanix, Inc.

Fig. 8-13. The Robertson 320, 16″ × 20″ horizontal process camera.

built to be suspended from overhead rails (rather than having the rails built into the base). This allows the operator to move more easily around the camera to adjust lights and load the copyboard.

Basic Parts of the Camera

The basic parts of a process camera are the *lens*, front case, *bellows*, *camera back* (rear case), *copyboard*, and *lights*. See Fig. 8-12. There are many more additional parts and features on any specific camera, Fig. 8-13. The student should locate and become familiar with the comparable units on any camera used.

The Lens and Front Case

The process lens is the most delicate, critical and expensive of all the camera parts. See Fig. 8-14.

Lens Construction. The lens is composed of several separate optical glass elements assembled into a barrel, Fig. 8-15. The entire assembly generally is threaded into a lensboard, mounted on the front case of the camera. The front of the lens is provided with a slip-fit protective cap which should be kept on the lens whenever it is not in actual use.

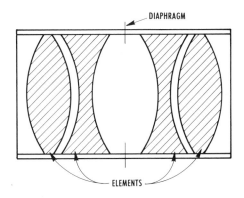

Fig. 8-15.   **Schematic cross section of a typical process lens.**

Focal Length.   The abbreviation FL is used to indicate the focal length of a lens. Focal length, for a particular lens, is expressed in inches. Generally, this number is engraved or stamped on the inner surface of the lens-retaining ring as FL 10½″, or 14″ FL. Each lens has a *single, definite focal length*. In general, cameras for larger film sizes require lenses of longer focal lengths.

In reproduction photography, focal length is expressed as follows: FL equals one-quarter of the distance from the camera copyboard to the

C.P. Goerz — American Optical Company

Fig. 8-14.   **Goerz ARTAR lens, 16″ FL.**

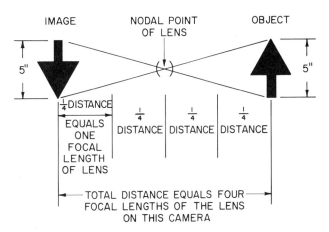

Fig. 8-16.   **The focal length of a lens equals one-quarter of the distance from the copyboard to the ground glass when the focused image on the ground glass is the same size as the object on the copyboard. In the example above, the image and the object are the same height. If the total distance from object to image is 40″, the lens is a 10″ FL lens.**

camera ground glass, when the focused image on the ground glass is the *same size* as the object on the copyboard. At this setting for same size (or 100%), as is shown in Figs. 8-16 and 8-30, the bellows extension equals the copyboard extension, and each is twice the FL.

To determine the focal length of an unmarked lens, place a piece of copy on the copyboard. Adjust the camera so that the image is in focus and is the same size as the copy. Measure the distance from the copy to the image on the ground glass, and divide this by four.

Diaphragm.   The diaphragm (or iris) is an arrangement of metal blades inside the lens barrel. When the knurled lens collar is rotated, the diaphragm blades can be seen to open or close, forming a circular "mask" or an *aperture opening* of the desired size to admit light through the lens.

Stamped on the knurled collar is a series of *f-stop numbers:* $f/11$, $f/16$, $f/22$, $f/32$, $f/45$, etc. Each number is called an *f-stop.* It expresses the diameter of the diaphragm opening as a fraction of the focal length of the lens. For example, a 16″ FL lens which is set at $f/32$ has an opening (aperture) of ½″.

$$\frac{FL}{f\text{-No.}} = \text{diameter of aperture}$$

$$\frac{16}{32} = \text{½″}$$

In Figure 8-17, note that the larger f-numbers represent the smaller openings. The f-numbers have been selected so that each successively larger number cuts the aperture area in half — $f/22^{*}$ is half as fast as $f/16$, and $f/45$ is twice as fast as $f/64$.

To set the lens for a particular f-stop, rotate the knurled collar until the desired f-stop index line matches the lens barrel index line. For example, in Fig. 8-14, the lens is set at $f/11$.

Manual Diaphragm Control.   Most process cameras are equipped with a manual diaphragm (iris) control, Fig. 8-18. This consists of a plate imprinted with a number of fan-shaped scales (bands) and a movable index pointer which is attached to the circular-adjustable lens collar.

The uppermost scale is the F or f-stop division scale. See A in Fig. 8-19. This scale is a greatly enlarged and finely subdivided reproduction of the f-markings on the lens barrel. When the index pointer is moved manually along the f-stop division scale, the lens aperture can be set most accurately for any desired full or fractional f-stop.

Below the f-stop scale are the individual f-stop percentage scales, or bands. See B in Fig. 8-19. There is one band for each of the f-stops inscribed on the lens barrel.

When set at the percentage reproduction desired on any selected f-number band, this diaphragm control will automatically adjust the lens for the proper f-number (aperture). In this way, the correct amount of light will be admitted and the exposure time will remain cons-

---

*$f/22$, as engraved on the lens collar, is actually $f/22.6$.

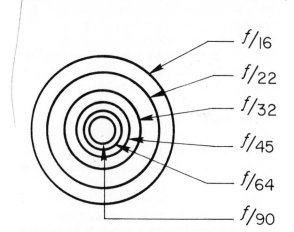

Fig. 8-17.   Relative sizes of aperture openings (F-numbers) of a typical process lens.

Robertson Photo-Mechanix, Inc.

Fig. 8-18.   The manual diaphragm control.

nuArc Company, Inc.

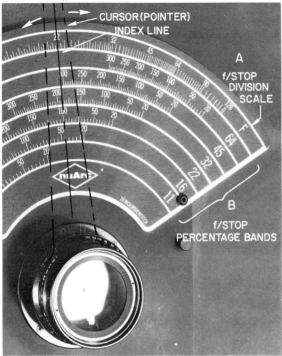

Fig. 8-19. Manual diaphragm control, showing pointer, index line, F-stop selection scale, and F-stop percentage bands (scales). Pointer index is shown set at 100% on the f/22 band.

Robertson Photo-Mechanix, Inc.

Fig. 8-20. Electric solenoid shutter mounted inside the front case.

Robertson Photo-Mechanix, Inc.

Fig. 8-21. Electric timer and control panel.

stant. An example in the use of the manual diaphragm control is given on page 138.

Shutter. For accurately controlling the length of exposure, some cameras are equipped with an electric solenoid shutter fitted behind the lens. An electric timer, adjustable for the number of seconds of exposure, operates the shutter. It can be set to hold the shutter open when focusing the camera and to make exposures at set lengths of time. See Figs. 8-20 and 8-21.

When the camera has no such shutter, exposure is made simply by removing the lens cap for the exposure time. If the lens also has no percentage scales for diaphragm control, an allowance must be made in exposure time for the amount of reduction or enlargement.

Filter Slot. This is the slot in the lens barrel through which square gelatin filters may be inserted when color work is being done. It also permits the insertion of "Waterhouse Stops" (diaphragms of paper or metal with small, spe-

cially shaped openings). If the filter slot is not being used, it should be covered or taped to prevent dust and stray light from entering.

Lens Care. As previously mentioned, of all the camera parts, the lens is the most delicate, critical and expensive. To minimize image errors (aberrations), several types of glass are used in lenses. Some are so soft that they are easily scratched.

Whenever you are not using the lens *for making an exposure,* cap it. If you remove the lens, cap both ends. This keeps dust from the surfaces of the lens.

Should dust settle on the lens glass, fan it off with a card. While there is a danger of a lens brush scratching the glass, it can be used occasionally if one is very careful. Never touch the

Fig. 8-22. **Manually operated flashing lamp mounted on the front case (shown swung over to project light through the lens).**

Fig. 8-23. **Placing copy on the copyboard of a horizontal camera.**

lens glass with your fingers, as perspiration may etch the surface. To remove any smudges remaining after a light brushing, use special lens tissue dampened lightly with lens cleaner. Do not use regular tissue or a handkerchief, as these may be abrasive. Never dismantle a lens. Leave this to a qualified lens mechanic.

When inserting (or removing) the lens assembly, hold one hand underneath the lens. With the other hand, turn the lens into the mount.

Flashing Lamp. A flashing lamp may be mounted on the front case of the camera for flash exposures of halftones through the lens, Fig. 8-22. When a contact screen is used on a manually operated camera, a yellow safelight at the back of the camera (in the darkroom) serves as the flashing lamp. See Fig. 9-22.

Fig. 8-24. **Foam padding behind the glass permits holding flat an object as thick as an open book in the copyboard plane.**

Copyboard

The copyboard is a flat board usually equipped with a hinged glass cover, Figs. 8-23 and 8-24. In use, the copyboard of a horizontal camera is turned to the horizontal, opened, and the copy positioned. The glass cover is closed and locked, and the copyboard is turned vertically to face the lens. A vacuum copyboard insures that the copy will be held tightly in a flat plane. An additional feature of some copyboards is the transparency opening, as shown in Fig. 8-25.

Fig. 8-25. **Transparency opening in the camera copyboard permits light to be transmitted from behind the transparent copy.**

Fingermarks, dirt and dust on the copyboard will be photographed with the copy. Therefore, handle the copyboard by the frame, keeping the fingers off the glass. If the glass is dusty, brush it with the camel's hair brush. If still dirty, clean it with a glass cleaner or, preferably, with a soft, clean cloth dampened with household ammonia. Clean both sides of the glass. It may be best to cover the glass when the camera is not in use.

Lights.   There are several types of lights for the copyboard. *Incandescent bulbs* (photofloods) are weak in blue-white light and therefore require long exposures. Also, except for the quartz-iodine type, they darken with use, further reducing efficiency. The white-flame carbon arc lights were the accepted standard for many years. Now, more of the powerful tungsten lamps, quartz-iodine lamps, and pulsed-xenon lamps are being used. *Pulsed xenon* (zee-on or zee-non) is an electronic flash which fires many times a second, giving good, clean lighting.

Some light arms are attached to, and move with, the copyboard. Distance to the lights remains constant. On some vertical cameras, the lights do not move with the copyboard, although corrections can be made for this. When the distance between copy and lights increases, the illumination drops off rapidly. If distance doubles, lighting drops to one-fourth; if it triples, lighting drops to one-ninth.

Light reflectors must be kept dust-free. Do not touch lamp bulbs, especially the tubular, quartz-iodine type. Fingerprints may darken the bulb. When necessary, all lamps should be replaced at the same time so as to maintain equal illumination. Quartz bulbs should be handled with a cloth.

Camera Back

The camera back, or rear case, contains the following components, either as built-in devices or as separate accessories set in place as needed:

The Ground Glass.   This device is used for focusing and adjusting the image prior to exposing the film.

The Film Holder.   This component may be a coating of sticky, "stay-flat" solution on a flat surface, or it may be a vacuum film holder (vacuum back) which holds the film flat to its surface by means of suction generated by a vacuum pump. A vacuum film holder is a necessity for good work with contact halftone screens. See Figs. 8-26 and 8-27.

On the simplest of cameras, contact screens may be used with a pressure frame, similar to a

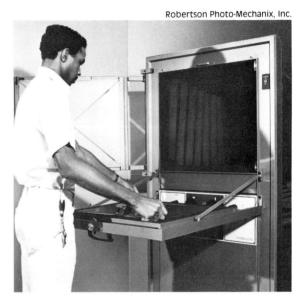

Robertson Photo-Mechanix, Inc.

Fig. 8-26. Loading the film on the vacuum film holder.

Robertson Photo-Mechanix, Inc.

Fig. 8-27. Vacuum film holder in operating position with ground glass swung out of position.

contact-printing frame. This consists of a board with a foam-rubber pad and a hinged glass cover. Exposure is made through the glass.

Gallery cameras which are used outside the darkroom must have a film holder which can be removed from the camera and taken into the darkroom for loading the unexposed film and for removing the exposed film. A thin, flat, metal slide passes through a slot in the film holder frame to cover the film entirely and protect it from the light. This cover is removed only during exposure of the film and is replaced immediately after the exposure is made.

Glass Halftone-Screen Device.   This may be a built-in device which lowers the glass halftone screen into position, allows it to be set for proper distance, and elevates it into a storage compartment when not in use. Or, it may consist only of screen bars in which the screen is mounted when needed and which can be adjusted toward or away from the film holder. Since the advent of the popular contact halftone screen and its simpler procedures, glass halftone screens are found on fewer cameras.

Bellows.   The bellows is that expanding box-like structure extending from the camera back to the front case, or lensboard. It insures that only the light picked up by the lens is directed to the film in the camera. When periodically cleaning the camera, use a vacuum to remove any dust from inside the bellows. Do not handle the bellows as this might wear holes in the corners of the folds.

Controls.   Most process cameras are equipped with two steel tapes or scales. These have

Fig. 8-29. Camera operator at the control panel of Chemco Spartan II roll film camera. Film selection, reproduction size, and exposure can be made from one location.

markings that indicate to the camera operator the proper position of the lens and of the copyboard for any reduction or magnification within the range of the camera, Fig. 8-28.

In addition to the automatic electric timer for timing the exposures, the operator may have switches for controlling the vacuum pump for the vacuum film holder, and possibly one for the vacuum copyboard. See Fig. 8-29. A master switch should be provided for turning off all power to the camera when desired.

Setting the Camera for "Same Size" Reproduction

The process camera is so designed that two distances can be varied:

1. Bellows (lensboard) extension — the distance from the film holder (or ground glass) to the center of the lens.
2. Copyboard extension — the distance from the center of the lens to the copyboard.

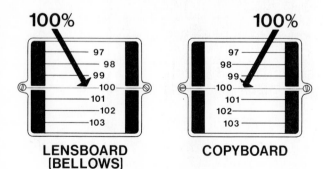

Fig. 8-28. Setting the camera tapes, or scales, for same-size (100%) reproduction.

Variations in these distances produce an image on the ground glass or film which may be an enlargement, a reduction, or the same size as the copy on the copyboard, Fig. 8-30.

To set the camera for a "same size" or 100% reproduction (so that the copy reproduced is neither enlarged nor reduced), set the copyboard and lensboard (bellows) extensions each at 100%. See Fig. 8-28.

• **Note:** If the camera has no calibration tapes, set the copyboard and lensboard (bellows) extensions so that each is equal to two focal lengths of the lens being used. See Figure 8-31. Use a tape measure to verify these distances.

Demonstration
Set the camera to "same size." Open lens fully — to the smallest *f*-number. Place a piece of copy in the copyboard. Measure the height of the inverted and reversed image on the ground glass. Compare it with the height of the copy. Both should be equal. Check the setting for maximum sharpness by watching the image with a magnifying glass while shifting the lensboard slightly each way. If this changes the size of the image, readjust the copyboard to regain the image size. If necessary, repeat, readjusting the lensboard and copyboard until size and focus are the best obtainable.

Settings for both tapes should read 100% when image is in focus and same size as the copy on the copyboard. If not, calibration of the tapes is necessary.

If the reflection of the camera lights intrude on the image on the ground glass, move the offending light(s) outward to eliminate these "hot spots."

Unless instructed otherwise, position the camera lights at an angle of 45° to the centerline of the copyboard, and aim them at the centerline. (See Fig. 8-31 again.) Usually, this is the most satisfactory lighting setup. Occasionally, however, a different pattern may give more even illumination. For example, for large

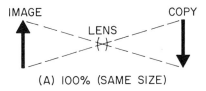

(A) 100% (SAME SIZE)

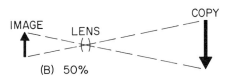

(B) 50%

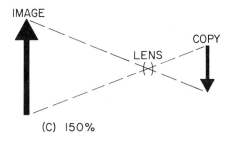

(C) 150%

Fig. 8-30. On the process camera, reductions and enlargements are obtained by changing the bellows and copyboard extensions.

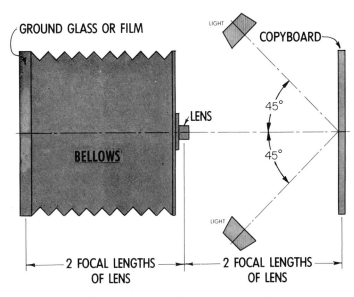

Fig. 8-31. Bellows extension and copyboard extension for same-size setting of camera.

pieces of copy, some camera operators leave the arms at 45°, but aim the lights at the far side of the copy, crisscrossing the lighting pattern. A photoelectric exposure meter can be used to check evenness of illumination, although this usually is not a problem when copy and negatives are small. It is best to check readings at the ground glass.

Determining the Basic Length of Exposure

Several factors, which may vary from shop to shop, must be controlled to produce a good negative. These are quality of copy, amount of lighting, exposure time, f-stop, focus, any enlargement or reduction, film type, developer, development time, and processing temperature. Begin by varying only one factor, *exposure time,* and hold all other factors constant and as ideal as possible. This will give a *basic exposure* from which specific cases can be adapted.

To determine a basic exposure, use good *normal copy* (black type or lines with fine serifs on bright white paper), with the camera set up for same size, as just described. The lens opening should be stopped down to the third-smallest f-number. For example, if the stops are f/11, f/16, f/22, f/32 and f/45, use f/22. This third stop should be close to the setting which gives the sharpest image and is most frequently used. With a diaphragm control, set the pointer at 100% on the f/22 band.

Place the sheet of copy in the center of the copyboard, and place a *sensitivity guide* (gray scale) alongside the copy, as in Fig. 8-32.

• **Note:** A sensitivity guide should be included along with the copy for every exposure. It is best placed in an open area near the center of the copy (and later blocked out), but may be included at the edge of solid copy. This serves as a general check on exposure, as well as a guide in developing. See also page 204.

With fresh film in the camera each time, make three exposures of the copy *including the sensitivity guide,* using a different length of exposure each time. Expose the first film for what you consider a normal exposure (perhaps 20 seconds). Expose the second film for half that length (10 seconds), and then expose the

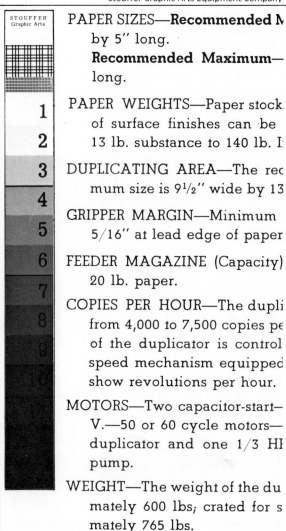

PAPER SIZES—**Recommended N** by 5″ long.
Recommended Maximum— long.

PAPER WEIGHTS—Paper stock of surface finishes can be 13 lb. substance to 140 lb. I

DUPLICATING AREA—The rec mum size is 9½″ wide by 13

GRIPPER MARGIN—Minimum 5/16″ at lead edge of paper

FEEDER MAGAZINE (Capacity) 20 lb. paper.

COPIES PER HOUR—The dupli from 4,000 to 7,500 copies pe of the duplicator is control speed mechanism equipped show revolutions per hour.

MOTORS—Two capacitor-start— V.—50 or 60 cycle motors— duplicator and one 1/3 HF pump.

WEIGHT—The weight of the du mately 600 lbs; crated for s mately 765 lbs.

Fig. 8-32. The 12-step camera operator's sensitivity guide shown placed next to copy.

third for double the first (40 seconds). Use your usual film (for example, Kodalith Ortho, Type 3), and cut notches along the edge to identify each piece by its exposure time.

Develop the test films at the same time in fresh developer by the time-and-temperature method, as described in Chapter 11. Use the recommended developer and procedures — for example, Kodalith developer at 68°F. for 2¾ minutes, with continuous agitation. After rinsing and fixing these films, examine them over a light table.

Determine from the test strips the length of exposure required to make Step 4 (of the sensitivity guide) just black, but leave Step 5 gray or with only a few black specks. See Fig. 8-33.

If necessary, make further refinements in exposure time, until you get a good Step 4 development. Record this time for future use. This is your standard basic length of exposure for normal copy at same-size reproduction.

Determining the Best F-Number of the Lens

Most lenses have a particular *f*-stop which will give the sharpest image. In determining the basic exposure, it was assumed that the third stop was close to this best setting. You may wish to test this experimentally for your particular lens. All future exposures for line work could then be made using this same *f*-stop. This is referred to as the *constant-aperture system* (described on page 139).

To determine which aperture, or *f*-number, will give best results for your lens, set up the camera for same-size reproduction, as before. Place a page of small type matter in the copyboard. Make a series of exposures on different pieces of the film. For each exposure, use a different f-stop each time. (With a diaphragm control, set it at 100% on each f-stop band used.) Begin with the f-stop and the exposure time determined for your basic exposure.

All exposures must be the equivalent of this basic exposure. Each time the aperture size is doubled (next smaller f-number), the exposure time must be cut in half. When the aperture size is cut in half (next larger f-number), the exposure time must be doubled. For example, if the basic exposure has been found to be 20 seconds at *f*/22, then make your series of tests as follows:

    f/11   5 seconds
    f/16 10 seconds
    f/22 20 seconds (basic exposure)
    f/32 40 seconds
    f/45 80 seconds

In each of these combinations, the same amount of light is reaching the film, but note how much longer it takes to pass through the smallest opening (*f*/45). If each exposure is made on a separate piece of film, notch each

A. **Step-4 development looks like this in the developer with overhead safelights, and appears about the same when cleared, dried, and placed on white paper and illuminated by overhead light.**

B. **When viewed by transmitted light, however, Step-4 does not appear absolutely black.**

Fig. 8-33. Step-4 development.

test sheet so it can be identified with its exposure. Carefully develop this film by the time-and-temperature method, as was done for determining the basic exposure.

The sharpest image on the developed films indicates which of the f-stops is best for that particular lens. If little difference is found in sharpness at various f-stops, then the most convenient combinations can be used. Times less than 10 or 15 seconds are difficult to duplicate exactly and much longer ones are wasteful. If a range of f-stops produces a satisfactory image, then a *diaphragm control* (with its percentage settings) can be used to adjust the exposure for reduction and enlargement. This is called the *constant-time system* and is further explained on page 138. Record your results for future use.

Posting Camera Settings

When several basic camera settings have been determined, it is handy to post a chart next to the camera giving the *basic camera settings for same size*. Include the following:

1. Angle and distance of lights (if adjustable).
2. Best length of exposure for same size.
3. Best f-stop.
4. Lensboard (bellows) extension.
5. Copyboard extension.

Procedure with Typical Darkroom Camera for 100% Reproduction

The procedure for using a darkroom camera at 100% reproduction is described here in

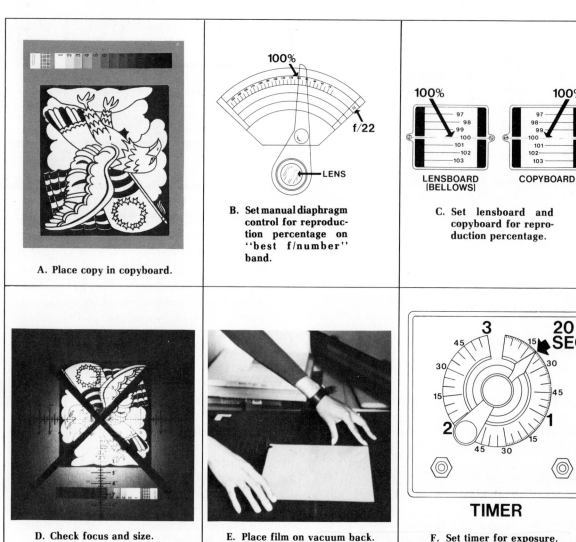

A. Place copy in copyboard.

B. Set manual diaphragm control for reproduction percentage on "best f/number" band.

C. Set lensboard and copyboard for reproduction percentage.

D. Check focus and size.

E. Place film on vacuum back.

F. Set timer for exposure.

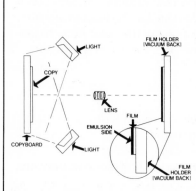

G. Make exposure.

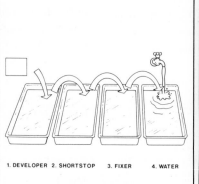

H. Process the film.

I. Evaluate the negative.

Fig. 8-34. Some basic procedures in line photography.

more detail. It applies to most darkroom cameras equipped with the usual devices, including a manual diaphragm control.

1. Clean the copyboard glass, inside and out.
2. Position the copy (inverted) in the center of the copyboard. Include a sensitivity guide (gray scale) at the edge of the copy or, preferably, in a gutter between columns of type. Place the copyboard in the exposure position. Set the light carriers to 45° angles; aim at the centerline.
3. Set the lens at the best f-number, or set the diaphragm control for 100% reproduction on the proper f-number band.
4. Remove the lens cap.
5. Set the bellows and copyboard extensions each for 100% reproduction.
6. Turn off the overhead room lights, and turn on the safelights. Check your film data sheet for proper safelight. Most of the lith-type films use a Series 1A (light red) safelight.
7. Turn on the camera lights, and check for focus and size of image. To adjust the size, change the position of the copyboard. To sharpen the focus, slightly move the lensboard back and forth. To bring the image back to size, you may need to slightly readjust the copyboard. Repeat readjusting copyboard and lensboard if necessary until focus and size are the best obtainable.
8. If there are hot spots, move the lights until their image does not intrude on the image of the copy.
9. Determine the amount (size) of film needed.
10. Shut off the camera lights, and swing the ground glass out of position.
11. Remove a sheet of film from its light-tight storage, handling it by the edges. Cut from it the size piece needed. Return the extra film, and *close the container.*
12. Turn on the vacuum back (or open the film holder). Holding the film by the edges, carefully place it in the center with the emulsion side of the film facing you (and, ultimately, the lens). The film may be smoothed flat with the back edge of the palm of the hand. To avoid scratching the emulsion or making fingerprints on it, cover the film with a clean sheet of paper during the smoothing operation.

> • **Note:** The emulsion is the lighter of the two sides. If the film sheets are notched by the manufacturer, the emulsion side will be facing you when the sheet is held with the notch on the top edge at the right-hand corner.

13. Close the vacuum back (or position the film holder).
14. Set the timer for the length of exposure desired and make the exposure. The camera lights must be on during this time.
15. After making the exposure and then turning the camera lights off, open the camera back. Remove the film by shutting off the vacuum and catching the film by the edges as it is released. (Or film may be removed by stripping it from the adhesive coating).
16. The film is now ready for processing.

See Chapter 11 for processing directions. Cap the lens if no other shots are to be made.

Procedure with Gallery Camera

The procedure for making line negatives with the gallery camera is substantially the same as that for the darkroom camera. Of course, since the gallery camera is located outside the darkroom, its film holder must be taken into the darkroom for loading the film and for removing the exposed film. After it has been loaded into the holder, the film is covered with an opaque slide. Just before the exposure, the holder is positioned in the camera. The slide is removed only for the time of the exposure and is replaced before removing the holder from the camera. Most slides are replaced in a reversed position to indicate the film has been exposed. Silver-side out means unexposed film; black-side or marked-side out means exposed film.

Reductions and Enlargements

Very often it is desirable to enlarge or reduce an illustration or some type matter so as to fit a given space or purpose. Most process cameras have markings and mechanical arrangements for setting the desired reductions and enlargements within their range. However, to help you understand the process camera better, instructions are given here for setting the camera *with* and *without* these devices.

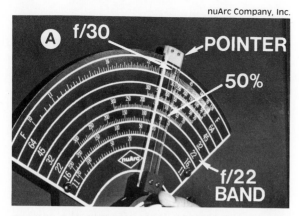

nuArc Company, Inc.

Fig. 8-35. The present setting of the diaphragm control in this illustration is 50% on the f/22 band. When the diaphragm pointer was moved from 100% to 50% of the f/22 band, the effective lens aperture was reduced from f/22 to f/30, as indicated by the arrow at "A" on the uppermost "F" scale.

Using the Manual Diaphragm Control

The manual diaphragm (iris) control, with its percentage bands, is most often employed when the photographer is using the *constant time* (constant length) *method of exposure* for making negatives at 100% and at reproduction sizes of *other than* 100%. In this constant time method, each exposure — whether same-size, reduction, or enlargement — is always made for the *same length of time*. However, the lens aperture (*f*-number) is varied to admit more light for an enlargement or less light for a reduction. The method works like this:

First, a series of test negatives is made at 100% reproduction size to determine the *best length of exposure* and the *best f-number* of the lens for the copy being used. (This procedure is explained beginning on page 134). For example, assume that the best test negative was produced with an exposure of 20 seconds at a setting of 100% on the *f*/22 band of the diaphragm control. This means that 20 seconds and *f*/22 are the basic exposure factors at 100% reproduction.

Now, to make a negative at *other* than 100% reproduction size, this procedure is followed:

1. *Basic (Assumed) Exposure factors:*
   20 seconds basic exposure.
   f/22 diaphragm control percentage band.
   Camera has manual diaphragm control and percentage calibrated tapes.

2. *Problem:*
   A type form which measures 25 × 50 picas is to be reproduced at 50%. What are the required camera settings?

3. *Determine Percentage of Reproduction:*
   This percentage may be stated in the problem or indicated on the copy. Otherwise, it may be computed as explained on page 111. (The problem here states that 50% reproduction size is required.)

4. *Settings for This Exposure:*
   Set timer for 20 seconds (the basic length of exposure).
   Set camera tapes for both copyboard and bellows (lensboard) extensions at 50% reproduction size.
   Set diaphragm control pointer at 50% on the *f*/22 band.

This setting of 50% on the *f*/22 band will automatically reduce the lens aperture from *f*/22 to *f*/30, as shown at "A" in Fig. 8-35. This reproduction of 50% will then actually be made at an aperture of *f*/30 while keeping the length of exposure constant at the established basic 20 seconds. An exposure of 20 seconds at *f*/30 admits *less light* than an exposure of 20 seconds at *f*/22. This makes sense, because *it takes less light for the 50% reproduction.*

Determining CE and BE by Formulas

Your camera may have a diaphragm control, but it may not have *calibrated percentage-setting tapes*. When a camera is without tapes, the copyboard extension (CE) and the bellows extension (BE) can be computed for the required enlargement or reduction by the following procedure:

1. *Basic (Assumed) Exposure Factors:*
   20 seconds basic exposure.
   f/22 lens aperture.
   10½″ focal-length lens (on the camera).
   Camera has no percentage-calibrated tapes.

2. *Problem:*
   A type form which measures 25 × 50 picas is to be reproduced at 50%. Determine the camera settings.

3. *Procedure:*
   Step 1 — Determine percentage of reproduction. This percentage may be stated in

the problem or marked on the copy. Otherwise, it may be calculated as explained on page 111. In this case, the problem here states that a reproduction of 50% is required.

Step 2 — Determine CE (copyboard extension). In the following, FL is the focal length of the lens; R is the reproduction percentage required for this negative and is stated as a decimal.

CE = FL + (FL ÷ R)
CE = 10.5″ + (10.5″ ÷ .50)
CE = 10.5″ + 21″
CE = 31.5″

Step 3 — Determine BE (bellows extension).

BE = FL + (FL × R)
BE = 10.5″ + (10.5″ × .50)
BE = 10.5″ + 5.25″
BE = 15.75″

4. *Camera Settings:*

Set CE at 31.5″. Set BE at 15.75″. Set the diaphragm control pointer at 50% on the f/22 band. Set the timer for the basic 20-second exposure.

The Constant Aperture Method

In the *constant aperture* method, the lens aperture (f-number) remains the same for any size reproduction. However, the *length of exposure is varied* to suit the reproduction size.

• **Note:** If your camera has a diaphragm control, the percentage band settings will not be used. Use only the aperture settings on the lens collar or on the topmost F scale of the diaphragm control, Fig. 8-35.

The procedure is as follows:

1. *Basic Exposure Factors:*

First, determine the basic 100% exposure, as explained on page 134. Assume that this basic 100% exposure was made at an aperture of f/22 with an exposure of 20 seconds.

2. *Problem:*

A type form which measures 25 × 50 picas is to be reproduced at 80%. If the basic aperture setting of f/22 is to be maintained, what is the required new length of exposure?

Table 8-1
New Exposure Time for Various Reproduction Sizes When Using the Constant Aperture System
(Lights are attached to, and move with, the copyboard.)

		Same-Size Basic Exposure Time		
		10 Seconds	20 Seconds	30 Seconds
Reproduction Size Required	300%	40	80	120
	275%	35	70	105½
	250%	30½	61¼	92
	225%	26½	53	79
	200%	22½	45	67½
	175%	19	38	57
	150%	15½	31	47
	125%	12½	25	38
	100%	10	20	30
	95%	9½	19	28½
	90%	9	18	27
	85%	8½	17	25½
	80%	8	16¼ ◀	24¼
	75%	7½	15	23
	70%	7¼	14½	21½
	65%	6¾	13½	20½
	60%	6½	12¾	19¼
	55%	6	12	18
	50%	5¾	11¼	17
	45%	5¼	10½	15¾
	40%	5	10	15
	35%	4½	9	13½
	30%	4¼	8½	12¾
	25%	4	8	12
	20%	3½	7¼	10¾

Example: An 80% reproduction, based on a same-size basic exposure of 20 seconds, requires a new exposure time of 16¼ seconds (at arrow on the table).

To Extend the Table: For new exposures based on a 40-second same-size basic exposure, double the exposures shown in the 20-seconds column. For new exposures based on a 15-seconds 100% basic exposure, use one-half the exposures shown in the 30-seconds column.

3. *Procedure:*

On Table 8-1, above, read across from the 80% reproduction size to the column for 20 seconds basic exposure. The new exposure time, as indicated by the arrow, is 16¼ seconds.

4. *Camera Settings:*

Set BE and CE each for 80% reproduction. (For a camera without calibrated tapes, compute BE and CE as explained earlier.) Set the lens at the basic aperture of f/22 (on the lens collar or on the topmost F scale of the diaphragm control). Set the timer for 16¼ seconds — the new exposure time.

Remember that in this constant aperture method the same basic aperture (f-number) is issued for all reproduction sizes. However, the length of the exposure is varied, depending on the reproduction size. The new length of exposure is easily determined by use of Table 8-1.

Colored Line Copy and Paper

Camera line copy that is in a color other than the usual black or that is not printed on white paper may be photographed to appear as though it were black-and-white camera copy. This is done by using a selected combination of filter and film. A filter will transmit light of certain colors while it absorbs light of other colors. (This is illustrated in Fig. 10-9.)

Film and Filter Combinations

Table 8-2 suggests combinations of films and filters to use for photographing the listed colors of the original copy. For example, camera copy consisting of a black ink printed on a yellow sheet may be photographed as though it were black ink on white paper by using a No. 16 (orange) Kodak Wratten Filter and Ortho film. (Where more than one filter is recommended, the first listing is preferred.)

There is a multitude of differences in shades of colors, and no one perceives all colors the same. Experience may indicate other combinations than those listed. If so, post a record of satisfactory results for future use, showing samples of the copy, the numbers of the filters,

Table 8-2
Film and Filter Combinations For Copying or Dropping Various Colors

TO PHOTOGRAPH AS BLACK (to hold a color) use the film and filter* suggested below:			Color of Copy Being Photo- graphed	TO PHOTOGRAPH AS WHITE (to drop a color) use the film and filter* suggested below:		
Blue-sensitive Film	Orthochromatic Film	Panchromatic Film		Blue-sensitive Film	Orthochromatic Film	Panchromatic Film
Not recommended	Orange (16) Yellow (15, 12) Green (61, 58) Yellow (9, 8)	Green (61, 58)	Magenta (process red)	No filter needed**	Can try: ** Blue (47B) Magenta (30) Blue (47)	Red (25, 29)** Magenta (30) Blue (47B)
No filter needed	Blue (47B) Magenta (30) Blue (47)	Blue (47B, 47)	Red or Orange	Not recommended	Not recommended	Red (29, 25, 23A)
No filter needed	Blue (47B) Magenta (30) Blue (47)	Blue (47B, 47)	Yellow	Not recommended	Orange (16) Yellow (15, 12) Green (61, 58) Yellow (9, 8)	Red (29, 25, 23A) Orange (16) Yel (15, 12, 9, 8) Green (61, 58)
No filter needed	Blue (47B) Magenta (30) Blue (47)	Magenta (30) Red (25) Blue (47B, 47)	Green	Not recommended	Orange (16) Yellow (15, 12) Green (61, 58) Yellow (9, 8)	Green (58)
Not recommended	Not recommended	Red (25)	Cyan (process blue)	No filter needed	No filter needed	Blue (47B, 47)
Not recommended	Orange (16) Yellow (15, 12) Green (61, 58) Yellow (9, 8)	Green (58) Red (25)	Blue or Violet	No filter needed	Magenta (30) Blue (47B, 47)	Blue (47B, 47)

(Courtesy Eastman Kodak Company)

*Numbers are for Wratten filters, also known as follows: 8-K2, 9-K3, 15-G, 25-A, 29-F, 47-C5, 58-B, 61-N.

Try in order listed; variations in color of copy and experience may suggest other filters.

**To drop magenta, it is best to use pan film and a No. 25 filter.

the kind of film used, and the length of exposure or filter factor.

Filters

Filters are of two forms — gelatin film and gelatin cemented between sheets of optical glass. They usually are square — 2″ × 2″ or 3″ × 3″, depending on lens diameter. The filter is inserted into the filter (Waterhouse Stop) slot of the lens barrel, or it is inserted into a filter holder mounted on the front of the lens barrel. As a precaution, check the focus carefully when doing critical work with filters. Also, close the filter slot (or place a piece of tape over it) when you are through using the filters.

Filter Factors

When a filter is used during the exposure, the filter absorbs part of the exposure light. This absorption requires an increase of exposure over that when no filter is used. The number of times by which an exposure must be increased for each specific filter and film combination is known as the *filter factor*.

A factor of 2, for example, indicates that the standard exposure for that film and setup should be multiplied by 2 because of the filter interference. Sometimes, suggested factors for filters are included on data sheets for films. Otherwise, the factor for a specific film and filter combination is arrived at experimentally and should be recorded for future use.

Questions

1. What is meant by line photography?
2. What is a latent image? What causes it on the film?
3. Describe what happens during the developing of the film.
4. Compare the appearance of the image on the ground glass with the appearance of the copy on the copyboard.
5. How does a vertical camera differ from a horizontal one?
6. What are the basic parts of the camera?
7. What precautions are observed in handling the lens?
8. Explain the term *FL*.
9. Describe the copyboard. Tell how to care for it.
10. How is the film held in place on the camera?
11. What function is served by the bellows? What may happen if the bellows develops a leak?
12. Where can one find information that indicates the particular kind of safelight to use for a given film?
13. On the ground glass, how are slight changes made in the size of the image? How does the user adjust for critical focusing?
14. What is meant by the expression "same-size" in photography?
15. Describe two methods for determining the emulsion side of a piece of unexposed film in the darkroom.
16. Describe the manual diaphragm control.
17. Describe the constant time method of exposure.
18. Give a description of the constant aperture method of exposure.

Problems and Projects

1. Determine the basic exposure time for your camera setup.
2. Determine the best f-number of your lens.
3. Make a chart/drawing for a same-size (basic) exposure. Show the settings for BE and CE, the angle of lights (and distance, if adjustable), the "best" f-number, the diaphragm control index setting on "best" f-number band, and the "best" length of exposure.
4. A 10″ FL lens is set at f/16. Compute the effective (actual) diameter of the aperture.
5. If the diaphragm control is set at 50% on the f/16 band, what is the actual f-number setting of the lens?
6. Assume a camera is without calibrated tapes. It has a lens of 10″ FL. What are the BE and CE settings (in inches) for:
   a. a 200% reproduction.
   b. a 125% reproduction.
   c. a 50% reproduction.
7. Using Table 8-1, determine the new length of exposure for each of the following:

a. a 225% reproduction; basic exposure is 20 seconds.
b. a 125% reproduction; basic exposure is 30 seconds.
c. a 40% reproduction; basic exposure is 10 seconds.

New Terms

aberrations	band
anti-halation	base side

bellows extension	normal copy
diaphragm	process lens
f-stop numbers	pulsed xenon
filter factor	rail
gallery	right-reading
gray scale	safelight
incandescent bulbs	sensitivity guide
linear	shutter
lens mount	solenoid
nodal	vacuum pump

Halftone Photography

Camera copy which contains *gradation of tone* (continuous tones) typically is reproduced by the halftone process. This procedure involves printing a broken pattern in which dots, though in an equally spaced pattern, vary in size in different areas. This creates the illusion of lighter and darker tones in the copy, Fig. 9-2.

Gradation of Tone

Gradation of tone is found in pencil drawings, original photographs (snapshots, portraits, landscapes, equipment, and processes), oil paintings, watercolor renderings, lithographs, crayon art, etc. (Refer back to Fig. 7-2, page 109.) In each of these original pieces of camera copy, the tones vary. The elements of the illustration *are not all* solid black or solid white. Rather, there is a gradual variation of

tones ranging from the lightest parts of the illustration to the darkest. Examine a snapshot and you will see this gradation of tone, or continuous tone.

Optical Illusion

Most photographs which are used as illustrations in newspapers and textbooks are printed by the halftone process. Examine Fig. 9-1 under a magnifier, and you will see that a printed halftone illustration is actually an *optical illusion*. There is no gradation of tone. Rather, the picture is composed of thousands of dots and checkerboard squares of varying sizes, as shown in Fig. 9-2. Held away from the magnifier, however, the printed halftone illustration *looks* like a picture. In fact, if the dot pattern is

Campbell Photos, Inc. Campbell Photos, Inc. Campbell Photos, Inc.

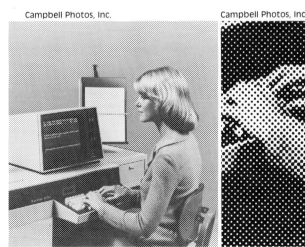

Fig. 9-1. A 65-line halftone print.   Fig. 9-2. Enlarged portion of Fig. 9-1.

Fig. 9-3. A 300-line halftone print.

very fine, as shown in Fig. 9-3, the printed half-tone may closely reproduce most of the details of the original photograph. It more closely resembles gradation of tone. This is because there are 18,000 more dots than there were in Fig. 9-1.

Reflection of Light

Actually, our eyes see *reflected light* when we look at a printed halftone. We see light reflected from the paper — not the black ink. The black ink merely serves to absorb light and control the reflection.

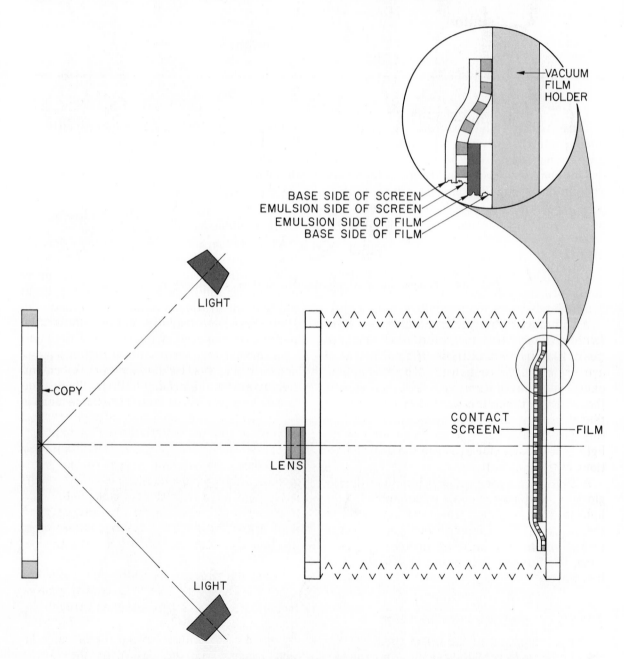

Fig. 9-4.   Basic camera setup for halftone photography. Film is base side toward the vacuum back, its emulsion side toward the lens. The contact screen overlaps the film and is in direct contact with the film, making emulsion-to-emulsion contact with the film. Base side of the screen faces the lens.

A. This represents the continuous-tone camera copy.

B. This is the halftone (film) negative.

C. This is the halftone printed on paper.

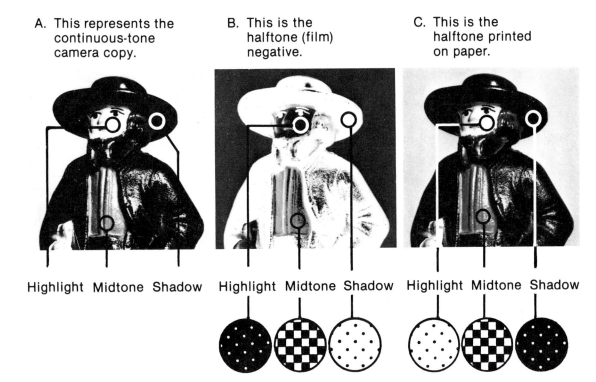

Fig. 9-5.   **Comparison of typical highlight, midtone, and shadow areas.**

Areas of a printed halftone which are white (with extremely tiny staggered black dots) appear as nearly white areas. If the black dots are larger, they cover more of the white paper, causing it to reflect less light. The appearance then is gray. When the black dots are so large that they cover most of an area and leave only tiny pinpoints of white paper, very little or no light is reflected. Our eyes see the darker portions of the illustration.

A dull-white paper reflects less light than a glossy-white paper. Yellow paper reflects less light than white paper. The color and finish of the paper on which the halftone illustration is printed then may improve upon, or detract from, the final printed effect of a halftone illustration.

Theory of Halftone Reproduction

The ink fountain of the offset press carries ink of a single tone of one color — for example, black. On the printed sheets of paper, then, the press can print only solid black dots, lines and areas, or it can leave an area of the paper blank.

To make a satisfactory offset printing plate which will reproduce the effect of a printed continuous-tone illustration requires a particular procedure. The original continuous-tone illustration (camera copy) must be photographed in such a way as to produce a film negative composed of dense, opaque dots and squares and clear, transparent areas — no semi-opaque areas. Such a negative is called a *halftone negative*. It is produced from continuous-tone camera copy (such as an original photograph) by placing a halftone screen over the film in the camera before making the exposure. See Fig. 9-4.

When the exposure is made, light reflected from the copy (on the copyboard) passes through the camera lens and then through the tiny openings of the halftone screen, *before* it strikes the film emulsion where it causes a *latent image* to be formed. When the film is developed and processed, the image is seen to be composed of *dots*. There is one dot for each opening of the halftone screen through which the light passed. Each screen opening acts as a tiny individual lens or film gray scale to produce its characteristic dot pattern on the film emulsion.

Halftone Dots

The size of any individual black dot on the film emulsion is determined by the intensity of the light rays from a corresponding area of the copy on the copyboard being focused through a

single screen opening. Original continuous-tone copy usually has a rather wide range of tones. Therefore, the varying amounts of light (or intensities of light) which are reflected from the copy areas and pass through the screen openings will produce a range of dot sizes on the film. See Figs. 9-5 and 9-6.

The highlight, or lightest, areas of the copy reflect the greatest amount of light. This produces on the negative the largest black dots, which appear as black or nearly black opaque areas. These dots are so large and overlapping that they leave only tiny pinpoints of clear area on the film. This *darkest* area on the *negative* is called the *highlight area*.

Areas of the copy that reflect a moderate amount of light and thus produce a checkerboard effect on the negative are called *mid-tone areas*. Exact size of these alternating black and clear squares depends upon the shading of the copy mid-tone areas. The checkerboard pattern of the 50% tone is similar on both the negative and its print.

The shadow (darkest) areas of the copy reflect the least amount of light. They produce, on the negative, transparent areas of tiny pinpoint black dots or sometimes no dots at all. The *lightest* areas on the *negative* are called the *shadow areas*.

Note that all the areas produced on the negative must be definitely *transparent* or definitely *black opaque*. The same high-contrast film as used for line photography is used also for halftones. There can be no semi-opaque or "brown" dots. When the halftone negative is used in exposing a plate, the transparent areas transmit light of equal intensity (though differing in size) to the sensitized coating on the offset plate. In

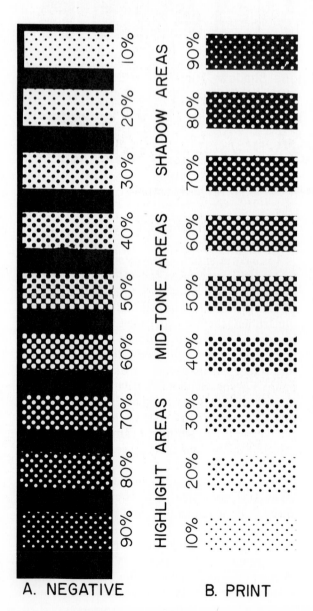

A. NEGATIVE   B. PRINT

Fig. 9-6. Approximate values of halftone dots (enlarged): (A) negative; (B) print. In each of the above, the percentage figure indicates the percentage of the area that is taken up by the black dots; 10% means that the black dots take up 10% of the total area; 90% means that the black dots take up 90% of the area. Note that a 10% highlight area on a print is produced from a corresponding area of the negative having a 90% dot. Actually, the black dots in the 90% area of the negative are so large that they overlap somewhat, leaving only a tiny white space (or dot).

the subsequent developing of the plate, then, all transparent areas will produce a hard, firm image area which will print well on the press sheets.

A comparison of the two sides of Fig. 9-6 should clear up any misunderstanding that the beginner may have in referring to *shadow* and *highlight* areas of the halftone negative. Remember that a negative is just the reverse of the printed illustration. Black on the negative becomes white when the work is printed, and clear areas become black. (Again, see Fig. 9-5).

In looking at a *halftone negative*, then, remember that the percentage size of the dots refers to the percentage of *black area on the film*. On a *halftone print*, the percentage size of the dot refers to the *percentage of area covered by the ink*. For instance, a 30% dot means that the black dots cover 30% of the area on the print where they occur.

In Fig. 9-6, also note that a 10% shadow dot on the halftone negative will produce a 90% shadow dot on the halftone print. An 80% high-light dot on the negative will produce a 20% highlight dot on the print.

In summary, in black-and-white work, (1) halftone dots are always *black*; (2) on the negative, the size of the black dot is determined by the intensity of light from the reflected copy; and (3) the percentage size of the dot (whether on the film or printed paper) refers to the percentage of the area which is *black*.

Screening Methods

Continuous-tone copy may be broken into a halftone pattern by one of three techniques. The image may be passed either through a glass halftone screen or through a flexible plastic contact screen; or it may be exposed directly on Kodalith Autoscreen Ortho Film. Autoscreen film has a screen pattern built into its light sensitivity. (See page 174.)

Glass Screens

The glass screen (Levy screen) is the traditional halftone screen. It is made of two sheets of glass, each ruled in one direction with cut-in, parallel lines. The rulings are filled with an opaque (light-stopping) material. The two sheets

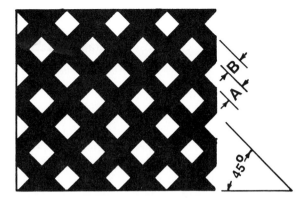

Fig. 9-7.   Enlarged portion of a glass halftone screen, 1 to 1 ratio. Lines "B" and openings "A" are the same width. The number of diagonal lines per inch (counted at 45°) represents the ruling of the screen.

of glass are then cemented face-to-face, with the lines on one at right angles to those of the other, Fig. 9-7.

Glass screens are more expensive than the contact screens, described below. Their use, though much more complex in nature, follows the same general procedures as for the contact screens. Further instructions on glass screens are not given in this book.

Eastman Kodak Company

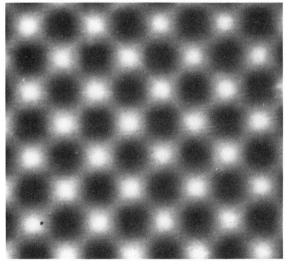

Fig. 9-8.   Contact screen (enlarged). Note that the vignetted dots form a 45° pattern. The number of dots in one inch, counted along a 45° line, represents the ruling of the screen.

Contact Screens

Contact screens have largely replaced the glass halftone screens for halftone photography. They are made of a flexible film support with a vignetted-dot pattern in the film emulsion. See Fig. 9-8. These screens are used in direct contact with the film on the camera vacuum film holder. The emulsion side of the screen is positioned against the emulsion (dull) side of the film, and the contact screen is on the side toward the lens, Fig. 9-4. They are available in screen rulings from about 50 lines per inch to about 300 lines per inch. See Table 9-1.

Table 9-1
Halftone Screen Rulings (Lines or Dots) Per Inch
of Commercially Available Screens

50	110	175
65	120	200
75	133	250
85	150	300
100		

Each vignetted dot (square) of the contact screen, as shown in Fig.9-8, varies in density from a tiny, almost transparent opening in its center to a surrounding almost-opaque area at its edge. Thus, in effect, each dot acts much as a film gray scale. A weak light will penetrate only the tiny center portion; a stronger light will pass through an increasing area; and an intense light will pass through a large portion.

Types of Contact Screens

Because of the many kinds and purposes of contact screens, the manufacturer's instructions packaged with each individual screen should be studied carefully. Some types of contact screens are described below.

Gray Contact Screen (for Negatives). . This screen has silver-content vignetted dots. It may be used for making halftone negatives from black-and-white camera copy. It is always used when photographing colored original camera copy and when making direct-screen halftone color separation negatives.

Magenta Contact Screen. This screen has vignetted dots of a magenta-colored dye. Magenta contact screens are used for making halftone negatives from black-and-white camera copy. Because of their magenta color, they are not used for making halftone negatives from colored camera copy. Magenta contact screens allow additional control of the range of tones in the halftones by the use of magenta and yellow filters over the light source.

The *magenta negative contact screen* is used primarily for making halftone negatives from black-and-white camera copy. The *magenta positive contact screen* is used primarily for making halftone screened film positives from continuous-tone film negatives in the indirect method of color separation.

The magenta positive contact screen is also used for making halftone screened paper prints of rulings finer than 100 lines per inch.

Kodak PMT Gray Contact Screen. This screen is used for making screened paper prints on Kodak photomechanical transfer (PMT) papers.

Special Effects Screen. Several types of special effects screens are shown in the three lower examples in Fig. 9-9. Their use produces interesting, unusual, and eye-catching effects. They are used in the same manner as conventional dot contrast screens.

Kinds of Screen Dots

Contact screens are available in several kinds of dot patterns. Among them are the *conventional square dot*, the *elliptical dot*, the *dual dot*, and the *round dot*. Figure 9-10 shows the 50% area of the conventional square dot and the elliptical dot.

Given dot shapes may be suited to different types of reproduction. For instance, the elliptical dot screen gives smoother tonal rendition in the middletones.

Care of Contact Screen

Contact screens should be protected from scratches, dirt, and liquid stains. They should be handled only by the edges and kept in their original folders and cartons when not in use.

Caprock Developments, Inc.

ROUND DOT (100)   SQUARE DOT (100)   ELLIPTICAL DOT (100)   MEZZOTINT (75)

STRAIGHT LINE (62)   WAVY LINE (60)   CONCENTRIC CIRCLE (60)   MEZZOTINT (150)

Fig. 9-9.   Halftones made with Caprock contact screens.

The screens should never be handled with wet or damp hands, and never laid down on tables or counter tops.

The contact screen should be smoothed in place on the film holder, by covering it with a clean sheet of paper and rolling it flat with a soft rubber roller.

If necessary, the screen can be dusted with a photo chamois — never with a camel's hair brush. Liquid stains may be removed according to instructions packaged with the screen.

To facilitate handling, screens may be taped into a cutout area of a larger sheet of acetate. Each side of the screen can be identified for the beginner with a tape label: "Emulsion side — This side toward film" and "Base side — This side toward lens." Other pertinent information can be added, such as date purchased, lines per inch, type of dots, and kind of screen.

Small screens can be used by beginners. It is necessary only that the screen be about an inch larger in width and height than the film. Test the size with your particular vacuum-back set-

tings to check that enough vacuum is developed to hold the screen tightly in place over the film.

Understanding Densitometry

A brief explanation here introduces the basic concepts of densitometry needed to produce better halftones, as well as those needed for understanding the information in film and photographic manuals.

A   B

Fig. 9-10.   Middletones of negatives made with (A) a conventional square-dot contact screen and (B) an elliptical-dot contact screen.

Basic Terms

Densitometry is the measuring of the optical density (the degree of blackness or lightstopping ability) of a particular tone area of a film negative or positive; of a photographic print, painting, or other tone copy; or of the printed reproduction. Density comes from the amount of developed silver or dye in the photographic process and from the amount of light-absorbing pigment in art and printing processes.

The factors which can be measured in densitometry are opacity, density, transmittance, and reflectance. These will be defined first.

Opacity is the ability of a material (such as developed silver deposit, ink, dye, or paper) to prevent light from passing through it. Opacity values are computed as follows:

$$\text{Opacity} = \frac{\text{Total amount of light that hits an area}}{\text{Amount of light that gets through that area}}$$

or, again,

$$\text{Opacity} = \frac{\text{Incident light}}{\text{Transmitted light}}$$

Opacity is expressed in decimal numbers from 1.00 (no opacity) to a practical point of 100.00 (which might seem quite opaque in normal light), to 1000.00 (at which only a very bright light might penetrate enough to measure).

Density means much the same as opacity, except that it is measured on a different scale. This is the factor measured by a densitometer. Each reading obtained on the densitometer scale is actually an opacity reading, except that the density reading is expressed as a logarithm (to the base 10) of that opacity. This gives smaller numbers and simpler calculations.

Figure 9-11 illustrates density. Suppose that a sheet of film is opaque enough to pass only 1/10th of the incident light falling on it — reducing 100 units of light to 10. A second layer of this film doubles the density, but further

Table 9-2
Multiplying the Effect of Density

Layers	Density	Light Passed	Opacity
0	0	100	1
1	1	10	10
2	2	1	100
3	3	0.1	1,000
4	4	0.01	10,000

reduces the 10 units of light reaching that layer to 1 unit. Three layers triple the density, but further reduces the light to .1 units. Thus, we see density is additive, but the effect is multiplied, as shown in Table 9-2.

Theoretically, the density numbers could continue indefinitely. However, for practical purposes, they run from 0.00 to a little less than 2.00 for light reflected from a print, and to nearly 3.00 for light transmitted through a negative or positive. At these upper points, there is so little light left that it is not very visible or even measurable.

Transmittance, or transmission, is a percentage indicating how much of the light striking the surface (incident light) is transmitted (passed) through an area of the film negative or film positive (at 90°). If $1/20$th of the incident light is transmitted, the transmittance is expressed as 5%. On a halftone negative, this would occur with 95% dots.

Reflectance is a percentage indicating how much of the exposure light (incident light) which strikes the surface is reflected from a

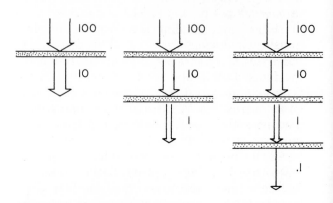

Fig. 9-11.   Density and transmission.

Table 9-3
Relationships of Density to Light, Tones, and Opacity

1 Density (Transmission or Reflection)	2 Percent of Light (Transmitted or Reflected)*	3 Halftone Dot Percentage (Related to Col. 2.)	4 Opacity
0.00	100% (clear or white)	0%	1.00
0.05	90% (light)	10%	1.12
0.12	75% (medium light)	25%	1.32
0.30	50% (middle tone)	50%	2.00
0.60	25% (medium dark)	75%	4.00
1.00	10% (very dark)	90%	10.00
2.00	1% (black and dense)	99%	100.00
3.00	0.1% (very dense)	99.9%	1000.00

*Approximated slightly for clarity.

tone area of, for example, a photographic print. See Fig. 9-13. If only ¹/₁₀th of the incident light is reflected, the reflectance is expressed as 10%, and the tone may be called a 90% (dark) gray. A black-and-white halftone having a perfect checkerboard pattern (equal black and white squares) gives a 50% gray and therefore has a reflectance of 50%. However, its density (being measured on a different scale) is only about .30.

Key points, approximated slightly for clarity in Table 9-3, show the basic relationships of density to transmitted and reflected light (and thus tones) and opacity.

The eye sees equal changes in *density* as equal steps in *tone,* and most gray scales are on this basis. The litho camera operator, stripper, and press operator usually think in terms of dot size, shown in column 3 (difference between column 2 and 100%). This is accurately measured on the density scale (column 1). It must be pointed out that there is no direct relationship between density and halftone dot percentage. Dot size also depends on film sensitivity and exposure. Note that a very small difference in density at the bright end of the scale makes a large percentage change in amount of light. At the dark end of the scale, however, a much larger change in density is necessary to make a similar change in light.

Density Readings. Transmission density and reflection density are readings taken by transmittance or reflectance which are ad-justed for variation in the light source. They eliminate light intensity as a variable so that all tone values are expressed as relative to a set zero point.

Transmission density readings are used with negatives and with positive transparencies. See Fig. 9-12.

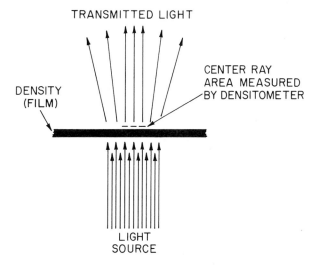

Fig. 9-12. **Transmission. When light is directed at (through) a photographic density such as a film negative or film positive, some light rays are absorbed by that density. Of the light rays transmitted through, some rays are scattered away from the measurable or center area.**

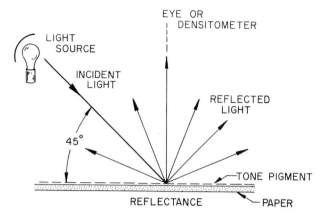

Fig. 9-13.   Reflection.

Reflection density is a density reading of reflectance from a print or from artwork which is illuminated by a light at 45°, and measures the light which is reflected 90° to the surface, Fig. 9-13. The actual amount of reflectance varies with brightness of the illumination. It also is affected by the overall color and surface of the paper, as well as the tone in a specific area. Bright white and a glossy-coated finish on the paper are capable of more reflection. When the blank paper or an extreme highlight is used as the zero point on the density scale, all other tone values are expressed in relation to that point. Sometimes a block of white magnesia chalk is used for a standard zero reference point.

Density Range.   Subtracting the minimum density from the maximum density of a negative or print gives us the density range of that item. Thus, density range is an indication of the amount of contrast in the negative or print. The term *density range* sometimes is used when referring to color materials and the term *density scale* when referring to black-and-white materials. Actually, they have the same meaning.

Densitometers

A densitometer is a device for measuring optical density. The most inexpensive tool for this purpose is a *calibrated gray scale* with the numerical density of each step labeled, as in Fig. 9-14. Accuracy in its use can be aided by punching a small hole in the middle of each step and between steps to limit the area of the copy being measured. Such use of the punched gray scale is shown in Fig. 9-35. Using a punched and calibrated gray scale is a big improvement over guessing at tone values, but the visual judgment involved is still a considerable factor.

Visual types of densitometers, Fig. 9-15, refine the gray scale technique. These use a system of lenses to superimpose a small circular area of tone from the copy directly onto a calibrated continuous gray scale. (The steps blend together.) Readings can be made in .01 units, but visual judgment is still somewhat a factor, as individual readings may vary a few points, and colors are a problem.

Photoelectric types of densitometers, Fig. 9-16, are more accurate and reliable because they eliminate personal variation. They are usable with filters for color, are read much more quickly, and have many additional applications.

Transmission, Reflection, and Combination Units.   Either the visual or photoelectric types can be designed to measure transmission den-

Eastman Kodak Company

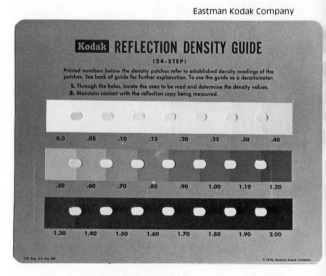

Fig. 9-14.   This type of calibrated gray scale can be used as a simple densitometer for measuring densities of reflection copy.

Eastman Kodak Company

Fig. 9-15. Visual densitometer.

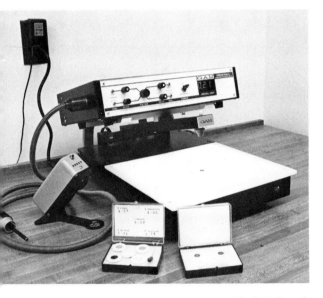

Fig. 9-16: Photoelectrical densitometer with digital readout for transmission and reflection use.

sity, reflection density, or both. Transmission readings are used for negatives and positives. Therefore, the units must have a light under the copy stage, and reflection readings require a toplighted stage. Combination units require both lighting systems and thus are more expensive. Most units are purchased for use at a particular work station. This would mean using a reflection unit for copy and a separate transmission unit for negatives.

Uses of Densitometers. The primary interest here is the use of the densitometer to

measure the density range of tone copy and perhaps to check the halftone negative made from that copy. Advanced manuals or the instruction book for your densitometer will give details for many additional uses. Following are some of these uses:

1. Check camera lighting for level and evenness.
2. Determine camera exposures for changing conditions.
3. Determine exposure factors for colored filters used on the camera.
4. Check evenness of image at camera back.
5. Determine exposure times for continuous-tone photo prints.
6. Determine percentage grayness or percent dot.
7. Check ink level on press sheets.
8. Calculate exposures for color correction masks and separation negatives in process color work (see next chapter).
9. Check on amount and purity of process color inks.
10. Check trapping of one color over another in multicolor work.
11. Determine paper opacity and brightness.
12. Monitor the density of phototype production.

Thus, it can be seen that the densitometer is a basic tool in quality-control work for graphic processes.

Film Sensitivity

To obtain a full range of tones, both the exposure and development of film (or any photographic emulsion) must be controlled and correct. A knowledge of three important factors related to sensitivity will give a better grasp of the process. The first of these is the *contrast* of the film, as shown by the characteristic curve. The second factor is the *color sensitivity* of the film, as indicated by the terms blue-sensitive, orthochromatic, and panchromatic. The third factor is *film speed,* as indicated by the exposure index.

Characteristic Curve. A characteristic curve, Fig. 9-17, illustrates graphically the con-

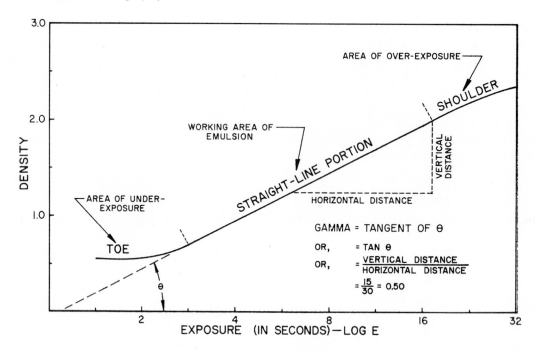

Fig. 9-17. Characteristic curve and its parts.

trast *characteristics* of the photographic emulsion under controlled conditions of exposure and processing. Notice the three portions of the curve: the toe portion, the straight-line portion, and the shoulder portion. In the curved sections, there is a changing relationship between density and exposure. However, in the straight-line portion, there is a constant relationship — a corresponding increase in density for each increase in exposure time.

The steepness (or slope) which the straight-line portion of the curve forms with the horizontal edge of the graph is referred to by the Greek letter *gamma* (γ). Gamma indicates the *contrast* obtainable with that emulsion — *due to development.*

The characteristic curve, or sensitometric curve, for a typical litho (very high-contrast) film is shown in Fig. 9-18. Litho film is a type intended for reproducing line and halftone copy for making printing plates by almost any printing process. It has a rather steep straight-line portion and thus is said to have a *high gamma.* A relatively small exposure change results in a great increase in density. This sharp jump in

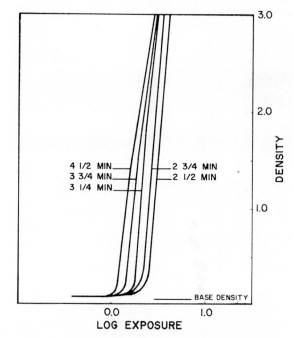

Fig. 9-18. Curves for Kodalith Ortho, Type 3 film. This is an improved extra high-contrast film. (Exposed to arc light, developed in Kodalith Super Developer with continuous agitation at 68° F. for the five times shown.) Zero point on exposure scale is recommended exposure.

density gives a clean break between image and nonimage area in reproductions.

Color Sensitivity

The color sensitivity of films is shown in the form of *wedge spectrograms* in film data books, Fig. 9-19. The height of the white patch in the spectrogram indicates the sensitivity of the emulsion to the various colors — provided the same kind of exposure light is used. Only the three main or primary colors of light (red, green, blue) are labeled. Yellow is located where red and green merge; violet is the left part of the blue band (next to the ultra-violet [U.V.], light which is invisible to the eye). There is a more detailed discussion of the nature of color in the next chapter.

Blue-sensitive films, sometimes called "color-blind" films, are sensitive only to blue light. They are blind to the other two-thirds of the spectrum — the greens, yellows, and reds. This is very convenient in the darkroom, because a relatively bright (yellow or red) safelight can be used for general illumination and the film will not be fogged.

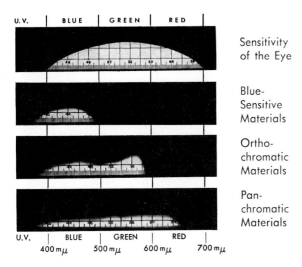

Fig. 9-19. Color-sensitivity classes for photographic emulsions. Blue-sensitive materials have only the near-ultra-violet and blue sensitivity inherent in every silver-halide emulsion. Orthochromatic materials have this sensitivity plus high green sensitivity. Panchromatic materials have a wide sensitivity which approximates that of the human eye.

Orthochromatic films are the standard film for copying black-and-white copy. Ortho films are sometimes called "red-blind" films because they are sensitive to blues, greens, and yellows, but are blind to red light. This means that any red in the camera copy (paper or ink) will reproduce as black on the negative. More importantly, since the ortho film is blind to red light, a red safelight can be used in the darkroom when working with this film. The red safelight will give enough illumination for most camera and developing work.

Panchromatic films are sensitive to all colors and reproduce tones in shades of gray which appear in a natural relationship to each other. However, the film must be handled and developed in total darkness, which is not convenient unless the process is completely automated (as in modern development of snapshots). In printing work, pan film is used to reproduce colored copy in tones of a single color, especially when it is necessary to distinguish between reds and blacks. It also is used with colored filters (especially reddish ones) to emphasize or drop out certain colors on the copy. Its largest printing use is in color-separation work for process color reproduction in full, natural color. Special pan films are available for this purpose.

Film Speed

Films vary considerably in the amount of light they need. <u>Fast films</u> require <u>very little light</u> — a small diaphragm opening and a short exposure. <u>Slow films</u> require <u>longer exposures</u> and larger diaphragm openings to admit more light. Each film has an A.S.A. exposure index number which makes exposure calculations more exact. A film with an exposure index of 10 will require twice as long an exposure as one with an index of 20. For film exposure indexes and information, consult the data sheet packed with the film or consult manufacturers' data books.

GOOD REF.

Basic Considerations in Making a Single-Color Halftone Negative

• **Note:** Either the *gray* contact screen or the *magenta* contact screen may be used for operations described in this chapter.

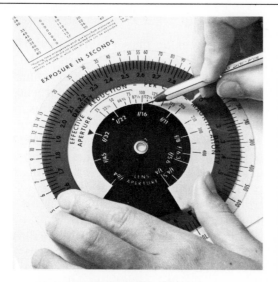

A. Calculate the exposures.

B. Place the copy in copyboard.

C. Set lens or diaphragm control.

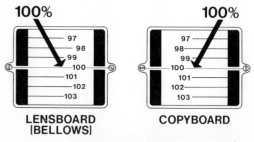

D. Set lensboard and bellows extensions.

E. Place film on camera back.

Fig. 9-20.   Major steps in making a single-color halftone negative with a contact screen.

F. Place screen over film.

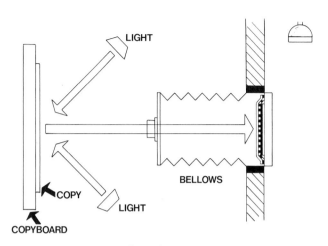

LIGHT

LIGHT

COPY

COPYBOARD

BELLOWS

G. Make main exposure.

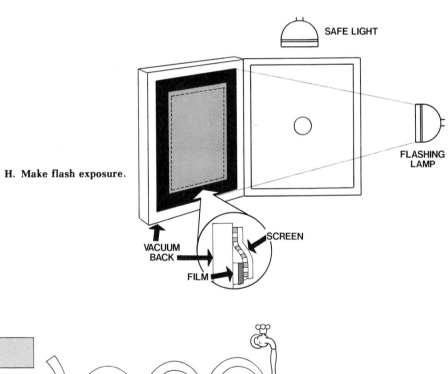

SAFE LIGHT

H. Make flash exposure.

FLASHING LAMP

VACUUM BACK

SCREEN

FILM

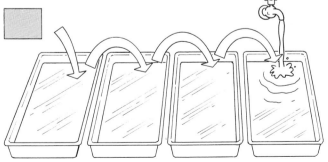

I. Process the film.

1. DEVELOPER   2. SHORTSTOP   3. FIXER   4. WATER

Highly skilled operators employ a number of methods in making single-color halftone negatives. It is suggested that the beginner master the two-part method presented here. In this method, the film-and-screen setup is first given a white-light *main* (or *detail*) exposure and then a yellow-light *flash* exposure.

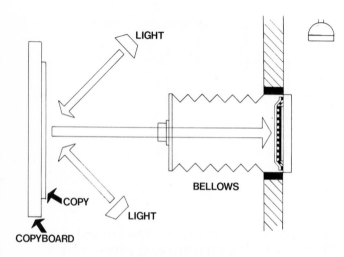

Fig. 9-21.   **Setup for main exposure.**

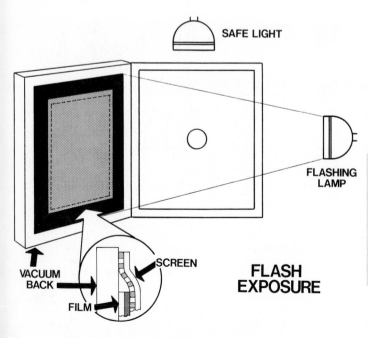

Fig. 9-22.   **Setup for flash exposure.**

Overview of the Two-Part Method

Following is a brief description of the two-part method for making a single-color halftone negative: (See also Fig. 9-20, page 156.)

1. Main and flash exposures are calculated.
2. The copy is mounted in the camera copyboard.
3. Camera settings are made for such factors as reproduction size, lens setting, and focus.
4. Under safelight conditions, the film is mounted on the film holder.
5. The contact screen is mounted over the film. Thus, when the camera back is closed, the screen is between the film and lens.
6. The *main exposure* is made. White light from the copyboard lights is reflected from the copy, through the lens, through the screen, and onto the film, Fig. 9-21.
7. Still under safelight conditions, the camera back is opened, and *a flash exposure* is made. Here, light from the flashing lamp goes directly from the lamp through the screen and onto the film — *not through the lens!* See Fig. 9-22.
8. Remove the screen and film.
9. Store the screen.
10. Process the film.

The Main Exposure

In the *main exposure*, Fig. 9-21, white light is directed at the copy on the copyboard, reflected from the copyboard to pass through the lens, then through the screen, and onto the film emulsion.

• **Note:** The above holds true for *reflection* (opaque) copy, such as a photograph on photopaper. For *transparent* copy, such as film slides, the transparency is mounted in an opening of the copyboard. The lights are positioned *behind* the copyboard, from where they direct the light *through* the transparency onto the film, Fig. 8-25.

A main exposure, in itself, will seldom reproduce the complete tonal range of the copy. Usually, it will satisfactorily reproduce the highlight and middle tones, but will fail to reproduce all the tones in the shadow areas of the copy.

The Flash Exposure

The flash exposure, Figs. 9-22 and 9-31, is sometimes also called the *supplementary flash exposure,* or the *controlled flash exposure.* A lamp suitable for darkroom flash exposures can be made from a darkroom safelight holder, Fig. 9-31. This lamp, positioned 6 to 8 feet from the camera back, has a safelight filter — Wratten Series 00 (light yellow) and a 7½-watt frosted lamp. A Wratten Series OA (greenish yellow) safelight can be substituted. Since it transmits less light than the Series OO, the Series OA should be used with a 60-watt frosted lamp at a distance of 4 feet and with about twice the exposure needed with the Series OO filter.

- **Note:** Yellow filtered light is used with magenta screens. Yellow light may also be used with the gray screens, but is not necessary.

The flash exposure generally occurs *after* the main exposure. *With the safelight and film holder vacuum still on,* the camera back is opened after the main exposure has been made, and positioned so that the film-screen setup faces the yellow flashing lamp at 90 degrees. The yellow-light flash exposure is then made *from the flashing lamp directly onto the film-screen setup.*

- **Note:** If Newton's rings (concentric bands of light) become a problem with the gray contact screen, try flashing without the filter.

Some cameras are equipped with a flashing lamp mounted on a pivot on the lensboard. This lamp can be positioned in front of the lens so that its light is directed *through* the lens and screen, onto the film, Fig. 9-23. In neither this case nor the one above is the flashing light reflected from the camera copy mounted on the copyboard.

The flash exposure serves to add some dot pattern in the shadow areas of the negative, as well as to improve detail, thereby lightening the dark end of the scale. This essentially compresses the density range to that which can be printed.

Consolidated International Equipment and Graphic Supply Company

Fig. 9-23. Camera lensboard assembly with three-way turret lens mounting and automatic flashing lamp, controlled from within the darkroom.

In Fig. 9-24, note that the left-hand half of the *negative* was given a main exposure and the right-hand half was given a main exposure *plus* a flash exposure. The print made from that

Fig. 9-24. Halftone negative (left) and print (right) show the effect of adding a flash exposure. The upper-left half of the negative received no flash; the lower-right half received normal flash exposure. Note how the shadow dots in the darkest portion of the lower-right half of the print (produced from the shadow dots in the corresponding part of the negative) bring out added detail.

negative demonstrates clearly that the area on the left, which was given only a main exposure, shows the highlight areas normally, but is lacking in shadow details. However, the right-hand area, which was given a main exposure *plus* a flash exposure, shows greater shadow detail. This illustrates that the flash exposure affects only the shadow areas of the printed picture.

• **Note:** The use of a third exposure — the *highlight* (*no-screen*, or *bump*) *exposure* is explained on page 172.

Calculating Halftone Exposures

Halftone exposures sometimes must be as much as eight times as long as exposures for line work. This is because the exposure light rays in a halftone exposure must overcome and penetrate the dye density of the halftone screen emulsion.

Lengths of the halftone main and flash exposures may be calculated by means of computers. These may be electronic computers, the Kodak Graphic Arts Exposure Computer (Q-12), or the Kodak Halftone Negative Computer (Q-15). The Q-12, Fig. 9-25, is a general exposure computer whereas the Q-15 is more specialized. For illustrative purposes, the Q-12, is used here and referred to as "the computer." A discussion of the basic properties of the Q-15 may be found on page 170.

The computer must be calibrated (adjusted) and set according to particular shop conditions, such as the individual contact screen, the

Eastman Kodak Company

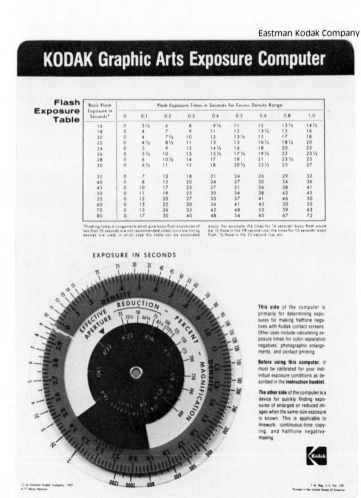

KODAK Graphic Arts Exposure Computer

Flash Exposure Table

Basic Flash Exposure in Seconds*	Flash Exposure Times in Seconds for Excess Density Range								
	0	0.1	0.2	0.3	0.4	0.5	0.6	0.8	1.0
16	0	3½	6	8	9½	11	12	13½	14½
18	0	4	7	9	11	12	13½	15	16
20	0	4	7½	10	12	13½	15	17	18
22	0	4½	8½	11	13	15	16½	18½	20
24	0	5	9	12	14½	16	18	20	22
26	0	5½	10	13	15½	17½	19½	22	23½
28	0	6	10½	14	17	19	21	23½	25
30	0	6½	11	15	18	20½	22½	25	27
35	0	7	13	18	21	24	26	29	32
40	0	8	15	20	24	27	30	34	36
45	0	10	17	23	27	31	34	38	41
50	0	11	19	25	30	34	38	42	45
55	0	12	20	27	33	37	41	46	50
60	0	13	22	30	36	41	45	50	55
70	0	15	26	35	42	48	53	59	63
80	0	17	30	40	48	54	60	67	72

*Flashing-lamp arrangements which give basic flash exposures of less than 16 seconds are not recommended unless accurate timing devices are used, in which case this table can be expanded easily. For example, the times for 14 seconds' basic flash would be ½ those in the 28-second row; the times for 10 seconds' basic flash, ½ those in the 20-second row, etc.

EXPOSURE IN SECONDS

This side of the computer is primarily for determining exposures for making halftone negatives with Kodak contact screens. Other uses include calculating exposure times for color-separation negatives, photographic enlargements, and contact printing.

Before using this computer, it must be calibrated for your individual exposure conditions as described in the instruction booklet.

The other side of the computer is a device for quickly finding exposures of enlarged or reduced images when the same-size exposure is known. This is applicable to linework, continuous-tone copying, and halftone negative-making.

Fig. 9-25. Kodak Graphic Arts Exposure Computer Q-12.

Eastman Kodak Company

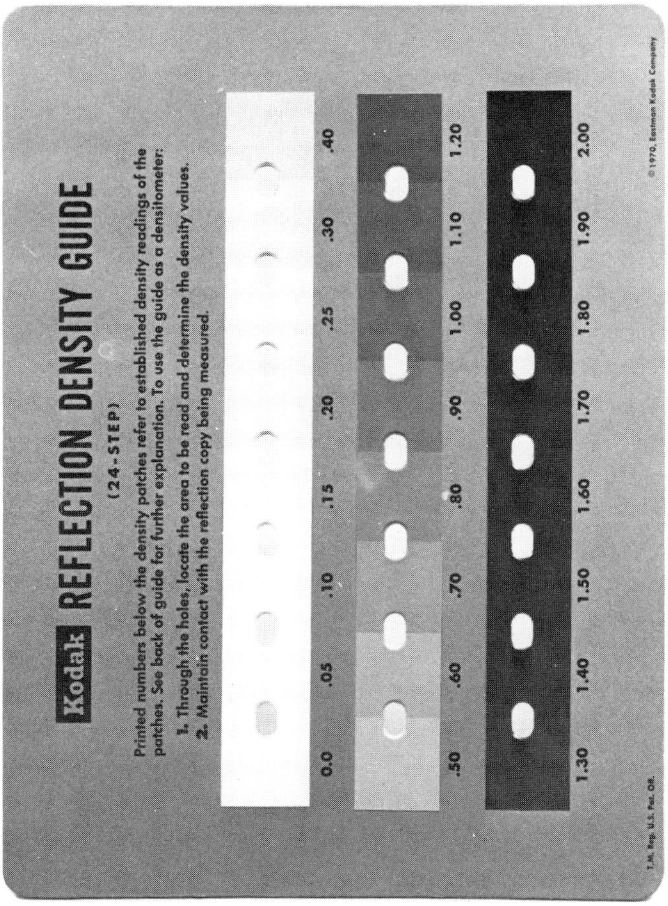

Fig. 9-26. Mount a calibrated-step gray scale on the copyboard.

camera and lens, the camera lighting, the film, the developer, and the processing procedure. Once this calibration is done, it need not be repeated as long as the equipment and conditions remain the same. If conditions change, simply repeat the calibration procedure.

Kodak Graphic Arts Exposure Computer Q-12

• **Note:** This method is suggested for use with cameras equipped with a diaphragm (iris) control. For cameras not so equipped, follow the instructions packaged with the computer.

It is desirable that a *halftone negative exposure worksheet,* such as the one shown in Fig. 9-37, be used in conjunction with this computer as an aid in making calculations and as a record of the procedures used. It is referred to hereafter simply as "the worksheet."

Directions for the calibration and use of this computer are given below. (Additional instructions are contained in the Kodak pamphlet packaged with the computer.) The procedure requires that you make a negative with, first, a *main exposure* and then a series of *flash test exposures.* Proceed as follows:

Making the Main Exposure

1. For the main exposure, mount a calibrated-step gray scale (density guide) on the camera copyboard, as if mounting line copy, Fig. 9-26.
2. Set the camera lensboard (bellows extension) and copyboard extension for 100% reproduction size. Set the lens for 100% on

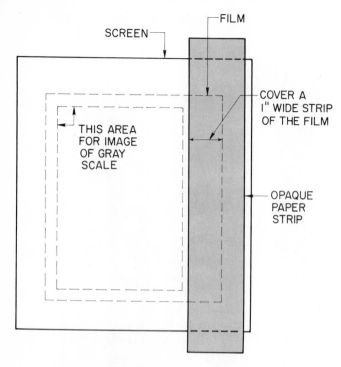

Fig. 9-27. Cover a 1″ width of the film with a strip of opaque paper.

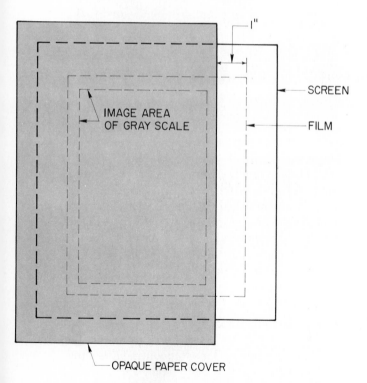

Fig. 9-28. With opaque paper, cover the area of the film-screen setup that received the main exposure. Then, remove the strip of paper from the un-exposed part of the film-screen setup.

the *f*/16 band of the diaphragm control. Adjust the copyboard lights to the proper distance and angle so as to avoid hot spots.

3. On your worksheet, enter 100% as Item 1, and enter *f*/16 as Items 2 and 9.

4. Position a sheet of ortho-type litho film on the vacuum back with the emulsion side toward you, so the emulsion side will later be facing the lens (during exposure).

5. Place the selected contact screen over the film, emulsion side against the film so as to make an emulsion-to-emulsion contact. (Refer back to Fig. 9-4, page 144.) For proper vacuum seal (draw-down), the contact screen should overlap the film on all sides by at least 1″.

> • **Note:** if you are calibrating the computer for use with Kodalith Autoscreen film, *no contact screen* is used in making the test negative.

6. Cover a 1″ width of one edge of the film with a piece of opaque paper taped in place over the film-screen setup, Fig. 9-27.

7. Close the camera back. Make the main exposure with white light reflected from the copyboard, through the lens, then through the screen, and onto the film (Fig. 9-4). For the length of this main exposure, use either:
   a. Two 35-ampere arc lights for 20 seconds; or
   b. *Four times the line exposure with arcs or pulsed-xenon lamps; or*
   c. Six to eight times the line exposure with incandescent lamps.

8. Assuming that a 20-second main test exposure has been made, enter the time as worksheet Item 3.

Without disturbing the film-screen setup, proceed to make the series of flash test exposures described below:

Making the Series of Flash Test Exposures

1. With the *vacuum still on*, open the camera back. In this position, the film-screen setup faces the darkroom flashing lamp. Only the light from the red safelight is on. (Figures 9-22 and 9-31 show the flash exposure setup.)

2. Tape a piece of opaque paper (as a mask) over that part of the film-screen setup that received the main exposure. Then remove the strip of paper covering the unexposed part of the film-screen setup (Fig. 9-28), but do not move anything else. Be sure that the 1″ width of film under the screen is not covered by the mask paper.

3. Divide the 1″ uncovered width of film into 5 equal parts, Fig. 9-29.

4. Cover all but Part 1 with a strip of opaque paper, Fig. 9-30. Give Part 1 a flash exposure of 20 seconds. See Fig. 9-22.

5. Now, with Parts 1 and 2 uncovered, expose for a flash exposure of 10 seconds.

6. With Parts 1, 2 and 3 uncovered, flash for 6 seconds.

7. With Parts 1, 2, 3, and 4 uncovered, flash for 8 seconds.

8. Finally, with the entire strip uncovered, flash for 16 seconds.

9. The individual parts of the width of film will have been exposed for these total lengths: 60, 40, 30, 24, and 16 seconds, as shown in Table 9-4. Enter these total exposures in Item 4 of the worksheet.

Table 9-4
Total Length of Flash Exposures on each of Five Parts of the 1″ Width of Film

Part No.	Exposures in Seconds	Total Exposure in Seconds
1	20 + 10 + 6 + 8 + 16	60
2	10 + 6 + 8 + 16	40
3	6 + 8 + 16	30
4	8 + 16	24
5	16	16

Process the Test Negative

Process the film as recommended by the film manufacturer, using fresh developer with continuous agitation. If subsequent test films are to be processed, use fresh developer for each piece of film. Keep all processing consistent.

Determining the Basic Density Range

1. Examine the gray scale image on the main exposure section of the test negative. This should show an area of the gray scale with

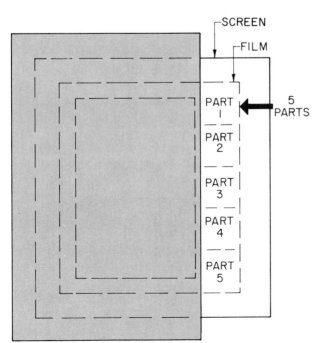

Fig. 9-29.   Divide the strip of film into 5 equal parts.

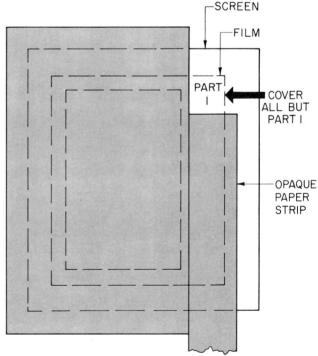

Fig. 9-30.   Cover all but Part 1 with a strip of opaque paper, and "flash" for 20 seconds.

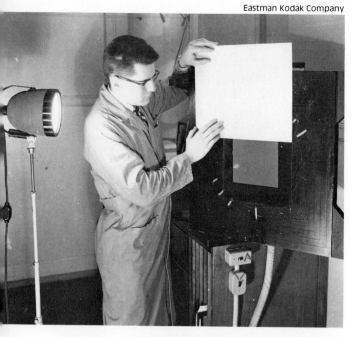

Fig. 9-31. One setup for making the flash exposures on the test negative. The yellow light is exposed directly through a contact screen.

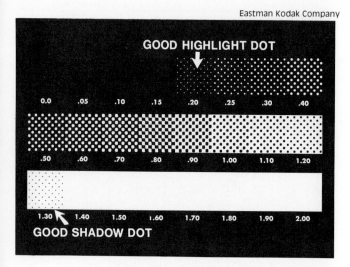

Fig. 9-32. The main exposure portion of the test negative, shown diagrammatically. A satisfactory test negative should have highlight dots that are nearly closed up, as in the .20 step, and shadow dots missing, as in step 1.40.

highlight dots nearly closed up, as in step .20, and an area with shadow dots missing, as in step 1.40. See Fig. 9-32.

2. If your test negative does not show this range of densities, make another negative, this time using a longer or shorter main exposure.

3. Locate the densities of areas where there are both a good highlight dot and a good shadow dot, as pointed out in Fig. 9-32. A good highlight dot is shown at density .20. It is a small, transparent dot with a good dense black background. A good shadow dot is shown at density 1.30. It is a small black dot in a transparent background.

> • **Note:** To read a step gray scale, it is sometimes necessary to estimate between steps in order to determine or to match the desired density.

4. Enter 1.30 and .20 as worksheet Items 5 and 6, respectively.

5. Subtracting the highlight density of .20 (Item 6) from the shadow density of 1.30 (Item 5) results in a *basic density range* of 1.10 for this screen-and-camera setup.

Item 5 — Shadow density of main exposure test negative 1.30

minus

Item 6 — Highlight density of main exposure test negative 20

equals

Items 7 and 15 — Basic density range 1.10

6. Enter the basic density range of 1.10 as worksheet Items 7 and 15.

> • **Note:** The *basic density range* is actually the *density range* of a particular contact screen as used in a particular camera setup. Expressed as a sum, it represents the range of density of original copy that a screen will reproduce as a halftone negative with a single white-light main exposure — without an added flash exposure. Figure 9-32 shows that this screen-camera setup reproduced a range of densities from 1.30 to .20 — a basic density range of 1.10.

Calibrating the Computer

1. Calibrate (set) the computer using these four *values* derived from the test negative procedure and recorded in Section *A* of the worksheet:

    100% reproduction size (Item 1);
    f/16 lens aperture (from Item 2);
    20 seconds main exposure (Item 3); and
    highlight density of .20 (Item 6).

2. Rotate the computer dials, positioning 100% reproduction size opposite the f/16 lens aperture. See A in Fig. 9-33.

3. Holding the bottom dial with one hand so that it will not turn, rotate the red density dial until .20 (highlight) density is positioned opposite the 20-second main exposure time.

4. With a short piece of masking tape, fasten the dials together *and to the base* of the computer, as in *C* of Fig. 9-33. The computer is now calibrated for computing the main exposures for copy of other densities and reproduction sizes. (This assumes one is using a camera equipped with a manual diaphragm control.)

Determining the Basic Flash Exposure

1. Examine the test negative for the series of test flash-exposure results, Fig. 9-34. These are the exposures which were made on the 1″ width of film that was covered during the main exposure.

2. Choose the flash exposure area which has produced a normal shadow dot. Do not necessarily choose the smallest printable dot. Rather, choose the size dot you feel is required for the negative you will make. In this case, the area is chosen that was exposed for 24 seconds, Fig. 9-34. This 24-second exposure is regarded as the *basic flash exposure* for this screen-and-camera setup.

3. Record 24 seconds as worksheet Item 17.

Using the Computer

As an example in using the computer, assume this problem:

Eastman Kodak Company

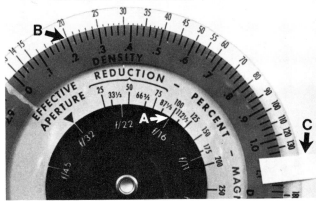

Fig. 9-33.   Setting the Kodak Q-12 computer. Position f/16 aperture opposite 100% reproduction size, as at A. Rotate the top red density dial so that the density of the step which produced a satisfactory highlight dot (.20) is opposite the exposure time (20 seconds) which produced it, as at B. Then, tape the dials together, and to the base, as at C.

Sample Problem

An original photograph has been selected as camera copy. It is to be reproduced as a 150% halftone negative. What are the required lengths of the main (detail) and flash exposures? What is the lens diaphragm setting? What are the lensboard and copyboard settings?

Enter 150% as worksheet Item 8. This will be the size of the halftone negative in the problem. Continue as below:

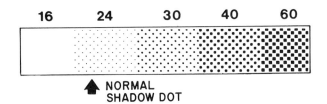

Fig. 9-34.   The area exposed for 24 seconds is our choice of normal shadow dot on the strip of 5 test flash exposures on the test negative.

Determining Highlight and Shadow Densities of the Camera Copy

1. On the original camera copy (the photograph to be reproduced), select and measure the densities of highlight and shadow areas that you consider to be the most suitable. The *highlight area* should be of lightest density, and the *shadow* area of the darkest density. If the copy lacks a suitable highlight area, use the white photo border as the highlight area.

2. Measure these densities with a densitometer, or with the calibration gray scale (reflection density guide). If using the latter, place the gray scale over the copy. Looking through the holes, match a chosen area of the copy with a density patch on the gray scale. Beneath the matching density patches, read density value, Fig. 9-35.

3. Assuming that the copy has a highlight density of .10 and a shadow density of 1.40, enter .10 as worksheet Items 10 and 13; enter 1.40 as Item 12.

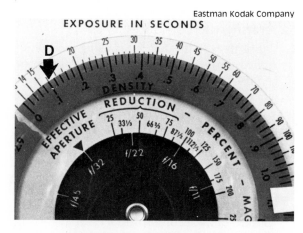

Eastman Kodak Company

Fig. 9-36. Opposite the copy highlight density of .10 on the red "density" scale, read the main exposure of 16 seconds on the outer scale, as at D.

Determining the Main Exposure

The computer has already been calibrated, and the dials have been taped together and to the base.

1. On the computer, locate the highlight density of camera copy .10 on the red *density* scale. Opposite this, on the outer *exposure in seconds* scale, read the main exposure of 16 seconds. See Fig. 9-36.

2. Enter 16 seconds as worksheet Item 11.

Determining the Flash Exposure

1. Using the worksheet, determine the *density range* of the camera copy, as below:

Item 12 — Shadow density of copy . .   1.40
 minus
Item 13 — Highlight density of
 camera copy 10
 equals
Item 14 — Density range of
 camera copy 1.30

2. As shown above, the density range of the camera copy is 1.30. Enter this as worksheet Item 14.

3. Again, using the worksheet, determine the *excess density range* of the camera copy, as follows:

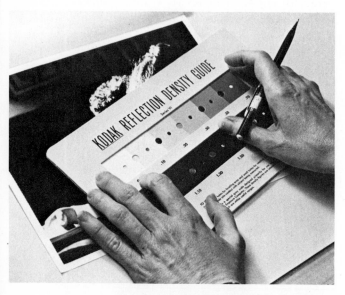

Fig. 9-35. Measuring highlight and shadow densities of the copy. Looking through the holes of the guide, match chosen density areas of the copy with patches on the guide. Beneath the matching density patches, read the printed density values.

Item 14 — Density range of
      camera copy 1.30
                 minus
Item 15 — Basic density range 1.10
                 equals
Item 16 — Excess density range 20

4. The excess density range is .20, as shown above. Enter this as Item 16 on the worksheet.
5. Using the *flash exposure table* printed on the computer, and also shown as Table 9-5, locate the point where the *basic flash exposure* of 24 seconds (Item 17) intersects the *excess density range* of .20 (Item 16), and read the answer — 9 seconds. The required flash exposure for this halftone negative then is 9 seconds. Record this as worksheet Item 18.

Resulting Factors

The extreme right-hand column of the completed worksheet now gives these settings and exposure times for making the halftone negative of the sample problem:

1. Set diaphragm control pointer at 150% on the f/16 scale.
2. Set lensboard and copyboard at 150%.
3. Make a main exposure of 16 seconds.
4. Make a flash exposure of 9 seconds.

Basic Procedure for Making Single-Color Halftone Negative

The following is the basic procedure for making a single-color halftone negative, using a contact screen and the two-part exposure method. Try making one for practice.

For calculating the lengths of the exposures, use the Kodak Graphic Arts Exposure Computer Q-12. Measure densities with the Kodak Reflection Density Guide, the Kodak Calibration Gray Scale, or a densitometer. Also, a copy of the halftone negative computer worksheet, Fig. 9-37, should be used.

Table 9-5
Determining the Length of the Shadow Flash
Exposure Time in Seconds

		Excess Density Range								
		0	0.1	0.2	0.3	0.4	0.5	0.6	0.8	1.0
	16	0	3½	6	8	9½	11	12	13½	14½
	18	0	4	7	9	11	12	13½	15	16
	20	0	4	7½	10	12	13½	15	17	18
	22	0	4½	8½	11	13	15	16½	18½	20
Basic Flash Exposure (seconds)*	24	0	5	9	12	14½	16	18	20	22
	26	0	5½	10	13	15½	17½	19½	22	23½
	28	0	6	10½	14	17	19	21	23½	25
	30	0	6½	11	15	18	20½	22½	25	27
	35	0	7	13	18	21	24	26	29	32
	40	0	8	15	20	24	27	30	34	36
	45	0	10	17	23	27	31	34	38	41
	50	0	11	19	25	30	34	38	42	45
	55	0	12	20	27	33	37	41	46	50
	60	0	13	22	30	36	41	45	50	55
	70	0	15	26	35	42	48	53	59	63
	80	0	17	30	40	48	54	60	67	72

(Eastman Kodak Company)

For example: Where the basic flash exposure of 24 seconds intersects the excess density range of 0.2, read the flash exposure time of 9 seconds — as indicated by the arrow.

*Flashing-lamp arrangements which give basic flash exposures of less than 16 seconds are not recommended unless accurate timing devices are used, in which case this table can be expanded easily. For example, the times for a 14-second basic flash would be ½ those in the 28-second row; the times for 10 seconds, basic flash, ½ those in the 20-second row, etc.

Student _____ Job No. _____

Camera _____ Film _____

Screen Identification _____

Halftone Negative Exposure Worksheet

A. Test Negative

1. Reproduction size of test negative . . . . `100 %`

2. Diaphragm band . . . . `f/ 16`
   (Enter also as Item 9, below)

3. Main exposure . . . . `20`
   seconds

4. Flash test exposures (total exposure on each section)

   | 1. 60 | 2. 40 | 3. 30 | 4. 24 | 5. 16 |

   seconds

5. Shadow density of main exposure test
   negative . . . . `1.30`

6. Highlight density of main exposure
   test negative . . . . `.20`

7. Basic density range of camera/screen (Item 5, less
   Item 6.) Enter also as Item 15, below . . . . `1.10`

B. Main Exposure

Halftone Negative Exposure Factors

8. Reproduction size of required negative
   (Obtain from job specifications) . . . . `150 %`

9. Diaphragm band (Same as Item 2, above) . . . . `f/16` *

10. Highlight density of camera copy
    (Enter also as Item 13, below) . . . . `.10`

11. Main exposure length (Use the computer and
    data from Item 10 to calculate this) . . . . `16`
    seconds

C. Flash Exposure

12. Shadow (maximum) density of camera copy . . . . `1.40`
13. Highlight (minimum) density of
    camera copy (Same as Item 10, above) . . . . `.10`
14. Density range of camera copy
    (Item 12 less Item 13) . . . . `1.30`
15. Basic Density range of camera/screen
    (Same as Item 7, above) . . . . `1.10` *
16. Excess density range (Item 14, less Item 15) . . . . `.20`
17. Basic flash exposure
    (From test negative procedure—
    the chosen flash exposure) . . . . `24` *
    seconds
18. Flash exposure length (Using data from
    Items 16 and 17, and the Flash Table (Table 9-5) . . . . `9`
    seconds

Fig. 9-37. Handwritten entries in the extreme right-hand-column boxes of the Halftone Negative Exposure Worksheet are the factors for making the main and flash exposures for Sample Problem halftone negative.

On worksheets for additional halftone negatives, providing the camera-and-screen setup and exposure conditions remain the same,
1. You need not enter factors for Items 1 through 7; and
2. You can copy data directly from the starred (*) boxes — Items 9, 15, and 17 — on the first completed worksheet.

This form may be reproduced in quantities for your use only.

1. Select the contact screen to be used. It should be at least 1″ larger in width and length than the film which will later be mounted on the film holder of the camera.
2. For your camera copy, select a black-and-white original glossy photograph with good contrast, 4″ × 5″ or 8″ × 10″ in size.
3. From the job specifications determine the required reproduction size (percentage) and enter it on the worksheet.
4. After making a test negative (as previously explained), calibrate and set the halftone computer. Record pertinent factors on your worksheet.
5. Make density readings of selected highlight and shadow areas of the copy. Record these densities on your worksheet.
6. Using the calibrated computer and the data entered on the worksheet, calculate the required lengths of the main and flash exposures. Enter these on your worksheet.
7. Prepare the processing solution trays.
8. Clean the copyboard glass of smudges, fingerprints, and dust.
9. Place the copy in the copyboard. Position the copy upside down on the copyboard so that its image will appear right-side up on the ground glass.
10. Check the angle and distance of the copyboard lights.

> • **Note:** In order to prevent unwanted reflections, do not let overhead lights or window lights strike the camera or the copyboard.

11. With a piece of stiff cardboard, briskly fan dust off the lens surface. Then, on the selected *f*/band of the diaphragm control, set the lens for desired reproduction size.
12. Set the lensboard (bellows) and copyboard extensions for the desired reproduction size.
13. Turn copyboard lights *on*. In the darkroom (with white lights *off* and safelight *on*), focus and adjust for best image and correct size. If "hot spots" intrude on the image, move the copyboard lights outward. Then, turn copyboard lights *off*.

14. Still under safelight conditions only, place a sheet of unexposed orthochromatic litho film on the vacuum back of the camera, and turn on the vacuum. The emulsion side of the film should be toward the operator, and, ultimately, will face the lens during exposure. (The emulsion side of the film is the lighter side. This is easily determined in the darkroom with only the safelight on.)
15. Check that the contact screen is at least an inch larger in each dimension than the film on the vacuum back. Clean the contact screen with a photo chamois. Then, center and place the screen over the film with the emulsion (dull) side of the screen in contact with the film — emulsion-to-emulsion contact. Then, with a soft rubber print roller, roll the screen flat — from the center, outward toward the edges.

> • **Note:** Be sure the screen is parallel to the sides of the vacuum back, so that the screen pattern will be at the proper 45° angle. To insure closest contact between the film and screen, it is recommended that a camera with a vacuum back be used.

16. Close the camera back and make the main exposure. This exposure is made with white light *reflected from the copyboard*, through the lens, and through the screen onto the film.
17. Now, with the safelight and the camera-back vacuum still *on*, open the camera back. Without disturbing the film and screen setup, position the camera back so the film-and-screen setup is at a 90° angle to the flashing lamp.
18. Make the flash exposure. This exposure is made with yellow light directed from the flashing lamp straight to the film-and-screen setup. This light is *not* reflected from the copy on the copyboard.
19. Carefully remove the screen and store it in its box.
20. Remove the film and shut off the vacuum.
21. Process the film. (See Chapter 11, beginning page 201.)
22. Evaluate the negative. (See page 171.)

Kodak Halftone Negative Computer Q-15

The Q-12 Computer that has been discussed is a "general" exposure computer. This means that when determining basic exposures for halftone negatives the computer does not make allowances for certain factors.

When a halftone negative is made with gray contact screens, the flash exposure will somewhat change the middletones. The Q-12, which treats the exposures as independent, cannot be calibrated to overcome this situation. The problem may be solved by use of the Kodak Halftone Negative Computer Q-15, an instrument more accurate than most electronic computers.

To understand the built-in highlighting effect of the Q-15, it is necessary to examine its parts, Fig. 9-38. Note the large M inside the triangle. This is part of the main exposure dial. It points to the density values on the density-of-copy scale. The main exposure dial has a window that displays basic exposure times. At the lower left of the illustration is the main exposure tab. It lies beneath the main exposure dial. The tab is used to place a *basic* main exposure time in the main exposure window. Beginning in the lower right of the figure is the basic quadrant flash dial, which is divided into basic exposure times. To determine the actual flash exposure

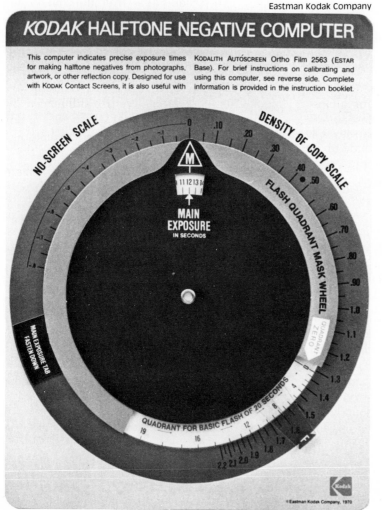

Fig. 9-38.   Kodak Halftone Negative Computer Q-15.

times, pointer F is used. The small arrows located on the quadrant dial are known as correction arrows. They permit adjustment of the *basic* main and flash exposures.

The Q-15 has two scales. The first of these is the density-of-copy scale mentioned above. It is used in setting up the computer. The scale ranges from 0 (white) to 2.2 (very dark). In the upper left of the figure is the no-screen scale used to calculate unscreened "bump" exposures.

As with the Q-12, this computer must be calibrated to the exposure and processing conditions of each particular shop.

The Q-15 will compensate for the effect of flash exposure on the middletones and highlights of negatives. When exposure is added to the highlights when flashing the negative, time must be subtracted from the main exposure. To allow for calculation of a shorter main exposure to offset the flash exposure, the correction arrows are used with pointers M and F.

This computer may also be calibrated so as to show middletone dot placement for almost any copy requirements. For more descriptive information on use of the Q-15, consult the appropriate Kodak publications.

Advent of computers has greatly added to efficiency of exposure calculations. Range of error for exposures is, by nature, quite narrow. Previously, if halftones were to be made from pictures with differing tone distributions, the camera operator had to experiment. Even then, the desired effect was not always achieved. This trial and error process was costly in terms of time and money. With the Q-15 (and to a somewhat lesser extent with the Q-12), accurate exposure times may be determined for different types of copy. These calculations will remain valid from day-to-day unless shop conditions change.

Evaluating the Negative

Ideally, a halftone negative should produce a plate which will print a reproduction as nearly like the original photo as possible. On the press, as the plate picks up ink and the soft blanket exerts pressure, the printed highlight dots tend to get larger and the printed shadow dots tend to fill in or plug up a bit. This dot spread also occurs in making duplicate negatives or positives and in platemaking.

The best halftone has no pure white, or pure black. Rather, the best range is from near white to near black. The generally satisfactory halftone negative should have shadow areas (lightest areas) of dots ranging in size from tiny 10% black pinpoints to dots about 25% to 30%. On the printed sheets, shadow areas reproduce as black with tiny white pinpoints or sometimes as solid black areas.

The highlight areas on the negative (darkest areas) should have about a 90% dot, so as to reproduce about a 10% dot on the printed sheet. Sometimes a smaller printed dot is preferable.

The mid-tones should range smoothly from about a 35% dot to a 70% dot. The characteristic checkerboard pattern should be in the center of the range.

In judging the negative, remember that the dots should be black — not brown. Also, the black dots on the negative are influenced by the amount of reflected light which strikes the film.

If the main exposure is too long, the dark areas tend to close up, thus making the pinpoint transparent dots disappear. Therefore, for *larger* transparent dots in the highlight area of the negative, *shorten* the main exposure. For a denser negative highlight area with *smaller* transparent dots, *increase* the main exposure.

To *add* black dots or to *increase* their size in the clear shadow areas of the negative, *increase* the flash exposure. For *smaller* shadow dots, decrease the flash exposure.

Remember that the main exposure controls the size of the highlight dots. The flash exposure governs the size of the shadow dots.

When film is developed under standard conditions and with fresh developer, the image should begin to appear in about 30 to 40 seconds. A shorter period than that indicates overexposure; a longer one, underexposure. Exposure should be such that the negative can remain in the developer for close to the recommended 2¾ minutes. However, if the dot size is inspected with a magnifier during the last few seconds, some correction can be made in devel-

oping time. A longer period gives smaller highlight dots and may allow brownish shadow dots
to turn black so they will print. Remember to
expose for the highlights and *flash for the
shadows.*

Controlling Contrast
with Contact Screens

There are several satisfactory ways of controlling contrast with contact screens.

1. The *shadow flash exposure* technique is the
   simplest.
2. *Still development* of the film will lower contrast while improving definition.

Fig. 9-39. Magnifiers shown are (A) linen tester, (B) tri-
pod magnifier, (C) swivel desk-stand magnifier,
(D) pen-clip pocket microscope, and (E) swivel
magnifier.

3. The *magenta contact screens* can be used
   with filters (yellow for lower contrast and
   magenta for higher contrast).
4. The *highlighting* (no screen, or bump) exposure method can be used to increase highlight contrast or even drop out highlight
   dots. In this method, an additional highlighting image exposure is made *without the
   screen.*

   For example: With only the film in place
   (*no screen*), the camera back is closed, and
   the highlighting (bump) exposure of the image is made. Light is reflected from the copy
   on the copyboard, through the lens, and onto
   the film. Then, the camera back is opened,
   the screen is placed in position over the film,
   and the main and flash exposures are made.

   This highlight exposure of the copy without the screen adds light selectively — a lot
   to the highlights, less to the midtones, and
   almost none to the shadows. The highlight
   exposure is usually 5% to 10% of the main
   exposure. If a highlight exposure is used,
   shorten the main exposure by the length of
   the highlight exposure.

Making a Negative from a Halftone Print

When an original glossy print of a photograph is not available for use as camera copy,
sometimes it is necessary to reproduce an
already printed halftone picture.

Shooting as Line Copy

Because a *halftone print* (a printed halftone
picture) is composed of solid dots and areas
which differ in size but not in tone, it may
actually be treated as camera line copy. That
is, a halftone negative may be made from it
without the use of a screen in the camera. The
screen pattern will be picked up from the copy
(dot for dot), provided that this ruling is not extremely fine or indistinct.

Halftone prints often are pasted up on a
mechanical along with other line copy, such as
type matter. The page then is shot as line copy
on one piece of film. Figure 7-2, page 109, was
produced from a number of pasted-up halftone
prints and then shot as line copy.

Of course, enlarging or reducing a halftone print will result in a correspondingly coarser or finer screen pattern or ruling. For example, if a newspaper halftone print which has a screen ruling of 65 lines per inch is reduced 50%, the resulting print will have a ruling of about 130 lines to the inch. Rulings reduced much finer than 150 lines per inch tend to plug, and so may be difficult to print.

A change in the screen ruling may or may not be objectionable, depending upon the original screen ruling and upon the intended use of the resulting printed piece. One way to avoid objectionable change in fineness or coarseness of screen pattern is to photograph the halftone print at same size and then crop the negative to the dimensions needed for the illustration.

Rescreening

Reproduction of a printed halftone illustration sometimes will involve a large reduction in size or will have screen patterns which are indistinct (or extremely fine). In such cases, the halftone print is photographed through a screen (or *rescreened*).

Occasionally, the dot pattern of the screen used in the camera may not exactly match the dot pattern on the print. This mismatching may result in a disturbing pattern on the negative, which is very evident and unacceptable. This is called *moiré* — pronounced "maw-RAY". See Fig. 9-40. Moiré may be avoided by any of the following methods:

1. A screen which has a ruling either 50 lines per inch finer or 50 lines per inch coarser than the screening on the original (at its new size) may be used.
2. In order to minimize the pattern when a screen is used, the copy or screen should be placed so that the resulting angle is 30° greater than that of the original. If the original angle was 45°, the one of the new print should be 75°.
3. The printed halftone may be enlarged, air-brushed, and then shot as an original photograph.
4. The original may be reduced greatly (to less than 40%), thus causing the original screen to drop out.
5. A clean piece of glass or clear film may be held before the lens and tilted back and forth during exposure.

Fig. 9-40. Moiré is an objectionable halftone dot pattern caused by faulty rescreening of an already screened halftone illustration. (This illustration actually is the accidental result of using a contact screen over an Autoscreen film.)

Theory

Unlike most films, Autoscreen film is not equally sensitive to light throughout its emulsion surface. Instead, the emulsion is composed of thousands of light-sensitive areas, each most acutely sensitive at its center. The same result is achieved on Autoscreen film as on other films exposed through a glass or contact screen. A weak exposure from the dark areas of the original produces an image only in the most sensitive portions of the emulsion, which are at the centers of the dots. A stronger exposure from the middle tones exposes less sensitive areas also, thus producing larger dots. With a maximum exposure from the highlights, an image is formed in all but small areas.

Advantages

Because no separate screen obstructs light from the film's emulsion, because the film has great sensitivity, and because the exposed Autoscreen negatives are processed by still development, Autoscreen film can record finer detail than other halftone processes. Another advantage is that type matter and original photographs can be shot at the same time on the same sheet of film without producing an objectionable screen pattern in the type matter. A third advantage is that Autoscreen film can be loaded into a *conventional view camera* to directly yield halftone negatives by photographing original subjects (or copy) at the scene, using a time exposure of several seconds.

Exposure

Two exposures are made: a main white-light exposure, based upon the highlight density of the subject (or copy), and a flash exposure to control contrast. The flash exposure is made at 6 feet, using a safelight filter Series OA (greenish yellow) and a 60-watt bulb. Usually, an exposure to such a light requires about 20 seconds. Detailed instructions for exposing and processing Autoscreen film are packaged with the film.

Figure 9-41 shows the highlight and shadow dots on a typical Autoscreen negative, as seen under an 8x magnifier. Highlight dots are about 95 percent, and the shadow dots are about 10 percent. Variations in dot sizes may be better for specific conditions.

Although main and flash exposures may be determined experimentally, it is strongly recommended that both exposure times be determined in the same manner as described previously for the white-light plus flash technique (the method used in making halftones with the contact screen) using the Kodak Graphic Arts Exposure Computer Q-12. *Do not use a halftone screen in the camera when making the test negatives.* Remember to use an OA (greenish-yellow) filter in the flashing lamp.

Using the computer, make the main test exposures on a single sheet of Autoscreen film. Calibrate the computer and then determine the exposure times. Remember to expose for the highlights and flash for the shadows.

• **Note:** The test flash exposures can be made on a separate piece of the Autoscreen film, providing you use fresh developer and the same processing procedure as for the main exposure test film.

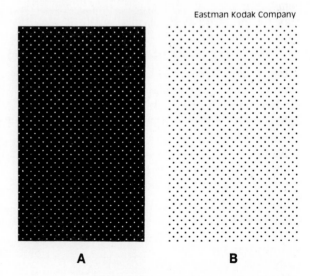

Eastman Kodak Company

A   B

Fig. 9-41.   Highlight and shadow dots, as seen on a typical Autoscreen negative, under an 8x magnifier.
A. Highlight dots are about 95%.
B. Shadow dots are about 10%.

Making Halftones with an Autoscreen Film

Through the use of Kodalith Autoscreen Ortho Film, highly satisfactory halftone negatives may be made without the use of a halftone glass or contact screen. Autoscreen film is very similar to other litho films, except that it has a dot pattern of 133 lines per inch built right into the emulsion. Thus, when the film is exposed and developed, it automatically produces a halftone negative.

Processing

The exposed Autoscreen film can be developed either by the *inspection* method or by the *time-and-temperature* method. (For complete information on these methods, see Chapter 11 on film developing.) For best results, the still-development technique described below should be employed.

Develop each negative in fresh Kodalith developer, using 1 part A, 1 part B, and 1 part water, at 20° C (68° F). Use a Wratten Series 1A (light red) safelight filter in a suitable safelight holder with a 15-watt bulb, at no less than 4 feet. Do not turn on the safelight until the film has been in the developer for 1½ minutes.

Whichever method of developing is used, remember that the dot quality of the negative may be impaired if the film is exposed to the safelight for a *total time longer than 3 minutes.*

Inspection Method. Use a white enamel tray for reflecting the light of the safelight from the bottom of the tray. Do not turn on the safelight until the film has been in the developer for 1½ minutes.

Agitate the developer vigorously for a few seconds. Immerse the film, and again agitate the developer for 2 minutes. Then allow the film to lie perfectly still in the bottom of the tray. Inspect at frequent intervals. *Total* developing time should be about 2¾ minutes for normal developing.

Time-and-Temperature Method. Develop for 2¾ minutes at 20° C (68° F.) employing constant agitation.

Further Processing. After developing, rinse the negative in the stop bath for 10 seconds, agitating continuously. Then fix, with *continuous agitation,* for 2 to 4 minutes or for twice the time that it takes for the film to clear. Finally, wash about 10 minutes in running water 18 to 20° C (65° to 70° F.).

To minimize drying marks, treat the negatives in Photo-Flo solution after washing, or wipe surfaces carefully with a photo chamois, a soft viscose sponge, a rubber squeegee or other soft squeegee (such as a windshield wiper blade). Then hang the negatives to dry in a dust-free place.

Originals Containing Type Matter

Type matter can be exposed together with pictures without the usual loss of legibility caused by the screening of fine lines. The detail exposure should be sufficient to close up the highlight dots in the white background of the type, and the flash exposure should be such as to give normal dots in the shadows of the picture area, Fig. 9-41. If special prints are to be made for combination with type matter, the highlights of the pictures should be slightly darker than the white paste-up paper or the paper on which the type is printed.

Duotones

A duotone is a halftone printed in two colors. Although it usually is made from a black-and-white photograph, it involves some of the techniques of color printing and so will be illustrated in the next chapter. The principal negative, usually printed in black or in a very deep color, is exposed and processed for nearly normal contrast, but it favors detail in the shadow end of the scale and has only sketchy highlights. The second negative, usually printed in a lighter color, must have the screen angled 30° to the first. It favors detail at the high end of the scale, so usually is lighter. Some duotones are printed black on black, so as to use a double layer of ink to increase the density range of the printed copy.

Questions

1. Which of the following pieces of artwork must be reproduced by the halftone process if it is to be reproduced by offset printing?

   a. Charcoal drawing
   b. Snapshot of a person
   c. Proof of handset type or phototype
   d. Portrait in oils
   e. Pen-and-ink map
   f. Typewritten page

2. Describe a halftone contact screen. During the making of a halftone negative, where is the contact screen placed?
3. What is meant when it is said that the screen and the film are in "emulsion-to-emulsion contact"?
4. Which tonal areas of the copy will reflect the most light? Which areas will produce tiny opaque dots?
5. What is the usual screen angle for shooting black-and-white halftones?
6. Describe two devices or instruments for measuring density.
7. Give the steps in the making of a single-color halftone negative.
8. What is the physical setup for making a main exposure? For making a flash exposure?
9. Why are exposures longer for halftone negatives than for line negatives?
10. After making a test negative, how do you compute the basic density range?
11. How is the density range of the camera copy computed?
12. Why should the screen be larger in dimensions than the film over which it is placed?
13. How would you increase the size of transparent dots in the highlight areas of a negative?
14. What is the procedure for increasing the size of black dots in the shadow areas of a negative?
15. When a printed halftone illustration is rescreened, what might be the cause of a resulting moiré pattern?
16. How does Autoscreen film differ from other litho film?

Problems and Projects

1. Use a magnifying glass to examine a halftone print or negative which was made with a coarse screen. Make a sketch of the shape of the dots in the highlight area, the midtone area, and the shadow area.
2. Make a satisfactory test negative, using a piece of average halftone copy assigned by the instructor. Prepare a wall chart showing the camera setup and exposure conditions which proved satisfactory for the main exposure:

   a. Angle of lights.
   b. Distance of lights (if adjustable).
   c. Bellows extension setting.
   d. Copyboard extension setting.
   e. Screen identification — type, ruling, etc.
   f. Diaphragm f-band and percentage setting (or f-number of lens).
   g. Length of main exposure.

3. Make a diagram of the setup for the flash exposure used in 2, above, Show:
   a. Distance of flashing lamp.
   b. Wattage of lamp.
   c. Series and color of flashing lamp filter.
   d. Length of the basic flash exposure for the setup in 2, above.
4. Prepare a list of steps for making a halftone negative, using a main and a flash exposure. Mount this on the wall near the camera.
5. Prepare satisfactory halftone negatives, using main and flash exposures. Keep a record of all computations and exposures made.
6. Prepare a display of printed halftone samples or clippings from newspapers, magazines, and advertising pieces. Label each with the screen ruling and other pertinent information — kind of screen dot, etc. Include examples of screened type and process color work.
7. Compile a list of tools, equipment, supplies, and materials needed for halftone photography. Using the shop catalogs, prepare a purchase requisition. Include prices, specifications, and quantities.
8. Make a satisfactory halftone negative from (a) a coarse-screened already printed halftone illustration, and (b) from a fine-screen already printed halftone illustration.

New Terms

bump exposure
calibrate
characteristic curve
checkerboard
circular screen
color-blind film
continuous-tone
cyan
draw-down
duotone
film speed
flash exposure

flexible
gamma
highlight
illusion
incident light
key points
litho film
magenta
main exposure
mid-tones
moiré

orthochromatic
panchromatic
prescreened
processing
reflectance
reflection density
sensitometry
shadow dot
two-part method
transmission density
wedge spectrogram

Chapter 10 Color Reproduction

Printing in colors (other than black and white) adds eye appeal and realism to the reproduction. The two main classes of color printing are flat color, Fig. 10-23, and process color printing, Fig. 10-18.

In *flat color printing* part of the type, part of the ornamentation or illustration, or a background tint are reproduced in color. Care should be taken not to use too much color in this type of color printing.

Process color printing, as in Fig. 10-4, reproduces an illustration in the full, original hues. It does this by overprinting halftones for each of the subtractive primary colors — yellow, magenta, and cyan — as well as one for black. See Fig. 10-15.

Color

Color is a visual sensation which occurs when light rays of varying wavelengths reach the eye. Without light, there is no color. Some aspects of light are examined here to help you understand how light creates the sensation of color.

Light

Natural light is produced by the sun's heat and is transmitted to earth in a wave form, Fig. 10-1. A bundle of rays is often referred to as a "beam" of light. The wavelengths of light rays are measured from one wave crest to the next. They are measured in millimicrons (mμ) or in Angstrom units (A^0 or A.U.). One millimicron equals one millionth of a millimeter. One Angstrom unit equals one-tenth of a millimicron, or one ten-millionth of a millimeter.

These rays are identical in all respects, except that they differ in wavelength, Fig. 10-2. Only a very narrow band of these rays is visible in the form of light. These are the rays whose wavelengths measure between 400 and 700 millimicrons (4000 and 7000 Angstrom units) in length, Fig. 10-3.

Demonstration.

With the aid of a prism, a beam of natural (white) light can be spread out into a visible spectrum, Fig. 10-4. The colors of the spectrum gradually blend into each other — violet, blue, green, yellow, orange, and red.

From the demonstration, then, it is evident that projected light is a combination of all the spectrum colors. Usually these basic colors are shown with the various hues around a closed circle (or polygon), as in Fig. 10-5.

Color Sensitivity to Light Sources

Color is sensitive to light sources under various conditions. The temperature of a light source, for instance, affects the spectral quality of the light given off. Also, if there is a loss in voltage to camera or to printing lights, the normally emitted white light may become undesirably reddish, with a resulting adverse effect on length of exposures and colors transmitted. As a protection, camera or printing light systems

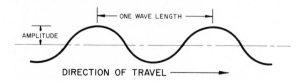

Fig. 10-1.   A ray of light travels in a wave motion.

should include a constant-voltage device. Usually, standardized daylight-fluorescent bulbs are used wherever colors are being checked or matched.

One of the most dramatic examples of the effects of light source occurs in the darkroom. Under the red illumination of the safelights, red, yellow and white all appear the same color, and greens appear to be black.

The human eye automatically adjusts to the more common of the color effects caused by varying light sources. However, films do not make these adjustments.

How We See Color

Color is nonexistent as a substance in itself. The sun or a lighted lamp appears to be a certain color because of the variety of wavelengths of light rays which it transmits to the eyes (or to a *spectrophotometer* — a device for measuring the brightness of the various portions of the spectrum).

A "white" lamp, when it is turned on, appears white. This is because it is transmitting

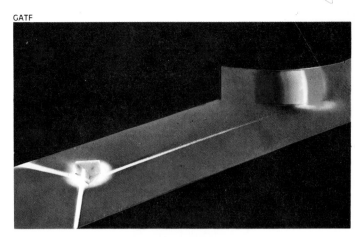

Fig. 10-4. Prism spreading white light.

When light, traveling in air, enters a more dense medium such as glass or water, it is refracted or bent to a new line of travel. The refractive index indicates the amount of bending — more dense media have higher indexes. This explains why a pole stuck into water appears bent. Glass lenses refract light to focus an image at a point. However, prisms and simple lenses refract the shorter wavelengths more than the longer wavelengths, so the prism above can spread out a narrow beam of light into a visible spectrum. Camera lenses tend to focus different colors at different points, unless color performance is corrected by the incorporation of several types of glass into a lens having several elements.

Some of the light hitting a lens or prism is reflected without entering the surface — note the beam extending toward the bottom of the picture above. Coatings on the surface of a lens minimize the light lost by reflection.

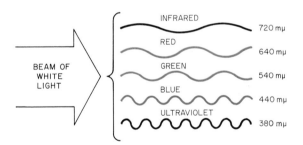

Fig. 10-2. White light has rays of many wavelengths.

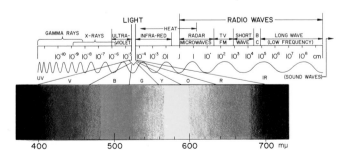

Fig. 10-3. Electromagnetic spectrum with visible portion enlarged.

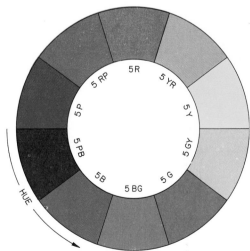

Fig. 10-5. "Hue" is the name of the color as it is identified on the color circle, such as red, blue, yellow, or green.

or radiating wavelengths of white light (which include all basic colors of the spectrum).

• **Note:** The term "apparent color" is sometimes used. For example, if an object appears red to the eye, it is said that the apparent color is red.

This same white light, when transmitted, for instance, through a red glass, causes the glass to appear red. The pigment in the glass transmits to the eye only those wavelengths of light in the red range of the spectrum. It absorbs wavelengths of all other colors.

Red printed areas on white paper have the apparent color of red because the ink and paper together reflect only those wavelengths of light in the red range of the spectrum. They absorb all other wavelengths. The unprinted portions of the white paper have the apparent color of white because the white paper reflects to the eye only wavelengths of white light.

• **Note:** It can be seen from the above that the color and finish of the paper being printed upon can have an important effect on the apparent color of the ink image.

Fig. 10-6. **Why is the tomato or glass of juice red? The pigment in both absorbs green and blue light but not red. Opaque objects reflect the unabsorbed light. Transparent objects transmit the unabsorbed light straight on through. In either case, only the light which is not absorbed is seen.**

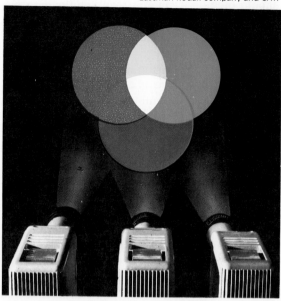

Fig. 10-7.   Additive mixtures of colored light.

These facts, then, are evident: (1) Except for an original source of illumination, color is apparent in an object only when that object *transmits* (allows light to pass through) or *reflects* light to the eyes, and (2) the *reflected* or *transmitted* apparent color (that which is seen) depends upon the wavelengths of the rays of light which reach the eyes because of the *transmittance* of a viewed transparent object or the *reflectance* of a viewed opaque object, Fig. 10-6.

Color Mixing

All color mixing can be described by either of two processes: *additive* color mixing and *subtractive* color mixing.

Additive Color Mixture

In an additive color mixture, light rays of certain colors are added to other light rays to produce (add up to) a new color. The additive primary colors are blue light, red light, and green light. A *primary* color is a basic one which cannot be made by mixing other colors.

If three projectors are set up, as in Fig. 10-7, one with a blue filter, one with a red filter, and one with a green filter, three circles of projected light are produced on the screen — blue, red and green. At the center, where the three projected circles of light overlap, the effect is white. (Blue, red and green light, mixed in the proper proportions, produces white light.) Where the blue circle of light overlaps the red circle of light, the resulting projected color of light is *magenta*; red light and green light overlapping results in *yellow* light; and green and blue light results in *cyan* light. This summation is then evident:

blue light	+ red light	=	magenta light
red light	+ green light	=	yellow light
green light	+ blue light	=	cyan light
blue light	+ red light		
	+ green light	=	white light
lack of any light		=	black

Magenta, yellow, and cyan are each a *complementary color* of one of the primary colors of light: green, blue and red, respectively. Complementary colors are opposites on the color wheel.

Primary	Corresponding Complementary
green	magenta (blue + red)
blue	yellow (red + green)
red	cyan (green + blue)

When each complementary color of light is mixed with its corresponding primary color of light, the mixture will be neutralized. That is, it will form white:

green + magenta (blue + red) = white light
blue + yellow (red + green) = white light
red + cyan (green + blue) = white light

The color formed by adding the individual beams of light is brighter than each of the components.

• **Note:** Additive light principles, discussed above, should be thoroughly understood, since the terms and principles are the foundation for process color separation.

Subtractive Color Mixture

In a subtractive color mixture, white light interacts with a colorant — in an ink, a dye, a pigment, or a filter, for example — which *subtracts* (absorbs or filters out) some of the colors from the white light and allows the unabsorbed

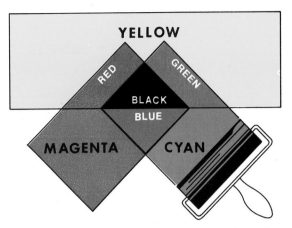

Fig. 10-8. **Transparent inks subtract from the reflectance of the paper. Paper reflects most of the light waves, causing it to appear white. Black ink reflects almost no light.**

colors to be seen by the eye. Each color formed by subtraction is not as bright as the original.

The principal subtractive primary colors of pigments are magenta, yellow and cyan. These are the names which identify the three colors of the transparent inks used in process color printing.

Figure 10-8 illustrates the subtractive method of mixing colored pigments. Three patches of transparent process color inks (magenta, yellow, and cyan) have been printed on white paper so that they overlap. Where a pair of the primary colors of pigments overlap, a complementary color is produced:

magenta ink	+ yellow ink	=	red
yellow ink	+ cyan ink	=	green
cyan ink	+ magenta ink	=	blue
magenta ink	+ yellow ink		
	+ cyan ink	=	black

Green, blue and red, respectively, are the subtractive complementary colors of yellow, cyan, and magenta transparent process inks.

Filter Action

A filter will transmit light of its own color and will absorb light rays of most other colors. For example, in Fig. 10-9, when white light (containing all colors) strikes the red filter, only those rays of the red wavelengths pass through. All rays of other wavelengths are absorbed, or blocked.

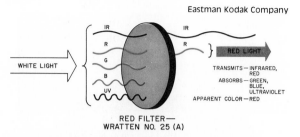

Eastman Kodak Company

Fig. 10-9. Filters subtract part of the light.

The blue filter transmits blue light and absorbs green and red light (yellow light). The resulting negative then is most opaque in blue areas and least dense (nearly clear) in green and red areas. The printing plate made from this, in turn, carries yellow ink in areas to be colored green or red (or yellow, which is their spectral combination). If screened, the halftone dots produce tones of yellow. Therefore, the blue filter produces the yellow printer, and the filter may be called *minus-yellow*.

In a similar manner, the green filter transmits green light and absorbs blue and red light (magenta light) — and may be called *minus-magenta*. The red filter transmits red light and absorbs green and blue light (cyan light), and may be called *minus-cyan*.

Stated another way: A filter will absorb its complementary color of light.

Figure 10-10 shows the portions of the spectrum range which the red, green and blue filters each transmit.

> • **Note:** In selecting filters for use in color separation photography, be sure to follow the recommendations of the film manufacturer for the particular process being employed.

> • **Note:** Since filters thus absorb some of the incident light, exposures through filters should be increased over normal "no filter" exposures. Relative increases in exposures (filter factors) may be determined experimentally or obtained from filter data books.

In color separation photography, three filters usually are used — a blue, a green, and a red, each for a separate exposure. This results in three separation negatives for making the plates which are to print the three colors of process inks — yellow, magenta, and cyan. A fourth printing — in black — may also be used.

> • **Note:** See also "Process Color Reproduction," pages 184-185, and Fig. 10-15.

How Inks Reproduce Color

A film of transparent or opaque printing ink appears colored because its particles of pigment absorb light selectively. Assume for this discussion that a red ink is composed of a finely ground, red-glass pigment suspended in a vehicle, such as linseed oil.

Transparent Inks

Refer to Fig. 10-11. If the refractive index* of the vehicle in the experimental ink is the same as that of the pigment, a beam of incident light will pass freely through the vehicle. The beam will reach the red-pigment particles which will absorb from the white light all colors other than red. They will transmit the red rays through to the surface of the white paper. The

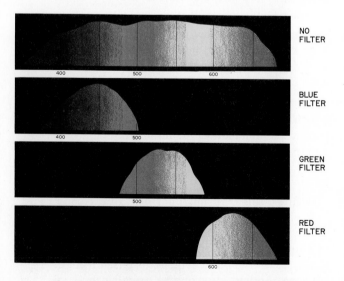

Fig. 10-10. Separation filters make panchromatic films sensitive to various sections of the spectrum.

* For brief explanation of refractive index, see Fig. 10-4.

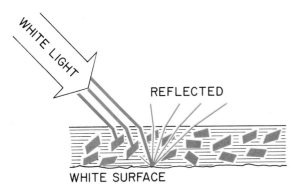

Fig. 10-11. Transparent red ink.

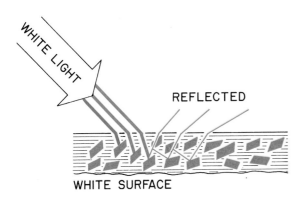

Fig. 10-12. Opaque red ink.

red rays will reflect back from the paper surface, giving the apparent color of red. However, if the surface below is such that it *will not* reflect the light rays, the resulting apparent color will not be red, but black.

If, in another instance, a transparent yellow ink is superimposed on a transparent blue ink, the subtractive effect produces an apparent green color. By overprinting with selected combinations of cyan, magenta, and yellow process inks, most colors can be reproduced.

Opaque Inks

Refer to Fig. 10-12. If the particles of the red-glass pigment have a higher index of refraction than that of the vehicle in the ink, reflection of the incident light rays will occur at every boundary between the pigment and the vehicle. All the red light rays will be reflected without striking the paper. Rays of light other than the reds will be absorbed.

With opaque inks, the color of the light that is reflected from the *printed image surface* depends very little on the color of the paper or on other colors printed under it. Opaque inks are required for true colors on colored paper or overprints. The apparent color of opaque inks is more constant than that of transparent inks when the amount of ink varies during a press run.

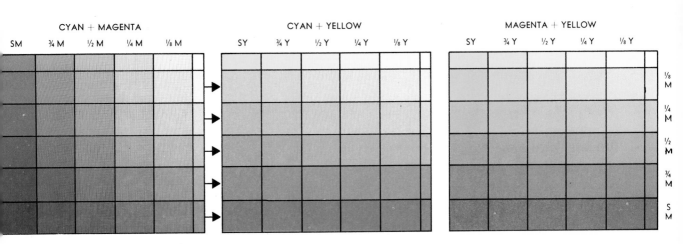

Fig. 10-13. Two-color combinations of process ink hues.

Combining Ink Colors

Either transparent or opaque inks may be mixed prior to printing so as to produce new colors according to the subtractive color theory. Mixing a second color to the first color can only *subtract* from the reflected light, thus producing another color.

Varying the size of the halftone dots with which any hue of ink is printed will vary the value, or tone, of that color. Note in Fig. 10-13 that if the cyan halftone dots cover 100% of the area, the effect is full-color value. A 50% dot size will lessen the value in that area. By varying the proportions of each color when overprinting, new hues can be produced. Figure 10-13 shows the range of hues available in two-color overprints of the primary colors of process inks, using various tones of each color. A tone of cyan produced by an approximate 25%-dot area is labeled "¼C". A solid tone of magenta is labeled "SM", and so on. Such a chart is very useful when producing artwork or selecting screen tints for color printing. For example, on the basis of this chart, the color "blue" in the illustrations for this chapter was produced by overprinting a solid cyan and a 25% magenta. The two-color overprints are most valuable for determining the best combinations to produce the key colors of R, O, Y, G, B, and V.

White and Black

The "colors" white and black are not really visible colors. White is the full reflection of visible rays of light of all wavelengths (all colors of light combined). Grays are the partial reflection of waves which can neutralize each other. Black is the total absorption by an object of all wavelengths of light — that is, the *absence* of color sensation.

Process Color Reproduction

You have already learned how process inks can produce a broad range of colors, Fig. 10-13. Now you will learn how a colored photograph or painting can be separated into its three component primary colors, so that the tones of each single primary are recorded as a halftone negative on monochromatic film. After this negative is made, the rest of the printing process is much like reproducing black-and-white halftones, except that colored inks are used and a much higher degree of quality control is required throughout.

The three colors of process inks are yellow, magenta and cyan. Carefully controlled tones of each are printed from separate plates in perfect register to produce the composite reproduction of the original color copy. While these three primaries theoretically should reproduce the full range of colors, usually a fourth plate, printed in black ink, also is used. The black serves to:

1. increase the density range,
2. improve shadow detail, and
3. make control of the other three colors less critical as to ink balance.

It is impossible here to give a complete description of the many procedures for process color reproduction. It is hoped, however, that this introduction will give the reader enough of an insight into the process so as to better understand its principles, be induced to study it further, and perhaps even undertake some elementary process color reproduction.

Materials and methods in the field of process color reproduction constantly are being researched and improved. The reader is advised to seek detailed and up-to-date information from the published materials of such organizations as the Graphic Arts Technical Foundation, the Eastman Kodak Co., the Gevaert Co. of America, or the Photo Products Division of DuPont.

Copy for Color Reproduction

Camera copy for process color reproduction may be *reflection copy* (on an opaque base) or *transparent copy* (which must be viewed and copied with transmitted light). Transparent copy has a much wider range of density and color values, so color separation techniques are somewhat different. Since printing inks have neither the density range nor the color purity of photographic materials, some adjustments must be made.

Reflection copy includes such items as watercolor paintings, oil paintings, casein paintings, pastel drawings, colored crayon drawings, carbro prints, dye-transfer prints, color photoprints, or hand-colored photographs, in almost any size.

Transparent copy includes such items as slides or transparencies on reversal (positive) color film (Kodachrome, Ektachrome, Anscochrome, etc.) or on negative color film (Kodacolor, Ektacolor, etc.), from 35mm to 8″ × 10″ (or even larger) in size.

Types of Process Color Separations

There are two basic procedures for making color separations. These are the *direct* and *indirect* methods, and are shown diagrammatically in Fig. 10-14. Since the direct method is the simpler of the two methods, it is used here for a basic explanation, even though indirect methods generally are used in the trade when separations are made on the process camera. The direct method typically is used for transparencies separated on an enlarger rather than a camera. On the camera, the exposure times may become so long as to be prohibitive.

The Direct Method

Making the Separation Negatives. The original color copy is set up on the copyboard. Four separate exposures are then made, each on a separate piece of film (usually a panchromatic litho film), with a different filter in the camera lens for each exposure, Fig. 10-15, page 186. The screen is rotated to a different angle for each exposure, Fig. 10-16. Colors of the original color copy which are recorded on the separation negatives appear on the negatives as black-and-white densities.

The *first exposure* records the cyan in the original copy. It is made with a red filter (the complement of cyan) in the lens and with the

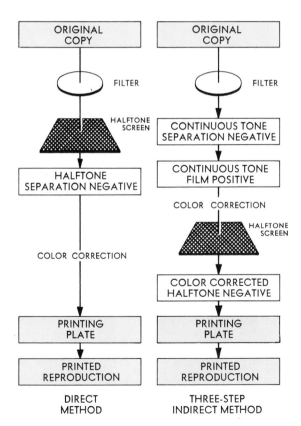

Fig. 10-14. Two of many possible methods of producing color separations. In each method, the procedures are repeated for each of the four colors.

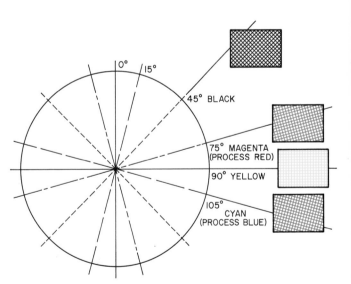

Fig. 10-16. Usual screen pattern angles for printing each of the four process-color plates. For halftones of a single color (black and white or any one color), the usual 45° angle is used, as shown above. The pattern of dots is least noticeable at this angle. Rows are most visible at 90° (as vertical and horizontal lines), so this 90° position is reserved for the lightest color (yellow).

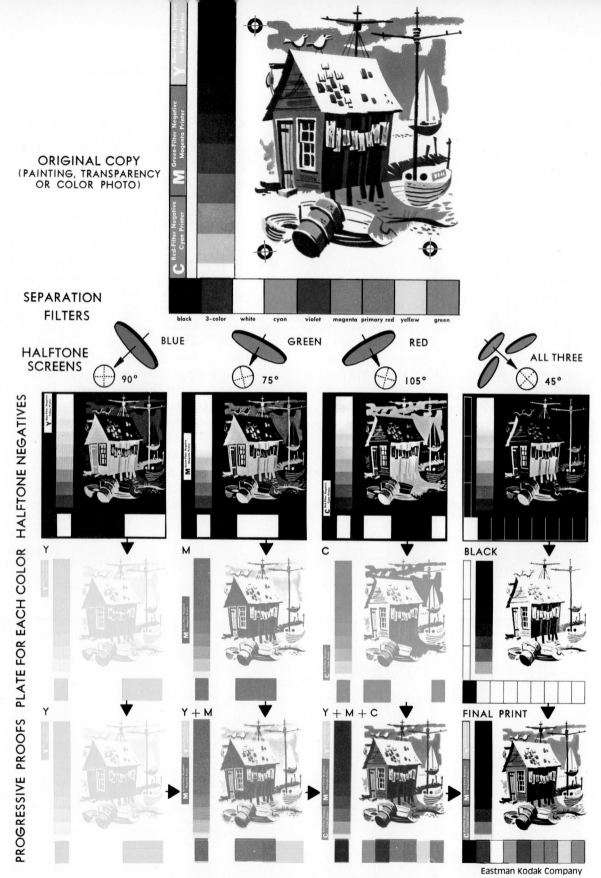

ORIGINAL COPY
(PAINTING, TRANSPARENCY
OR COLOR PHOTO)

SEPARATION FILTERS

black   3-color   white   cyan   violet   magenta   primary red   yellow   green

HALFTONE SCREENS

BLUE   90°   GREEN   75°   RED   105°   ALL THREE   45°

HALFTONE NEGATIVES

Y   M   C   BLACK

PLATE FOR EACH COLOR

Y   Y   C   FINAL PRINT

PROGRESSIVE PROOFS

Y   Y+M   Y+M+C   FINAL PRINT

Eastman Kodak Company

Fig. 10-15. Direct method of process color separation and reproduction.

screen at an angle of 105° over the film. This negative will be the cyan record negative, also known as the cyan printer negative. It will be used to expose the offest plate for printing the cyan ink on the press. Cyan (blue-green) is used to produce blues, greens, and purples. This action is summarized in Fig. 10-17.

The *second exposure,* for the *magenta* printer negative, is made with a green filter and the screen at 75°.

The *third exposure,* for the *yellow* printer negative, is made with a blue filter and the screen at an angle of 90°.

The *fourth exposure,* for the *black* printer negative, may be made as three partial exposures on the one piece of film. The first partial exposure uses the *red* filter; the second, the *green* filter; and the third, the *blue* filter. The screen is rotated to, and remains at, 45° for these three partial exposures. Some techniques use a single exposure through a yellow or orange (85B) filter.

Figure 10-15 shows the densities made on panchromatic film for each of the halftone separation negatives.

Color Correction.   Color correction provides a means of printing *less* ink of certain colors in appropriate areas of the reproduction printing,

in order to compensate for the color-absorbing deficiencies of process inks. For example, since magenta inks act as if they were contaminated with traces of yellow ink, some of the yellow should be removed below magenta areas wherever this combination is to overprint. Similarly, both yellow and magenta must be reduced under cyan, and all three must be removed under black.

Achieving a set of color-corrected separation negatives (or positives) may be accomplished by such techniques as photographic masking, electronic scanning, and hand-retouching of the halftone negatives or positives (localized dot etching). Figure 10-18 shows the correction achieved by photographic masking.

In *photo masking,* a special color film is prepared, which in one method is the same size as the copy. When placed over the copy for certain exposures, it automatically removes the necessary amounts of color intensity wherever needed. In camera-back masking, the mask is prepared to be placed in contact with the unexposed film. The light rays reflected from the copy must pass through this selective filter. Photographic masking, while removing most of the tedious handwork of localized dot etching, still requires careful judgment of the camera operator.

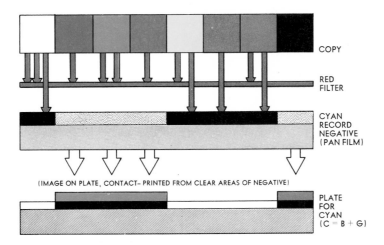

Fig. 10-17. Schematic showing basic action of the red filter in process-color separation (without color correction).

Fig. 10-18. Above: Uncorrected reproduction of a color photograph.

Below: The same copy color-corrected, using only the photographic masking methods.

The Indirect Method

The indirect method of color separation, diagrammed in Fig. 10-14, involves more steps than the direct method, but it is often preferred (especially when colors are corrected by hand). Also, it offers the convenience of color correcting on the continuous-tone film positives, plus the advantage of using the same set of color-corrected positives for enlargements or reductions prior to screening.

Note that in this method the separation negatives are exposed *without the screen* in the camera. This results in continuous-tone separation negatives from which continuous-tone film positives are made.

Color correction is done before these continuous-tone film positives are contact printed *through the halftone screen.* The final result is color-corrected halftone negatives for each of the printing plates.

Electronic scanners use computers to determine where the impulse from the colored image should be weakened for color correcting. This procedure completely automates the separation and correction. See Fig. 10-19.

If separations are being made for noncritical work or for experimental or demonstration projects, color correction may be omitted to simplify the procedure. This has been known as "short-run" process color or "pleasing" color. The technique is adequate for some types of copy and for some classes of work.

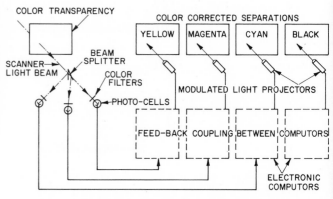

Fig. 10-19. Diagram of an electronic color scanner.

Making and Running the Plates

Plates are made from the separation negatives — one for each color to be printed. They are run on the press, in the progressive order shown — yellow, magenta, cyan, and black. Each plate transfers the correct amount of one of the colors to the paper. Four separate runs are made on a single-color press, and the ink is allowed to dry between each run. On a two-color press, the magenta is laid down directly over the wet yellow ink in one run, and then the black is laid over the wet cyan in a second run. It is necessary for the top ink to be thinner than the one first laid down. Otherwise, the top ink will not *trap* properly. That is, the second layer fails to adhere and it removes some of the first layer. Four-color presses apply all four inks (wet) in one run, and each color must be progressively thinner. The color balance may vary slightly, depending on the order in which the colors are run and on how well they trap.

Color Printing Procedures

Procedures for Flat Color

The easiest method of introducing color into a piece of printing is simply to print the entire form with a colored ink. While black ink normally is preferred for maximum legibility of text and line matter or for the maximum density range for halftones, such dark colors as browns, greens or blues may also be used. Another simple method of adding color is to print on colored stock. This is especially appropriate for pamphlet covers and posters.

In addition, it is possible to combine a single color of ink with a colored stock to obtain at least two colors. This requires little more work or expense than would be needed for black on white. There is also the possibility of obtaining a range of tones of a third color. For example, if an *opaque* blue (unaffected by the paper color) were printed on yellow stock, screened tone areas would blend the two colors producing shades of green — a 10% blue dot plus a 90% yellow paper giving a yellow-green, or a 90% dot giving a blue-green. Again, the two-color chart of overprints shown in Fig. 10-13 can be used for *ideas*, even if somewhat different colors and results are involved.

Methods of introducing more than one color into a job vary from the simpler methods of line separation to the more complex methods of process color separation of full-color originals, such as color photographs and transparencies.

Masked Separations

The masking separation may be used where lines or blocks of type matter (or illustrations) are to appear in different colors. See Fig. 10-20. From the single, stripped-up flat, a separate plate is prepared for each color. Each plate is exposed through a mask, so that only a portion of the flat is printed each time. Other masks are prepared for exposing plates for each of the other colors.

The masks may be prepared from flat-size sheets of goldenrod paper registered to the flat. The goldenrod sheet simply is placed in register over the flat on the lighted stripping table. Then the "windows" for the first color are cut out. The flat is labeled with the color for which it is intended. This is repeated, making a template mask for each of the other colors.

A separate plate is then exposed for each color to be printed. This is done by superimposing the appropriate template mask over the flat when exposing each plate in the platemaker.

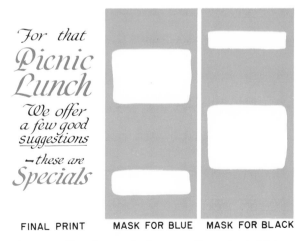

FINAL PRINT   MASK FOR BLUE   MASK FOR BLACK

Fig. 10-20. Template masks for separating a simple job into two colors.

Duplicate Negatives for Stripping

When the details being separated for color are too complex for convenient masking, it is best to make a duplicate negative for each color. Then the unneeded parts of each negative are opaqued. For example, look back at Fig. 10-2. It has lines in black, red, green and blue and is only one of many figures on that plate. From one inked drawing that included all details a negative and three duplicates were made. On the negative for yellow, all was opaqued except the red and the green lines. On the negative for cyan, only the green and blue lines remained. On the negative for black, only the three colored lines were opaqued, leaving the rest open. On the negative for magenta, all was opaqued except the red and the blue lines; then a piece of 25% tint screen was placed under the opening for the blue line, because blue is formed by cyan plus 25% magenta.

When colors must fit perfectly, the duplicate negative method is preferred, because the images are identical. If separate inked lines for Fig. 10-2 were attempted for the yellow and the magenta (to overprint as a single red line), they probably would not register as well.

Hand-Cut Ruby Film

By using the hand-cut ruby (peelable) film method of masking, considerable accuracy can be achieved in adding colors. It is commonly used for applying flat color to areas, to objects, or around an outline. See Fig. 10-21. The masking material is a separable two-ply acetate film — usually a ruby-red film adhered to a clear-film base.

The original artwork is keyed for colors and includes register marks. The acetate mask is taped in register over the artwork. The areas of the mask to be "opened" for the color are then outlined with a sharp knife. The stripper cuts through only the red layer of the two-ply mask (not cutting through the base layer). The red color is opaque to the blue light needed for exposing a plate, but it is clear enough to see through. The red layer is then peeled from the film, leaving a *window* in the red film. Register marks are copied on the film. Ruby film can also be cut to fit the master negative after it has been made.

This film is then stripped into a sheet of goldenrod to be used as the flat for exposing a plate to print that color. A separate acetate mask is prepared, with register marks, and is

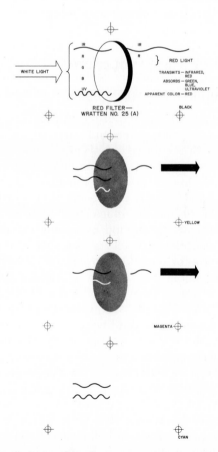

Fig. 10-21. Using hand-cut ruby film for color tint.

Fig. 10-22. Separations drawn on separate overlays. (See Fig. 10-9 for the color print of this.)

stripped up for each of the other colors to be printed.

Overlays

Line color work, such as multicolored maps, can be drawn on overlays by using a separate sheet or flap for each color to be reproduced. Each sheet is placed over the others and carries register marks. Transfer type, lettering, and film tint areas may be added where desired. Figure 10-22 shows black art and three overlays for the color. The resulting color illustration is shown in Fig. 10-9.

Overlays can be made on clear acetate sheets or even on tracing paper. Acetate requires lacquer-like ink which will adhere to the glossy surface. Also, some inks tend to chip off, but this can be minimized by a clear spray, or fixative, applied over the ink work. India inks can be used on tracing paper. Artwork is in black on white, no matter what the final printing color is to be.

Each color sheet may then be photographed separately as line copy, reducing as necessary. Clear acetates may be contact printed to produce the separate film negatives, or positives, for each color. Also, if the image is black enough, the drawings themselves may be used for exposing positive-working offset plates.

Key-Line Art

Adjacent colors which appear to meet actually should overlap slightly. This allows some variation in register without showing an unsightly gap between colors. Since such an overlap is difficult to draw accurately on overlays, key-line drawings are prepared. An example is shown in Fig. 10-23.

One drawing in black India ink incorporates all the colors. A fine line (the width of the desired overlap) is drawn where two colors meet, but the areas to be printed in color are not inked close to this margin. Usually the edge of the solid inking is left jagged to show it is unfinished.

Two identical negatives of the artwork go to the stripper, along with a drawing indicating the final appearance of the design. The stripper then opaques up to one side of the line and

Fig. 10-23. Key-line art (above) and its division into two colors by the stripper.

scrapes away unwanted emulsion on the other side. For example, study the yellow dot superimposed in the letter "F" in Fig. 10-23. On the negative, the key line is clear, with a ragged, narrow, black area surrounding it. The negative for yellow requires a clear round dot at this point, so the "F" is opaqued out up to the key line. Then a sharp knife is used to remove the emulsion on the ragged black ring inside the circular key line. On the cyan negative, the dot is opaqued and the ragged outline outside the key line is removed. On the yellow negative, it is necessary to opaque only ¼ " or so around the five yellow spots. The rest can be masked on the top side with tape or paper.

Tint Screens

When a flat shade of a color (including black) is required over an area, it usually is provided by placing a piece of screened photographic film over that area of the flat. Tint screens for a number of gray tones (usually designated by capital letters) are available commercially. While such screens could be made on the job by exposing flat halftone negatives from a clean piece of gray paper at various exposures, these are not accurate enough for most purposes.

Also, while the commercial screens can be contact-duplicated, even this is not as accurate as using the original commercial screen. (See page 116 for tints available.)

An easy method of incorporating the screen is to cut an opening in the goldenrod paper of the flat and then to tape the screen tint below the opening. If the tint is to register to another negative, the flat is registered with that negative below the goldenrod for the tint, and the image showing through the top goldenrod is used as a guide for cutting the opening.

Filter Separation of Line Copy

Line artwork in colors can be photographed one color at a time to produce separate negatives for each color. The appropriate filter and film combination to use is indicated in Table 8-2 on page 140. The negative for each color then can be stripped up for exposing its appropriate color plate. For example, if copy is in red and blue, a red filter (25) and pan film will copy the blue, but they will drop the red. A blue filter (47B) and pan film will copy the red but will drop the blue. Black cannot be filtered out, but it sometimes can be removed by opaquing or masking.

Duotones

Duotones are illustrations printed in two colors, commonly a principal (dark) color at a screen angle of 45° and a second (lighter) color at a screen angle 30° from the first — either 15° or 75°. See Fig. 10-24.

Usually black is used as the principal color, and some other color is used as the lighter color. Or the principal color may be a primary color and the other a complement or another primary color, such as: purple and yellow, blue and yellow, or red and green. Two such colors are capable of reproducing a considerable range of the spectrum.

Original copy for producing the duotone negatives is usually a black-and-white photograph. No filters are required. Duotones are produced from colored originals, such as color transparencies, by using filters to make the screened separation negatives.

In producing the negatives from black-and-white copy, the negative for the principal color should be made so that it is of normal contrast, but lacking somewhat in highlights. The negative for the lighter color may have a little more contrast and carry the highlights quite well. In this way, the second color of the duotone gives "sparkle" to the colored reproduction. Note the natural look of the silverware in Fig. 10-24.

Procedures for Process Color

Process color-separation methods and materials constantly are being researched as well as improved. For complete details of equipment, materials, and procedures for process color separation, including color-correction methods, the reader is referred to the following publications, among others:

Eastman Kodak Company:
  Basic Color for the Graphic Arts (Q-7)

Fig. 10-24. A duotone made from a black-and-white photograph.

At present, commercial-quality color-corrected process color separations may be beyond the scope of the average school's available time and equipment. However, the following discussion is presented with the hope that schools will acquire at least the minimum equipment and will do *some* process color separation, even though it might be experimental in nature. It even may be necessary to omit color-correction procedures.

Equipment

The basic items needed for elementary color separation procedures are described here. Other desirable items are mentioned and described in the publications listed above.

Camera

The process camera should be equipped with a color-corrected lens (apochromatic, for example); a vacuum back for holding the contact screen tightly against the film; a transparency opening in the copyboard (for transparent copy); a white-light source, such as pulsed-xenon arcs or high-intensity tungsten lights (3200° K).

For reflection copy, the lights generally are set at 45° to the center of the copyboard. Even intensity of light over the entire copyboard can be checked by using a photoelectric photometer, with a neutral gray test card in the copyboard. To get even illumination over large copy, it may be necessary to aim the lights at the far side of the copyboard.

For transmission copy, the camera should have lights which can be swung around (or placed) behind the copyboard, so that rays can be directed *through* the copy in the transparency opening. The copyboard should be covered with a dull-black material. The entire camera should be shielded so as to minimize reflected and room light.

With transmission copy, a condenser-type enlarger is more efficient than a process camera since shorter exposures are possible. An enlarger operates much like a process camera which has transparency illumination, except that in the enlarger the bellows cover the space between the lens and the copy (rather than between the lens and film). The effective lighting is much brighter and is completely enclosed.

Contact Halftone Screens

For the *direct method* of color separation, the Kodak gray contact screen is preferred because of its neutral color. For the *indirect method* of color separation, where halftone positives are to be made from the continuous-tone separation negatives, the Kodak magenta contact screens or the Kodak pre-angled magenta contact screens are used.

Contact Screen Angling

To achieve the four rotation angles, either the copy is rotated on the copyboard, or, more accurately, the contact screen angle is changed for each exposure.

Circular Screen. One method of achieving the angled positions of the screen on the vacuum back of the camera is to cut a single screen (as shown in Fig. 10-25), so that it is circular in shape, with four chords (straight sections) along its perimeter. A straightedge is then taped (with double-faced tape) to the vacuum back. Each of the chord sections of the screen is then butted, in turn, against the straightedge to achieve the four rotation angles.

Prior to using the screen, the screen alignment for each chord should be checked carefully with the Kodak angle indicator (as described in its accompanying instruction booklet). The

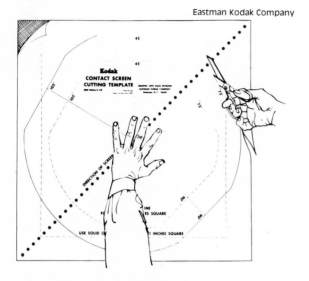

Fig. 10-25. Cutting a circular screen.

necessary corrections, if any, should then be recut.

Instead of using the butting method of positioning the screen on the vacuum back, more precise positioning is achieved by punching a pair of register pin holes along each of the four chord sections. The vacuum back is then fitted with a pair of register pins to accommodate these punched holes during each rotated position of the screen.

In preparing the "punched" screen, the screen angles must be precisely determined by use of the Kodak angle indicator.

Angling a Small Screen. For beginners and for small work, a smaller screen can be mounted in a cut-out window in the center of a sheet of acetate of the same outside dimensions as the template, and taped in place. The large sheet of acetate can be cut to the outline of the template and then checked for accuracy as for the large circular screen.

Set of Four Screens. A set of four separate screens — one designed for each rotation angle — may be prepared by using the angle indicator and a register punch. (Instructions are in the Kodak "Angle Indicator" booklet.)

Notch Coding the Screen Angles. To enable the worker to identify screen angles in the dark, each screen or screen chord can be notched with a code, such as one notch for 90° and two notches for 75°.

Testing the Angled Screen. After preparing the angled screen (or screens), it is best to perform the following test. Set up the camera for same-size reproduction, with a white card in the copyboard and a piece of orthochromatic litho film on the vacuum back. Make four successive exposures on the film (screen in place over the film), using a different screen angle for each exposure and having each exposure sufficient enough to make a 10% dot on the negative. Develop the film as for a halftone. If inspection of the negative reveals no objectionable moiré pattern, the screen is ready for use.

Size Screen Needed. The largest practical-size screen of each angle which can be cut from stock sizes of contact screens is listed in Table 10-1.

Films

Panchromatic film is used for making the halftone separation negatives from the original color copy (in the direct method), and for making continuous-tone separation negatives from original color copy (in the indirect method).

Orthochromatic film is used for making contact halftone negatives from continuous-tone separation negatives.

Masking film (Multimask or Tri-Mask) is used, in some methods of color correction, for making a correction mask.

Table 10-1
Screen Sizes Needed for Making Angled Screens

Size of Uncut Screen (in Inches)	45° Angle (in Inches)	75°, 90°, and 105° Angles (in Inches)
9 x 11	9 x 11	5 x 6
12 x 15	12 x 15	6 x 8
15 x 18	15 x 18	9 x 11
17 x 21	17 x 21	9 x 11
25 x 25	25 x 25	15 x 18
31 x 31	31 x 31	19 x 23

Safelights

For each type of film, consult the manufacturer's instructions (enclosed with the package) for the safelight and darkroom-handling of that particular film. Panchromatic and masking film generally require total darkness for all, or for a major portion, of the handling and processing procedures.

When handling film in total darkness, identify the emulsion side of the film as that side facing you when the film notches are at the top edge of the upper right-hand corner. If sheets are cut, place them emulsion-side up in the box or drawer. Use strips of taped-on cardboard on the film-cutting board and the camera vacuum back as an aid in cutting and positioning film.

Guides

Guides are mounted on the copyboard along with the copy to help in evaluating the separation and color correction; to identify the separation negatives; and to act as a quality-control check in the final printing.

Reflection copy guides include color blocks, gray scale, register marks, and color-control patches. In Fig. 10-15 on page 186 these are shown mounted. These guides are available as a set, in small or large sizes, as Kodak color separation guides. The small size is used for copy which is to be enlarged. The large size is used for copy which is to be reduced.

The transparent copy guide is for backlighted copy. The Kodak Tri-Mask guide is shown in Fig. 10-26. It includes color blocks and a modified gray scale. A photographic step tablet (11- or 21-step film gray scale) and register marks (on film or tape) should also be included on the copyboard.

The color blocks (one each for the cyan, magenta, and yellow printer negatives) indicate, after the negatives are processed, which negative is to be used for making each of the printer plates or positives.

The color-control patches (usually nine blocks) indicate, in the form of images on the film, a monochromatic record of the color densities. In one convenient strip on the negative, these patches show the effects of the color separation and of the color correction (if performed at this step). If the patches show up correctly, the corresponding colors in the copy are accurate as black-and-white densities.

Note, in Fig. 10-15, the reproduction of the color-control patches on each of the color-corrected separation negatives. The color-control patches on the cyan printer negative show the wanted colors — cyan, violet, and primary green — as equal in density. As further evidence of correctness, each of the three wanted colors shows up as equal in density to the three-color area. These correspond to the image areas of the separation negative which will permit printing of the cyan ink when the offset plate is exposed.

On the same cyan printer negative, the unwanted colors in the original copy — yellow, magenta, and primary red — have a density equal to the white patch area. Since cyan requires none of these colors in the press printing, these dense areas of the separation negative prevent the formation of an image. Thus, when the offset plate is exposed, no cyan is printed in those areas.

Notice particularly that, since these are color-corrected separation negatives (because of hand color correction), the black area on the color-control patches shows up as a matching density (black area) on the yellow, magenta, and cyan color-corrected separation negatives. These dense areas on the yellow, magenta, and cyan separation negatives prevent an image on exposure of the offset plates, thus printing no inks of those colors in that area. Where the printing of black ink is desirable, it is supplied by the black printer negative. This exposes the black printer plate in the proper area for the printing of the black color.

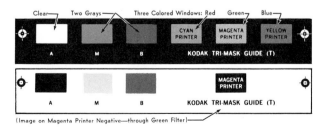

Fig. 10-26. Tri-mask guide (T).

The *gray scale* is used to measure and compare such elements as density and density range of the separation negatives. It is especially useful in color correction procedures.

Register guides on paper are intended for use with reflection copy. Register guides for transparent copy may be purchased ready-prepared on film or on transparent tape. However, they also may be produced in the shop as film positives by line-photographing the guides which are printed on paper. Then the negative is contact-printed onto ortho film which has been intentionally slightly fogged by exposing the film for a few seconds to a yellow flashing lamp. The fogging produces a slightly-grayish background on the film positives. This helps insure that the register marks will not be overexposed when included later with the copy on the copyboard.

Although not recommended, register marks sometimes may be scribed on the dark edges of transparent copy. This must be done *outside the working area of the copy* so as not to damage the original copy for further use.

For quality control of ink and identification during the press run, film images of color blocks, color patches, and register marks are stripped into the flat so as to print in the waste margin of the printing sheet. The color being printed or overprinted can be checked visually, or with a densitometer, against the master sheet and by comparison with the original color patches.

Filters

For the color separation procedures discussed later in this section, the following Kodak Wratten filters are recommended in this order of use (but others are possible):

23A (or 25) (red) for the cyan printer
58 (green) for the magenta printer
47 (or 47B) (blue) for the yellow printer

Densitometer

For serious work, acquisition of a densitometer should be considered.

Focusing the Camera

Camera focus should be checked and carefully adjusted at the magnification setting prior to exposing the film. For a camera equipped with calibration tapes, one check should be sufficient. Tape settings then may be used without additional focus checks.

Determining Exposures

The following procedures are suggested for arriving at the *f*-number (aperture), the main (detail) exposure time, and the flash (shadow flash) exposure time for each of the separation negatives, when using the direct method of producing color-separation negatives through filters.

f-Number of Lens. Usually an $f/22$ or an $f/32$ setting is the best lens setting to use for the separation exposures. The *f*-number which produces satisfactory halftone negatives usually is satisfactory for process color separation.

Main (Detail) Exposure. This procedure traditionally is based on the correct exposure of the cyan printer negative through the No. 25 (red) filter. Once this red-filter exposure time is determined, exposures through each of the other filters can be calculated by multiplying the red-filter exposure time by the filter ratio for each of the other filters as indicated on the film data sheet. If the newer No. 23A (red) filter is being used, its exposure time must first be increased by one-fourth to determine the equivalent time of the No. 25 filter. An approximate test exposure can be determined from the film instructions or by means of an exposure meter as follows:

With the lights set up as for an exposure, set a light meter according to the manufacturer's directions, using the film exposure index (speed number) given on the film data sheet. (For Kodalith Pan film, this is ASA 40 for pulsed-Xenon arcs, and ASA 32 for tungsten lamps.)

Select the exposure time which corresponds, on the meter scales, with the *f*-number to be used.

Corrected Exposure Calculation. The exposure time determined by use of the light meter must be corrected to allow for reproduction (magnification or reduction) size, interference of the halftone screen, and absorption of the filter (filter ratio).

Use this formula to find the corrected exposure time for the red-filter separation negative:

$E_{lmr} \times F_m \times 10$ = Exposure time when making the red-filter exposure.

where:

E_{lmr} = Exposure time obtained from the light-meter reading.

F_m = Factor of magnification. For 100% magnification, use the factor "4". For magnifications other than 100%, determine the factor by using the Kodak Copying Dataguide.

10 = A constant, to be included when using the Kodak gray contact screen. The screen offers an obstacle to the reflected light. In effect, using the "10" in the above formula, automatically multiplies the exposure by 10.

The corrected exposure time calculated above is for the cyan printer negative when exposed through the red filter.

Exposures for other filters are arrived at by multiplying the corrected red-filter exposure time by the filter ratio of the filter to be used. The filter ratios are given in Table 10-2 or on the film data sheet enclosed with the box of film.

Flash (Shadow Flash) Exposure. Position the continuous-tone color copy in the copyboard. Insert the specified red filter in the lens barrel. Observing the safelight precautions listed on the film data sheet, place a sheet of panchromatic film on the vacuum back. Position the screen over the film. Cover a 1"-wide strip of the film with black paper, and make a separation exposure of normal f-number and normal main-exposure length on this film. Open the camera back, and remove the strip of black paper. Make a series of test exposures on this strip, using only the flashing lamp. This is done to determine what length of flash lamp exposure will produce a density of 0.3 on this test strip of the negative, when the negative is developed to produce the desired highlight and middletone contrasts on the image portion. Flashing procedure and setup is the same as that described on pages 155-159, except that a Series 2 (red) filter usually is used with pan film.

Making a Set of Separation Negatives

The following are steps in making a set of separation negatives by the *direct method:*

1. Check the copy and work order for instructions.

Table 10-2
Separation Filter Ratios

These ratios are based on an exposure time of approximately 60 seconds through the filter No. 25.

Light source	Kodak Wratten Filter-Numbers					
	No. 8 (K2) Yellow	No. 23A Red	No. 25 A Red	No. 47 (C5) Blue	No. 47B Blue	No. 58 (B) Green
Pulsed-Xenon Arc	0.5	0.8	1.0	3.0	4.0	2.0
Tungsten*	0.6	0.8	1.0	10.0	12.0	4.0

*Photoflood, or other high-efficiency tungsten.   (Eastman Kodak Company)

Example: If the correct exposure to pulsed-xenon lights through the Wratten filter No. 25 (filter ratio 1.0) has been determined to be 60 seconds, the exposure through the No. 47B (filter ratio 3.0) would be 180 seconds (60 x 3.0), or 3 minutes.

Example of Exposure: To make a 1:1 line reproduction under average shop conditions using Kodalith Pan Film with two 1500-watt pulsed-xenon lamps at about 3 feet from the copyboard, use a trial exposure time of 10 seconds at f/22 through the Wratten filter No. 25. With a gray contact screen (negative) the exposure will be 4 to 8 times longer.

2. Install the proper safelights in the dark-room for the kind of film to be used.
3. Set the camera for reproduction size.
4. Set the lens diaphragm control for the desired reproduction size on the selected *f*-band.
5. Install a resolution guide in the copyboard (for focusing).
6. Set camera lights at proper position and angle.
7. Check the camera focus.
8. Mount the copy and guides on the copyboard.

> • **Note:** In mounting a transparency on the copyboard, place it between two pieces of glass to hold it flat. All copy should be secured with pieces of tape at the top edge in case the vacuum accidentally is shut off before all exposures are made.

9. Set the camera exposure timer for length of main (detail) exposure.
10. Determine the size of film needed. Kodalith Pan film, Estar base, is suggested.
11. Under proper safelight conditions, cut the film needed and place it in the box or drawer.
12. *For cyan printer negative:* Place the red filter, 23A (or No. 25, also called the A separation filter), in the filter slot of the lens barrel.
13. Place film on the vacuum back.
14. Place the gray contact screen at 105° over the film.
15. Make the main (detail) exposure.
16. Make the flash exposure.

Using a new piece of film, repeat the procedure for the magenta printer negative, rotating the screen to 75° and using a No. 58 (or B) filter. For the yellow printer negative, rotate the screen to 90° and use a new piece of film and a No. 47B filter, or a No. 47 (C5).

For the black printer negative, expose on one sheet of film, with the screen at 45°, successively and individually through the red, green and blue filters. Each exposure time should be roughly proportionate to the filter ratios. For example, in using the red filter, expose for 25% to 30% of the time as when exposing for the cyan printer negative. Likewise, a 25% to 30%

exposure through the green filter should be used, and a 35% to 45% exposure through the blue filter.

Color Correction

Normally, some form of color correction is included either during the separation exposures or after the separation negatives are made. When copy is a transparency masked with Tri-Mask film, often additional correction is not needed.

> • **Note:** In Fig. 10-18, the uncorrected reproduction lacks the purity of the colors that the corrected reproduction has — especially in the blues and greens. Color correction would have brought them out.

Processing the Negatives

Process the negatives by the time-and-temperature method. Again, observe safelight and processing instructions on film data sheet.

Evaluating the Negatives

Examine the negatives over a viewing table for obvious faults such as scratches and streaks.

Check to see that the shadow and middle-tone areas do not lack dots and that the highlight areas are not plugged up. For halftones, remember that the flash exposure controls the shadow dots in the clearer areas and that the main exposure controls the highlight area dots in the darker areas. Changes in exposures (main, flash, or both) may be necessary.

The gray scale images should show a complete range of tone, from 5% to 10% dots at the highlight end of the scale to 90% to 95% dots at the shadow end.

The color patches (reproductions on negatives) should be examined to see how well the colors have been separated — that is, which colors registered and which dropped out.

Check register by superimposing each of the negatives, in turn, over the cyan printer negative. Examine closely to see that the register marks coincide exactly.

Color Separation Pre-Press Proofs

After the color separation negatives (or positives) have been made and before the job is actually put into production on the press, color proofs of the job should be made. Proofs should be checked for color breaks, registration, fit, color values, copy details, proper stripping, and condition of tints and tones.

During the press run, the press operator will need a set of progressive proofs (usually four) comprised of, for example, (1) a proof sheet showing how the yellow plate should reproduce, (2) a proof sheet showing the magenta printed over the yellow, (3) a third proof sheet showing the addition of the cyan ink, and (4) a final progressive proof showing the black printed over the yellow, magenta, and cyan. (A set of four progressive proofs is shown in the bottom row of Figure 10-15.) The sequence of colors should be the same as that which will be followed in the actual press run.

Approval for the printing of a job may require a press test run in full color using the same plates, paper stock, and inks as those to be used for the actual press run.

Questions

1. What is color?
2. Name and describe the two main classes of color printing.
3. What is the range, in millimicrons, of natural visible light?
4. Name the colors of the spectrum.
5. What effect does a drop in camera-lighting voltage have on the color of light it transmits?
6. What is an "apparent" color?
7. Of what colors of projected light are the following colors composed? (a) magenta, (b) cyan, (c) yellow, (d) black, (e) white.
8. Of what colors of transparent process printing inks are the following printed colors composed? (a) green, (b) black, (c) red, (d) blue?
9. What color of light is transmitted through a green filter? Why?

10. If a transparent blue ink were printed on other than white paper, what changes would be expected in the apparent color?
11. What advantages are gained by using opaque (rather than transparent) inks?
12. What is meant by the expression: "changing the dot sizes in an area of printed color will change the value or tone of that color?"
13. Name the two kinds of copy for process-color reproduction, and give examples of each.
14. Briefly describe both the *direct method* and the *indirect method* of making process-color separations.
15. Explain the purpose of color correction.
16. Describe how two colors may be printed on a job by the masking-separation method.
17. What other methods besides masking can be used to produce separate flat colors?
18. What are key-line drawings?
19. How does a duotone differ from four-color process reproduction?
20. On notebook paper, make a table as shown. Fill in the information not given:

Indirect Method of Color Separation

Printer Negative	Screen Angle	Filter No. & Color	Ink Color on the Press
Cyan	105°	_____	_____
_____	_____	Green, No. 58 (B)	_____
_____	_____	_____	Yellow
Black	_____	_____	

Problems and Projects

1. Using your own press and materials, produce a color chart.
2. Make a list of the equipment, supplies, and aids needed to produce process-color separation negatives by the direct method.
3. Using the equipment and facilities in your shop, determine main and flash exposures for direct-method process-color separation negatives.
4. Make a set of four process-color separation negatives (direct method) from reflection copy.

5. Arrange for someone to come in and demonstrate one or more methods of color separation.
6. Plan a field trip to a place which specializes in process-color separation and process-color printing.
7. Contact firms who print process-color separation work and arrange for a loan or gift of (a) a set of process-color separation negatives, or (b) a set of progressive proofs of process-color printing.
8. Plan and produce a job involving a method of color separation other than that of process color.
9. Bring your shop files up-to-date with advertising literature and catalogs on equipment and supplies for process-color separation work.
10. Prepare angle markings on a gray contact screen and on the camera back.

New Terms

additive colors	oxidation
Angstrom	perfecting
black printer negative	photoelectric
chroma	pigment
complementary	pleasing color
composite	principal color
electromagnetic	prism
flat color	radiation
fluorescence	reflection copy
hue	scanner
incident	separation negatives
infrared	spectrophotometer
interposed	subtractive
magenta	tandem
masking film	transparent copy
neutral	ultraviolet
opaque ink	voltage
overprinting	wavelength

Film Developing and Darkroom Procedures

A darkroom must be provided for handling and developing film; for making contact prints, enlargements, combinations, and positives; and for performing other operations with sensitized materials which cannot be handled in normal room light.

Layout of the Darkroom

The layout of the darkroom will vary according to such factors as the number of persons to use it at one time, the equipment to be contained, the kind of operations to be carried out, and the funds available. Figure 11-1 illustrates a basic darkroom with a horizontal darkroom process camera installed through the wall. The temperature-controlled sink holds the four processing trays in the following order: developer, short-stop, fixer, and running water. A safelight is provided over the developing sink so that negatives can be inspected as the developing progresses. Or, a glass-top-lighted film viewer can be used on which wet negatives can be placed and inspected. Figure 11-2 shows a commercial darkroom installation, designed for high volume production. This layout shows additional uses, such as stripping and platemaking.

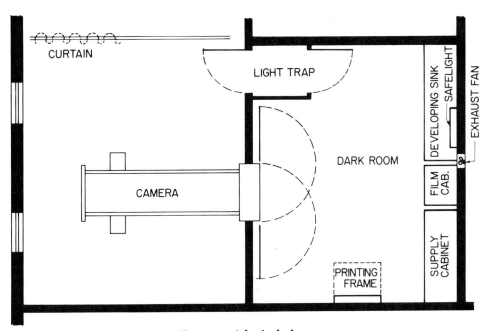

Fig. 11-1. A basic darkroom.

Chemco Photoproducts Company

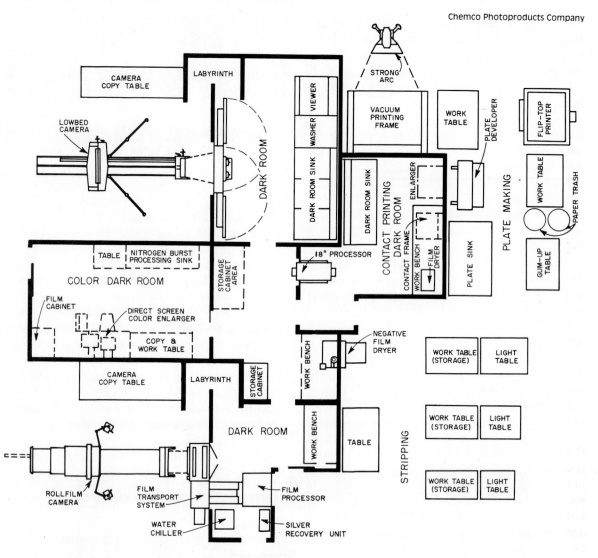

Fig. 11-2. Layout of darkrooms and related areas for handling a variety of work at high volume.

A red safelight is used for certain films, such as the orthochromatic film used for general work. However, always determine from the instruction sheet packed with the film or other sensitized material exactly what safelight to use.

For general room illumination in the darkroom, yellow overhead lighting is better than white. It causes less eye strain when you are going from a red to a yellow light or from a yellow to a red light.

Wall switches which control general room illumination should be located at least 60 inches

Table 11-1
Kodak Safelight Filters

OA	— Greenish yellow
OC	— Light amber
OO	— Light yellow
No. 1	— Red
No. 1A	— Light red
No. 2	— Dark red
No. 3	— Dark green
No. 6B	— Brown
No. 7	— Green
No. 8	— Dark yellow
No. 10	— Dark amber

(Eastman Kodak Company)

high; wall switches controlling safelights are placed at their normal 48-inch height. This insures that overhead lights are not turned on except intentionally.

In new construction, installation of a floor drain may be a convenient precaution.

On the wall or worktable is an exposure frame for making contact prints and combinations. Above the contact frame is the contact-frame exposure light.

A ventilating fan is a necessity for removing fumes and odors. If no fan is available, do not mix or weigh dry chemicals in the darkroom. Leave the doors open for ventilation when the room is not in use.

Shelves should be provided above and below the sink and worktables for graduates, trays, and other accessories. For safety, bottled chemicals should be stored on the *lowest* shelves.

A film-drying rack may be attached to the underside of the shelves over the sink.

A work-top, shallow-drawer cabinet should be provided for the storage and handling of film and other camera accessories.

Entrance to the darkroom is by way of a light baffle.

If a darkroom camera is used, an opening in the wall of the darkroom is provided to admit the back of the camera and its controls. Space between the camera back and the opening is sealed light-tight. In this manner the film need not leave the darkroom, and may be inspected and focused at greater advantage in the darkness of the darkroom.

If necessary, and if there is room, the darkroom camera may be placed and used within the darkroom, but it is best to protect the developing area from the bright lights.

Order of Trays

Four trays are generally used in the developing process. They contain developer, shortstop, fixer, and running water, Fig. 11-3. The trays are placed in that order in the sink, and always maintained in the same order to eliminate confusion in the dark. While commonly in order from left to right, the actual order may vary with the sink arrangement.

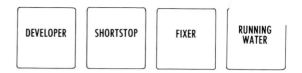

Fig. 11-3. **Order of trays in darkroom.**

Theory of Negatives

Reflected light during exposure of the film in the camera produces a *latent* image on the film. This is a chemical change in the composition of the film emulsion which cannot be seen until the film is in the developer.

The complete developing, or processing, of exposed film is accomplished by placing the film through the four successive tray baths — developer, shortstop, fixer, water. The action of the four baths is as follows:

The *developing* bath (chemically a base) causes the latent image to become visible as the developer solution frees the exposed silver particles in the film emulsion, causing these particles to form a dense, black or *opaque* background. At the same time, the particles of silver which were not struck by the light form a transparent image area on the film.

The *shortstop* bath is a mild acid which quickly neutralizes the action of the developer solution when developing has been completed.

The *fixing* bath is an acid which removes all unexposed particles of silver and the antihalation backing from the film.

Fig. 11-4. **Pelouze R-47 scales.**

The *running-water* bath washes away all traces of the chemicals used and prevents later darkening of the clear areas of the film.

Preparation of Tray Solutions

Purchase the developer and fixing chemicals recommended by the manufacturer of the particular film to be used. Follow the manufacturer's instructions in mixing the chemicals and in developing the film. See Figs. 11-4 and 11-6. In general, the procedure is as follows:

Developer

The developer is usually sold in concentrated powder form in two separate containers: one containing *Part A,* and the other containing *Part B.* Prepare each part separately according to the instructions on the package. Store them in two jugs marked "A" and "B." When you are ready to develop film, pour equal amounts of A and B into the developer tray and stir the solution. Such developers are discarded after they have been used.

Shortstop

The shortstop solution (stop bath) is prepared by pouring 8 ounces (liquid) of 28% acetic acid into a gallon of water. Be sure first to

Fig. 11-6.   Measuring liquids. For accurate measuring, hold the vessel level and sight top of liquid at eye level.

pour the water into the empty container, and then pour the 28% acid into the water. Store this in a jug labeled "Shortstop Solution." Discard after use.

• **Note:** Be certain to use *28% acetic acid* for the above shortstop solution. Under NO circumstances should *glacial (concentrated) acetic acid* be used, since the glacial acetic acid may cause blindness, irritation, or severe burns if allowed to come in contact with eyes, skin, or clothing.

Fixer

The fixer is generally purchased in powder form, and mixed according to the package directions. Store this in a jug marked "Fixer (Fresh)."

Fixer is also known as *hypo.* Wipe up spills thoroughly as they will look like white paint when dry. Fixer, if still clearing film in about 2 minutes, may be re-used.

Do not return used fixer to the jug of *fresh fixer.* Arrange to have two jugs — one marked "Fixer (Fresh)," the other marked "Fixer (Used)."

Water

The tray containing the water should be provided with some means for continuously changing the water. A tray siphon may be used, or a temperature-controlled faucet set at 68° F (20° C) may be allowed to run water continuously into the tray.

nuArc Company, Inc.

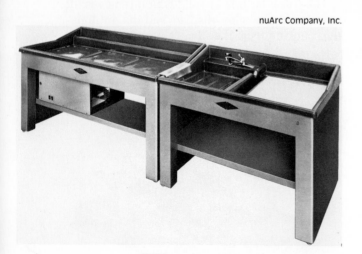

Fig. 11-5.   Darkroom sink installation with temperature control unit. Left-hand sink unit provides for developing, shortstop, and fixing; right-hand unit provides for washing (rinsing), squeegeeing, and viewing.

Filling the Trays

Select trays of a size a little larger than the film to be processed, and place them in order in the developing sink. Into each tray, pour enough of the appropriate solution to suit conditions — about ¾" deep will do to start.

For the first tray, equal parts of *developer* "A" and "B" solutions should be mixed. The second tray contains the *shortstop* solution. The third tray contains the *fixer* solution, and the last tray is at least half full of water at 68° F (20° C).

Now, place the sink overflow pipe in position. Turn water into the sink to achieve and maintain the tray temperature desired.

Developing Procedure for Negatives

The exposed film is processed in the darkroom with the overhead white (or yellow) lights *turned off,* and illumination provided only by the recommended safelight (at least until the film is in the wash bath). For example, the recommended safelight for processing Kodak Ortho Type 3 Film is a Kodak Safelight Filter, Wratten Series 1A (light red), in a suitable safelight lamp, with a 15-watt bulb, at not less than 4 feet.

Removing the Film

In the darkroom, with only the safelight on, open the camera back. As you hold the film only

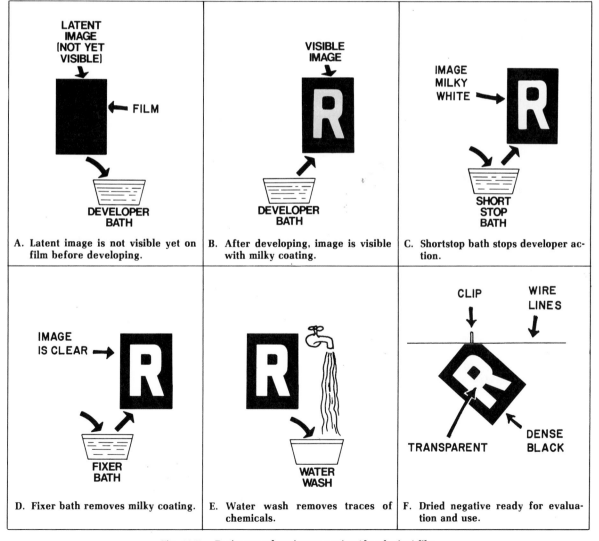

A. Latent image is not visible yet on film before developing.

B. After developing, image is visible with milky coating.

C. Shortstop bath stops developer action.

D. Fixer bath removes milky coating.

E. Water wash removes traces of chemicals.

F. Dried negative ready for evaluation and use.

Fig. 11-7.   Basic procedure in processing (developing) film.

by the edges, shut off the vacuum and remove the film.

Developing the Film

See Fig. 11-7. Holding the film by an edge, use the free hand to lift the nearest side of the developing tray about an inch or so. Then immerse the film, emulsion side up, in the developer and lower the tray. This action will cause the developer to flow completely over the film. Agitate the developer solution during the developing procedure by alternately raising and lowering the near edge of the tray, Fig. 11-8.

At frequent intervals as the developing progresses, check the increasing density of the

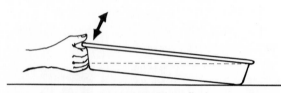

Fig. 11-8.   Agitating developer in tray.

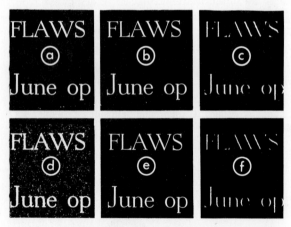

Fig. 11-9.   Judging the line negative after processing. (a) Underexposure — elements tend to thicken; (b) normal exposure; (c) overexposure — fine lines and serifs are lost; (d) underdeveloped — background not sufficiently opaque; (e) normal development; (f) overdeveloped — fine lines and serifs are lost.

Note: These illustrations are grossly exaggerated. Because of the wide latitude of exposure tolerance of a good line film, figure "a" shows only a little thickening of the lines, despite an exposure only one-sixth of normal; figure "c" was exposed four times the normal exposure to achieve the above results.

negative by lifting it out of the developer, letting it drip for a moment, immersing it quickly in water, and holding it up to the safelight for inspection. If the negative needs more developing, return it to the developing solution.

A well-developed negative, when viewed before the safelight, will have a dense, black background, and a clear, transparent image area. See Figs. 11-9 and 11-10 for examples of over- and under-exposure, as well as of over- and under-development.

> • **Note:** For additional information on the developing step, see "Three Methods of Developing Film," page 207.

Shortstop Rinse

When the negative is satisfactorily developed, lift it out of the developer. Allow it to drip a bit, and then immerse it in the shortstop bath for about 10 seconds, agitating it continuously.

Fixing Bath

From the shortstop bath, place the film in the fixing bath for 2 to 4 minutes, agitating frequently. Inspect the negative to see that all the "milky" coating is removed from the emulsion side of the film, and that the clear portions of the negative are perfectly transparent. Overhead lights may be turned on briefly after a few minutes of fixing (provided no one else in the darkroom is processing film or photographic

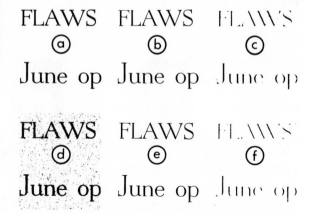

Fig. 11-10. Print made from the stripped-up negatives in Fig. 11-9. Compare each print with its corresponding negative.

Calumet Photographic, Inc.

Fig. 11-11. Tray processing of film.

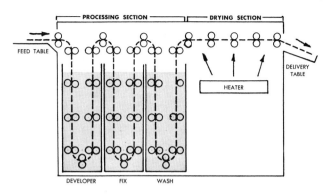

Fig. 11-12. Schematic of automatic film processor.

contact paper). The general rule for fixing film is to leave the film in the fixer for twice the length of time it takes to clear. Paper prints are usually fixed for 30 minutes.

Washing the Film

Wash the fixed negative in running water for 10 minutes (after the last negative was added to the wash tray). Do not hurry this step, as poor washing may not remove all unwanted chemicals and may result in a discoloration of the film later. Paper negatives (and photo print papers) absorb more of the chemicals during processing, and so must be washed much longer — usually 30 to 60 minutes.

Drying

After washing, treat the negatives in a Photo-Flo solution. Then squeegee or sponge off the excess water, and hang the negative by a corner in a dust-free place to dry.

Paper prints can be dried between sheets of white blotting paper for a dull finish. For a glossy finish, the wet prints are placed face down on chromium ferrotype plates and rolled to remove bubbles. The prints pop loose when dry. A print dryer with a heated ferrotype surface speeds the process.

Three Methods of Developing Film

Three methods of developing exposed film are by inspection, by time-and-temperature, and by aid of a gray scale (or sensitivity guide).

Inspection Method

In the inspection method, the operator develops the film until deciding, by visual inspection, that the film is sufficiently developed; then it is developed a bit more, for good measure. Consistency of quality in successive negatives depends a great deal upon the operator's "eye."

Time-and-Temperature Method

In the time-and-temperature method, the operator develops the film both for the length of time and in solutions of temperatures as specified by the manufacturer. In addition, other specifications of the manufacturer must be followed for the particular film being processed, such as exposure, processing solutions, and methods of agitation during processing.

This is the method of developing described in instructions by the manufacturer. However, because of the number of variables possible in different situations (including partial exhaustion of developer solutions), some operators may have difficulty in achieving consistently uniform negatives. Consequently, many operators may start out using only the time-and-temperature method, but later combine this with the inspection method.

Sensitivity-Guide Method

The sensitivity-guide, or gray-scale, method of developing exposed film gives good control of development and corrects for minor variation in factors such as exposure, temperature, and used developer. It requires that a sensitivity guide be placed alongside, and photographed with, the copy. In developing the film, the operator observes the progressive development of the steps of the guide on the film being developed in the tray. Step 1 develops most quickly. It first appears light gray, then speckled black, then solid black. In about 15 seconds, Step 2 turns black, then Step 3, etc. When the desired step turns black, the film is transferred to the shortstop bath, and the remainder of the processing is completed in the usual manner.

For this method, it is recommended that test negatives be developed in new Kodalith (or similar) developer at 68° F (20° C) for the manufacturer's recommended time (2¾ minutes). The exposure then should be adjusted to give a critical Step 4 with this development.

Figure 8-33 in Chapter 8 shows how the sensitivity-guide image looks on a negative which has been developed to Step 4. The caption notes the difference in appearance when viewed in the tray and when inspected by transmitted light.

> • **Note:** When the guide has been placed along the edge of the copy, use caution to prevent excessive tray agitation, as this may super-develop, or intensify, the edge and give a false reading.

Darkroom Photoprinting Operations

Included in darkroom photoprinting operations are the making of same-size *contact prints* on paper or film with use of the contact frame, and the making of reductions or enlargements by *projection printing* with use of the enlarger.

Contact Printing. Contact printing is the generating (creating) of a same-size image on film or on photopaper by placing a film negative (or film positive) in direct contact over a sheet of photoprint paper (or film) in a

contact-printing frame, and then exposing the setup to an exposure light source, Fig. 11-13. The exposed photopaper or film is then processed — usually in developer, shortstop, fixer, and wash water — and then dried.

Contact prints usually are made for these purposes:

1. To reverse the *tones* from positive to negative;
2. To *flop the image* from left to right; or
3. To make *duplicate copies* of the original film.

Further special techniques include darkening or lightening the image, screening continuous-tone negatives, combining the images from several sources (as in overprinting type on a halftone), and any of a number of special effects made possible by adding or combining solids, tones, and colors.

Introduction to Contacting

In contact printing operations, wherever possible when viewing the image as it will appear on the printed sheet, the emulsion side of the completed negatives and positives should be on the bottom (away from the operator). This is for

Fig. 11-13. Setup for contact printing. The adjustable point-source light is installed above the vacuum frame of a flip-top plate printer.

two reasons: (1) so that the film emulsion will be tight against the sensitized coating of the off-set plate during the plate exposure, thus preventing image spread, and (2) so that the film emulsion will be on the bottom of the flat, where it will not be cut into when the stripper cuts the "windows" into the goldenrod masking sheet.

Contacting Equipment. *A vacuum printing frame* is desirable for all-around contact printing work. A plate printer can be equipped with a point-source light for this purpose. See Fig. 11-13. Otherwise, a simple glass-topped printing frame can be equipped with a foam-rubber pad, about ½ inch thick. See Fig. 11-14.

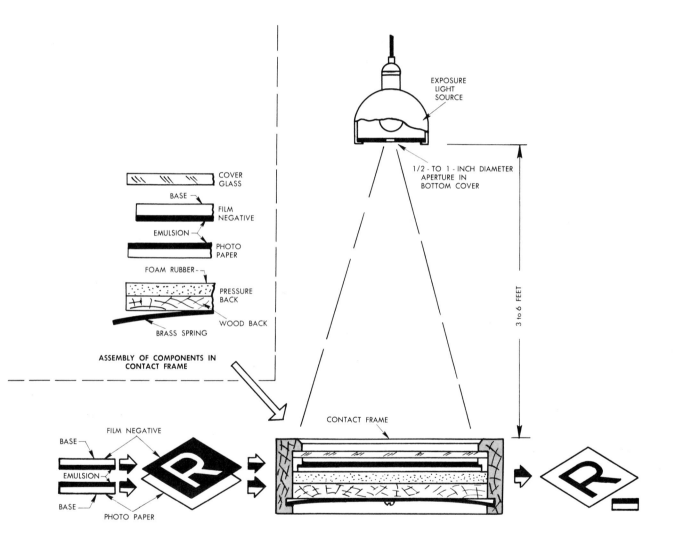

A. Film negative and photo paper are placed together; emulsion of film is in contact with emulsion side of photo paper. Film negative is readable from top side.

B. Assembled negative and photo paper are locked in contact frame. Film negative is on top (facing exposure light) and is in readable form. Exposure to light is then made.

C. After exposure, the photo paper is processed. Result is a readable positive photo print. Emulsion of print is on the upper surface.

Fig. 11-14. Basic procedure in contact printing.

The *light source*, if broad and placed close to the printing frame, allows light rays to reach the image from many angles and causes the duplicated image to be bolder than it was on the original being printed. On the other hand, a light projected from an absolute pin point minimizes the image spread, but it will duplicate any dust or speck on the cover glass and so requires more opaquing.

Usually, the light source should be spaced 3 to 6 feet or, at least, the diagonal distance of the printing frame from the cover glass. The opening over the light should be reduced to ½ inch to 1 inch in diameter. Most commercial lights are on a low-voltage circuit, controlled by a rheostat to vary the brightness. This allows light to be dimmed for use with faster emulsions, keeping the exposure time in a convenient range.

Exposures can be increased in accuracy by use of a timer control. A bright light source for exposing plates or blue-line proofs is often used with exposure frames, but should not be used for normal contact work.

Test Exposure. The first exposure made with a specific light setting or with a different photographic material must be determined experimentally. Use a section of the negative or positive being duplicated which will produce some fine lines, some solid areas, and some fine white areas surrounded by solids. A special test negative could also be used. Make the test exposures on a small strip of the material to be used for the contact print. Expose in the printing frame, as given in the specific procedures which follow, using a series of exposure times.

Hold a piece of opaque paper on the glass of the printing frame so that only about one-fifth of the test strip is exposed. Turn on the light for 5 seconds. Then uncover two-fifths of the test strip, and expose for another 5 seconds. Continue until five such exposures have been made. The test strip will have been exposed in five steps for 25, 20, 15, 10, and 5 seconds.

Develop the test strip according to the directions which came with the material and in the same manner to be used on the final print. After the strip has been in the fixer a minute or two, rinse in water and inspect in bright light.

The correct exposure should be a step or two longer than the one giving a noticeably gray-looking solid, but less than the step showing any spread in fine black or white lines.

A film negative gray scale could also be used as a test negative by making exposures in very narrow strips across its width. The correct exposure should just produce a solid Step 3 (three steps from the clear end of the negative).

It may be necessary to make additional test strips to refine the exposure time. Usually the light intensity should be adjusted so that the exposure time is in the range of 10 to 20 seconds. If the light is too dim (or too distant), the time will be excessively long. If the light is too bright, the exposure time may be so short that it cannot be timed accurately.

Contacting on Paper

A contact photo print (photographic print) may be made on photographic print paper from either a film negative or a film positive. On the film negative, the image is transparent and the background is opaque. On the resulting positive photo print, the image appears black and the background white (the white paper). The reverse is true when a film positive is used.

Contact papers (such as Azo or Velox), or enlarging papers (such as Medalist or Kodabromide) which are faster, can be used. These should be in a glossy (F) finish, a high-contrast (No. 4 or 5) grade, and a thin weight.

Contact prints are fastened to the paste-up (mechanical layout) along with the line copy. The entire paste-up is photographed as line copy on one sheet of film so as to facilitate stripping the flat.

Positive Print from Film Negative. To make a positive photo print from a film negative, place a sheet of photo paper, emulsion side up, on the bed of the contact printing frame. Place the film negative, emulsion side down, over the paper. Make the exposure and process the photo paper as specified by the instructions packaged with the paper. See Figs. 11-14 and 11-15 for the procedure. Figure 11-16 shows a positive print made from a film negative.

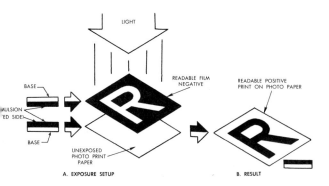

Fig. 11-15. Making a photographic contact positive print on photoprint paper.

Fig. 11-16. Positive photo print. Exposed and developed paper on which the image is black on a white background.

Fig. 11-17. Reverse photo print. A print on photographic paper where the image is white on a black background. A reverse print has the opposite, or reverse, tones of a positive print.

Reverse Photo Print. A reverse photo print, called a "reverse," is made by contact printing on photo paper from a *film positive*. The procedure is the same as for the positive print, above, except that a film positive is used instead of a film negative. The film positive will look much like Fig. 11-16 (except that white areas are clear film), and the reverse print will look like Fig. 11-17.

A one-step reverse print can be made as follows:

1. Make your film negative as usual;
2. On the emulsion side, paint over the image with white opaque;
3. Crop to size;
4. Paste this up on the mechanical (layout), or otherwise use as camera copy.

Instead of white opaquing the negative, you could back up the negative with bright white card stock. This latter method was used for the reverse in Fig. 11-22.

Halftone Contact Photo Prints. Since a halftone negative contains just halftone dots (no continuous tones), it may be treated essentially as a line negative when reproduction is by contact printing. The procedure follows that for other contact photo prints, except that a vacuum bed is essential for tight contact, and the dot structure of the print must be accurate. The contact-printing setup is the same as in Fig. 11-15. Halftone contact prints are sometimes called *Velox* prints because of the trade name of the paper used.

Since the original halftone negative is now contact-printed, and the print is then photographed as line copy to produce the negative for printing the plate, these extra, intermediary reproduction steps will change dot sizes somewhat. This should be anticipated and allowed for in making the original halftone negative. The smallest shadow dot may have to be about 20%, and the highlight dots about 80%, to produce a 10% to 90% range on the final print.

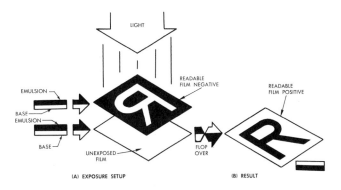

Fig. 11-18. Making a contact film positive from a film negative.

Contacting on Film

Film Positive from a Film Negative. To make a film positive from a film negative, proceed as shown in Fig. 11-18. Place a sheet of film such as Kodalith Ortho Thin-Base or a blue-sensitive contact film (emulsion side up) on the bed of the printing frame. Cover this with the film negative (also emulsion side up). Make the exposure to a point-source light and process the film.

Here, the emulsion of the negative is not in the usual direct contact with that of the film below since the base of the negative separates them. This is necessary so that the emulsion will be down in platemaking.

• **Note:** Some prefer to have both emulsions *down* rather than up, but if a thick-base film is used for the positive, the image may spread excessively as it passes through the base of the undeveloped film. This can be minimized by using thin-base or special contact film. The backing of these films is thin and clear enough to readily pass light rays, but even so, the exposure time may be somewhat longer.

Film Negative from a Film Positive. The same procedure described above (for film positive from film negative) may be used, except that a *film positive* is placed over the unexposed film on the bed of the contact printer. See Fig. 11-19.

Contacting on Duplicating Film

It is often necessary to duplicate film negatives (or positives) — in other words, to make a negative from a negative (or a positive from a positive), Fig. 11-20A and B. For example, this would be necessary when a job is to be run four-up on the press sheet, and three additional negatives (exactly like the original) are needed. Normal film always reverses tones, requiring that an intermediate film positive be made so that three extra negatives can be exposed from the intermediate. This means two additional generations of duplicates with possible loss of some fine detail each time.

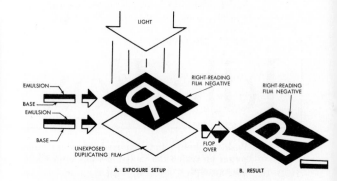

A. Base-side-to-emulsion contact maintains orientation of image. In this setup the exposure light passes through only one layer of film base.

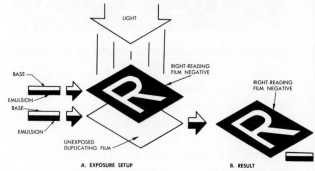

B. Emulsion-to-base-side contact also maintains orientation of image; however, the exposure light must pass through two layers of film base. Whenever possible, use method "A", above.

Fig. 11-20. Using duplicating film to make a duplicate right-reading film negative from a right-reading film negative. To make a duplicate right-reading film positive, substitute a right-reading film positive at "A".

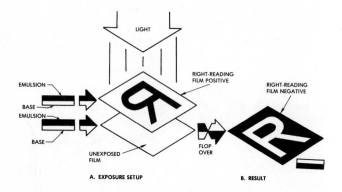

Fig. 11-19. Making a contact film negative from a film positive.

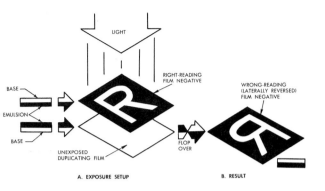

Fig. 11-21. Using duplicating film to make a laterally reversed image (wrong-reading image) film negative from a right-reading film negative or flopping an image from left to right. To make a similar film positive, substitute a film positive at "A".

Fig. 11-22. Diagonal reverse-position combination.

To make duplicate film negatives or duplicate film positives, use a *direct-duplicating film* such as Kodak Duplicating film, or Kodak High-Speed Duplicating film.

Direct-duplicating films can also be used to flop the image from left to right, also called *lateral reversal* of the image, Fig. 11-21. The duplicating film is exposed emulsion side up. This essentially puts the emulsion on the opposite side of the base, so as to allow an emulsion-to-emulsion contact in later operations (after the image has been flopped over). Choices of exposure for Kodak Duplicating and High-Speed Duplicating films include use of point-source light in contacting, exposure directly in a process camera, or exposure through the base or face of the film. Positives give positives; negatives yield negatives.

Negative-Positive Combinations. Figure 11-22 shows a negative-positive (reverse-positive) combination print. An easy method of making this combination uses regular film and photo paper, but requires three generations of exposures.

Prepare a film negative of the entire design, and make a positive photo print of it. Tape the print to a backing sheet. The negative should be taped, in register, over the print. Then, where desired, cut through both layers with a sharp knife. Tape half of each — the negative and the print — to a sheet of bright-white card stock.

Shooting this on the camera will result in a combination negative which will produce a reverse-positive combination print. See Fig. 11-22.

Contacting Spreads and Chokes

Sometimes, rather than carefully holding the same width of lines on the image, it is desirable to cause them to widen or to become thinner. These are called *spreads* and *chokes* (or weighting and thinning, or fats and skinnies). It may be necessary to make type look a little bolder or to produce special effects in large type. A common need for a spread is when color is added to a type reverse. The original negative (which was used to make the positive for the reverse) could be used for the color, but it would fit only when in *perfect* register. Since some variation is expected during the press run, it is desirable to have the color image overlap slightly.

A *spread* is contacted on film from a negative. The setup is nearly the same as for usual contacting, except the light must strike at an angle of about 20° to 45° — the greater the angle, the more the spread. For exposure, a small printing frame can be placed on a lazy Susan and spun to cause the spread in all directions. See Fig. 11-23. With large vacuum frames, it may be easier to swing the exposure light in a circle over the edges of the frame. Moving the light in a square pattern may produce sharper corners.

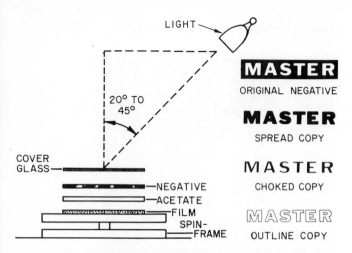

Fig. 11-23. Spreads and chokes. The setup is shown at the left, and examples are shown at the right.

There never should be an emulsion-to-emulsion contact between the negative and the film. For small spreads, the base of the film negative (as in Fig. 11-18) may be sufficient spacing. For larger spreads, a clear piece of acetate (.004″ to .006″ thick) between the negative and the film allows a greater under-cutting of the image on the negative. Experiment for the right effect. Either regular or direct-duplicating film can be used, depending on the results desired.

A *choke* is contacted in the same manner, except that a positive is used.

Outline letters can be produced from solid type by making a spread and a choke, and then making a regular contact print through the two in register. Another method is to make a normal positive from the negative and to use this in the following order to make a spread (from bottom

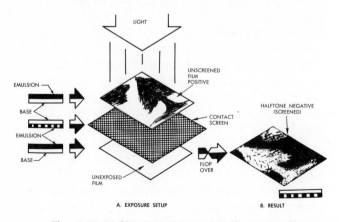

Fig. 11-24. Making a contact screened negative from an unscreened film positive.

layer upward): (1) unexposed film, (2) film positive, (3) clear acetate spacer, and (4) original negative. *In-line letters* (thin centers) are made in the same way, except the order of the positive and the negative is interchanged.

Off-Camera Contact Screening

Halftone Film Negative from Continuous-Tone Film Positive. A same-size halftone film negative can be made from a continuous-tone film positive by using the setup shown in Fig. 11-24. Kodalith Ortho Thin-Base Film, Type 3, is placed, emulsion side up, on the vacuum frame bed. Over this is placed the magenta contact screen (negative), with emulsion side down. The unscreened (continuous-tone) film positive is placed over the screen, emulsion side up. Main (detail) and flash exposures may be determined experimentally.

Autoscreen film can be used in place of the litho film. In this case, the contact screen is omitted.

Halftone Film Positive from Continuous-Tone Negative. This operation follows essentially the same procedure as in Fig. 11-24, except, of course, the continuous-tone *negative* and the magenta contact screen *(positive)* are used.

Special Techniques

Open or Blank Areas. An open or blank area may be produced on film negatives, film positives and prints in the contact-printing procedure by placing a piece of red or black opaque paper of the required size and shape over the appropriate area of the negative (or positive) in the printing frame. Stripping tape can also be used.

Silhouetted Halftone Prints. By opaquing the unwanted background on a halftone negative, the resulting halftone print will appear with a white background, as in Fig. 11-25.

Lettering on Halftone Illustrations. A simple way to have lettering appear on a halftone illustration is to place transfer-type letters (or to hand letter) directly onto the face of the original photo. The lettering can also be done on a *thin* piece of clear acetate fastened as a flap (an overlay) over the photo. If copied in one shot on the camera, Autoscreen film can be used to pre-

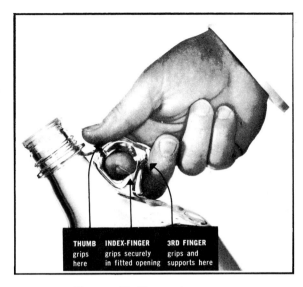

Fig. 11-25. Silhouetted halftone print.

vent a screen pattern from showing on the letters.

A more exacting method requires that the lettering be on the overlay. Then two separate negatives are made to be surprinted, or overprinted, later. A halftone negative is made only of the photograph with the overlay folded back. Then, at the same focus and without changing the location of the copy, the overlay is flopped into place, a clean white sheet is inserted between the overlay and the photo, and a line negative is made of the lettering. If any of the lettering is to appear in reverse (as white letters against a dark section of the halftone), it will be necessary to contact a film positive from the line negative of the lettering. The halftone should be on thin-base film.

These then may be combined in the darkroom by surprinting on film, so that a single negative is used in stripping and platemaking. This probably is desirable when the image must be repeated a number of times on the plate. Another method is to strip two separate flats and do the surprinting on the plate. This probably is desirable for a single (one-up) image on the plate.

Refer to Fig. 7-14 on page 115 as an example. This has four sections of type to be combined with the photograph — two lines are reversed, one is overprinted, and a pair are in a blocked-out area. The line positive must have all but the

two reversed lines scraped off, or removed chemically. Then this is placed *over* the thin-base halftone for one exposure. The clear positive must be larger than the halftone, because the film edge would cause a line to print. Tape placed on the top surface of the halftone negative forms the open area for the block-out. Then, the two unwanted lines on the line negative (which will be reversed and are on the positive) are opaqued. This negative is printed in register in a second exposure — either onto duplicating film or onto the plate.

Registering Multiple Exposures.   In the surprinting, explained above, the image for each exposure must be carefully located, so as to be in perfect register. There are several ways to do this. The *flap* method is accurate and easily done. The use of simple *register marks* is explained as a stripping procedure in Chapter 12 and is illustrated in Fig. 12-23.

Register pins, however, are the most accurate and now the most commonly used method of registering multiple exposures. See Fig. 12-33. They are used in darkroom printing operations, in stripping, in positioning flats for platemaking, and, occasionally, even as an aid in positioning plates on the press. The register pin is turned carefully to ¼″ diameter, is about $^1/_{16}$″ high, and is spot-welded to a thin metal backing which can

Raden C Auto-Step Company

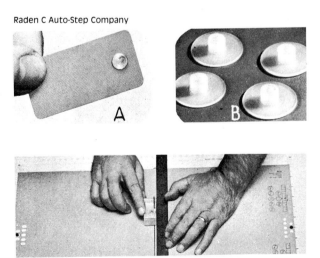

Fig. 11-26. Register pins (A) and buttons (B). The view below shows two pins being used with prepared step-masking sheets.

be taped in position. Similar plastic buttons without the backing are also available. Two ¼″ holes are punched in all sheets to be registered. The sheets can be aligned and then punched at the same time. Sometimes masking sheets are punched, and the film images are taped in register into openings on the sheets. Pins are placed in the two holes of a punched sheet. The pin backs then can be taped in position to a backing sheet which is placed in the exposure frame. For stripping work, the pins are taped directly to the glass of the light table. More complete directions come with the pins. Also, see Chapter 12.

Screened Type Effects.   Screened type effects, such as those produced in Fig. 11-28 with Phototypositor screens, are easily made. A patterned screen is interposed between the film negative (or film positive) and the print in the contact frame. For screened type, use a film negative of the type matter; for screened background, use a film positive.

Projection Printing

In projection printing (photo enlarging), the image on the film negative (or film positive) in the photo-enlarger negative holder is projected down to the sensitized photo material on the bed of the enlarger — usually in a larger size.

The Enlarger

Figure 11-29 shows the schematic construction of a table model photo enlarger. In operation, the light rays from the lamp are spread by the condensing system evenly over the negative.

The image on the negative is then projected through the lens to the photo paper or other sensitized photo material on the enlarger bed. After the image is exposed a suitable length of time, the photo material is processed.

Raising or lowering the enlarger head increases or decreases the size of the projected image. Image focusing is achieved by contracting or extending the bellows.

For projection printing operations which are to involve the use of the contact screen, a

Fig. 11-28. Screened type.

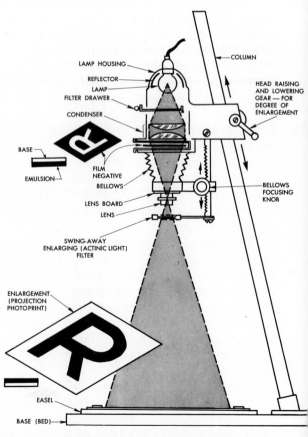

Fig. 11-29. Schematic of photo enlarger and projection printing.

Chemco Photoproducts Company

Fig. 11-27. "Protocol" film punch.

vacuum board is essential. However, if your enlarger is not equipped with a vacuum board, arrange the setup so that the vacuum-printing frame can be used for the enlarger easel.

A simple enlarger will suffice for the basic operations of contact printing. More elaborate enlargers extend to those large commercial models equipped for process-color separation and become increasingly more expensive.

Projection Printing Operations

Several projection printing operations are described below. Note that the first procedure, making a projection (enlarged) positive print from an unscreened film negative, includes the steps in the basic enlarging process. It is recommended that the student perform this procedure in order to become familiar with the basic projection-printing operation.

Making an Unscreened Positive Projection Print from an Unscreened Film Negative. This can be (1) the familiar enlargement of a snapshot negative, or other continuous-tone film negative; (2) an enlargement of a film negative whose image is type matter or other line work; or (3) an enlargement of a film positive, either line work or continuous tone. See Fig. 11-30.

Proceed as follows:
1. Clean the negative carrier.
2. Insert the negative into the carrier with the emulsion side down.
3. Shut off the overhead white lights; turn on the safelight.
4. Focus on a sheet of white paper.
   When making the enlargement, place the paper in exactly the position and plane that the projection (enlarging) paper will occupy. Proceed in this order: (a) first adjust for size; (b) adjust for sharp image; (c) recheck for size and readjust if necessary; (d) finally, recheck and readjust for sharpest focus (image).
5. Remove the paper used for focusing.
6. Insert a sheet of the projection (enlarging) paper into the easel — emulsion side up.
7. Make a series of test exposures, of varying lengths, across the sheet.

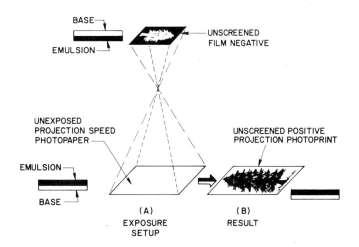

Fig. 11-30. Making an unscreened positive projection photoprint from an unscreened film negative. To make an unscreened projection reverse print, substitute a film positive in the enlarger negative carrier.

8. To determine the best length of exposure, develop by time and temperature according to package instructions.
9. Insert a fresh sheet of projection paper in the easel — again, emulsion side up.
10. Make the exposure, and process the print.

Making a Halftone (Screened) Positive Projection Print from a Continuous-Tone Unscreened Film Negative. (Figure 11-31.)   With

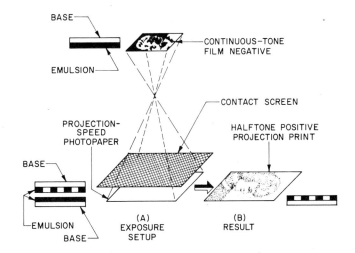

Fig. 11-31. Making a halftone (screened) positive projection print from an unscreened continuous-tone film negative.

this operation, snapshot negatives can be reproduced as halftone prints in the size and area needed for pasting up on the mechanical layout, and can then be photographed along with the line copy on one sheet of film.

For screen patterns of 133 or 150 lines per inch, use the gray contact screen; for coarser screen rulings of 120 lines per inch or less, use the magenta contact screen (negative). For main and flash exposures with either type of screen, use the white light and yellow flash as when the magenta contact screen is used in the camera.

Place the continuous-tone negative in the negative carrier of the enlarger, emulsion side down, and focus the enlarger. Place a sheet of the projection-speed paper on the vacuum-frame bed, emulsion side up. Place the halftone screen over this, emulsion side down, overlapping about an inch all around for good vacuum draw. Determine the main and flash exposures, experimentally, on different sections of the same sheet of paper. Using fresh paper, make the main and flash exposures. Process the print.

Making a Halftone Projection Film Positive from a Continuous-Tone Film Negative. To make a halftone film positive from a continuous-tone film negative, first place the continuous-tone film negative in the enlarger negative holder, the emulsion side *up*. Place a sheet of Ortho Type 3 film on the vacuum frame bed with emulsion *up*. Cover this film with the magenta contact screen (positive) with the emulsion side of the screen facing *down*. See Fig. 11-32. Be sure the screen overlaps the edges of the film by about an inch all around.

Determine the main and flash exposures experimentally, using different sections of a sheet of the same type film at varying exposure times. With a fresh sheet of film, make main and flash exposures, and process the film.

Supplies

Manufacturers of graphic arts films and photographic supplies include, among others, the following firms (listed in alphabetical order):

Agfa-Gevaert
Chemco Photoproducts
DuPont
Eastman Kodak Company
General Photoproducts Company
Polychrome Corporation
3M Company

The user is advised to consult latest catalog listings for complete offerings, and to follow the packaged instructions for exposure times and processing procedures. Also, it is suggested that, for possible economy, the user consider purchasing rollfilm.

Questions

1. List the usual items of equipment found in the darkroom.
2. What determines the color of the safelight to be used (if any) in the darkroom?
3. Why should bottled chemicals be stored on the lowest shelves of the cabinets in the darkroom?
4. Why is a ventilating fan needed in the darkroom? If there is no ventilating fan, how is the darkroom ventilated?
5. What advantage is there in having the back of the darkroom camera inside the darkroom?
6. Why are the trays always kept in the same order?

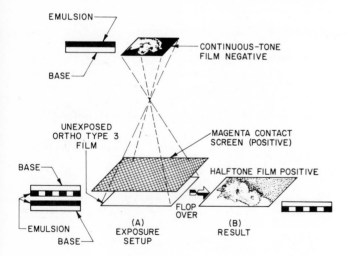

Fig. 11-32. **Making a halftone film positive from a continuous-tone film negative by projection printing.**

7. How is an image produced on a negative?
8. How is the concentrated developer chemical prepared for use?
9. Of what use is the tray siphon in the darkroom?
10. What is the recommended temperature for the water in the film-washing tray?
11. Tell how you would combine 28% acetic acid and water to make one-half gallon of shortstop solution.
12. Describe the inspection method of developing film.
13. How is film developed by the time-and-temperature method?
14. Describe a sensitivity guide (or gray scale).
15. Describe the gradual emergence of the image of the gray scale (or sensitivity guide) on the film in the developing tray.
16. What advantages are there in using a gray scale (or sensitivity guide) in processing film?
17. Outline the procedure in developing a negative.
18. Tell how to make a positive on film from a negative.
19. How is a contact print (positive photoprint) made from a negative?
20. Describe how to make a duplicate film negative from a film negative.
21. Tell how a combination negative is made.
22. How does one provide a blank space on a negative or print?
23. What kind of work is photographed on orthochromatic film?
24. Tell how to make an enlarged photoprint from a film negative.

3. Prepare a container of A and a container of B developer solution in the quantity specified by your instructor.
4. Prepare a container of fixer solution in the quantity specified by your instructor.
5. Using 28% acetic acid and water, prepare one-half gallon of shortstop.
6. Prepare the four trays for developing film. Use the quantities specified in these instructions, or those specified by your instructor.
7. Expose and develop a negative from the copy and problem specified by your instructor.
8. Make a film positive from the prepared negative in problem 7.
9. Make a contact print from the negative and the positive in problems 7 and 8. Provide a blank area on one.
10. Make a combination line and halftone negative from copy and problem specified by the instructor.
11. Make a halftone negative, using self-screening film.
12. Using duplicating film, make a right-reading film negative from a right-reading film negative.
13. On the enlarger, make an enlarged photoprint from a film negative.
14. On the enlarger, make an enlarged halftone negative by projection printing.
15. Prepare a wall chart showing how the sensitivity guide is placed next to the copy on the copyboard, and how the sensitivity guide looks when it is developed to a specified step on film. Make your own negatives and prints for this display.

Problems and Projects

1. Make a scale drawing of a darkroom for an offset plant, plan a new darkroom for the shop, or make plans for remodeling the present one. Use catalogs in the shop library for your planning. Estimate the cost of the equipment you have selected.
2. Make a wall chart showing the order of trays in the darkroom. Ink the drawing and photograph it, to be used later to make an offset plate for printing.

New Terms

acetic acid	illumination
Autoscreen film	negative-positive
choke	projection printing
developer	register pins
fixer	shortstop bath
flap method	spread
glacial acetic acid	squeegee
graduates	vacuum bed
hypo	vapors

Chapter 12 Laying Out and Stripping the Flat

Laying Out and Stripping Process

Stripping is the process of precisely positioning and fastening one or more film negatives, or film positives, onto a plate-size masking sheet so that those film images can be exposed in the desired positions on the offset plate. Stripping is also referred to as *image assembly*. The masking sheet with its taped-on film negatives, or film positives, is called *the flat*.

Basic Function of the Flat

Figure 12-1 illustrates basically how the flat is stripped up and how the flat is used to help produce an imaged plate for the offset press. The basic steps are as follows:

After all the film negatives and film positives have been made by the camera operator, the stripper tapes them, with the emulsion (wrong-reading) side up on a laid-out masking sheet of the same size as the press plate, in the exact positions called for by the layout.

The stripped-up flat is turned over on the stripping table so that it is in readable form, that is, base side up and emulsion side down. Windows are cut out of the masking material, exposing the desired portions of the film negatives, or film positives, below. See Fig. 12-1D.

The stripped-up flat is placed, readable side up, over a sensitized offset plate in the plate exposure machine. After a period of exposure to the intense exposure-light source, the plate is developed to bring out its image and to cause the image to be ink-receptive on the press.

Stripping Negative and Stripping Positive

Stripping negative, or negative stripping, refers to making a flat which consists mainly of film negatives. This negative-stripped flat is used in exposing a negative-working offset plate and produces positive images on that plate. See Fig. 12-3. Any film positive stripped into this negative-stripped flat will produce a reverse image on the developed negative-working offset plate.

Fig. 12-2. Stripping a large flat.

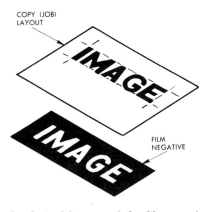

A. The desired layout and the film negative are supplied to the stripper.

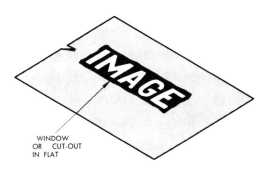

D. The flat is turned over, and the window is cut out.

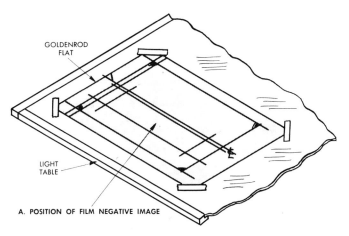

B. The flat is laid out. Note the position marked out for the film negative image.

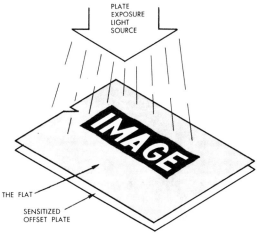

E. The flat, with image readable, is placed over a sensitized plate and the assembly is exposed to the platemaker light.

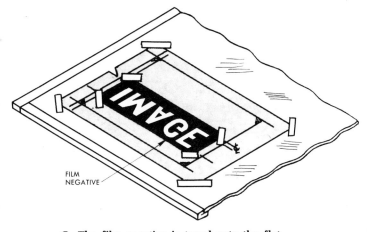

C. The film negative is taped onto the flat, emulsion up.

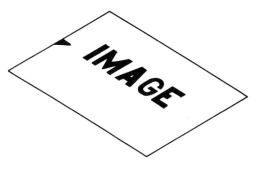

F. After exposure, the plate is developed and reveals a readable image.

Fig. 12-1.   Basic function of a flat.

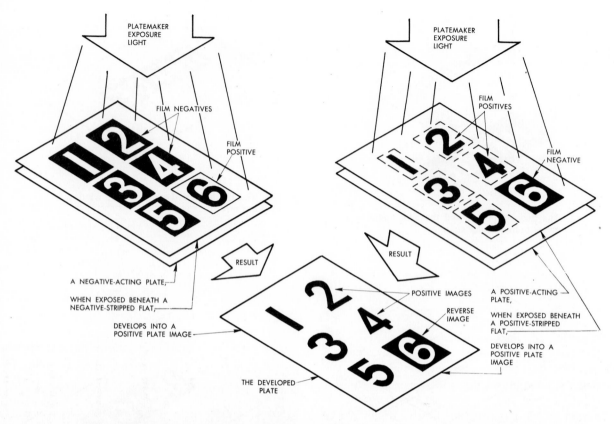

Fig. 12-3. Plate image resulting from exposure of film negatives to negative-working plate, and exposure of film positives to positive-working plate.

Stripping positive, or positive stripping, refers to the making of a flat which consists mainly of film positives. This positive-stripped flat is used in exposing a positive-acting offset plate and produces positive images on that plate, Fig. 12-3. Any film negative included on a positive-stripped flat will produce a reverse image on the positive-working offset plate. Detailed procedures for negative- and positive-stripped flats follow.

Stripping Negative

As described earlier, stripping negative refers to the making of a flat which is composed chiefly of film negatives.

Stock for the Flat

The stock, or base material, generally used for stripping a flat composed of film negatives

may be an 80-pound (118 g/m²) double-coated goldenrod paper, orange-colored sheet-plastic material, or other commercially available material sold especially for this purpose. Plastic materials are more dimensionally stable than the paper materials.

• **Note:** The term *goldenrod* is often used when the material of the flat is referred to — whether it is goldenrod paper, plastic, or other material.

The stock used for the flat allows non-actinic light to penetrate through the flat so that the images on the film can be seen through it, yet will not allow actinic light rays* to affect the

*A light ray which causes photochemical changes.

sensitized coating of the offset plate when plate exposures are made. Thus, the goldenrod acts as a light mask, the same as the opaque portions of the film negatives.

The goldenrod, or other masking sheet material, may be cut from bulk. Ready-cut sheets also may be purchased with layouts imprinted and prepunched for pin register systems for individual press-size use.

A flat which is cut wider than the plate width is useful when a job being laid out has a sheet width wider than the plate, Fig. 12-4. The extra width of the flat can accommodate film images which are to ''bleed'' off the edge of the sheet and will also prevent accidental exposure of the plate's edges.

After the exposed plate has been developed, the image on the plate is an exact duplicate of the image on the flat.

On a finished offset plate (unlike a type form), it is impossible to add spacing between lines. Neither can an illustration be moved in respect to other illustrations or type matter on the page. All images on the plate are fixed in their relative positions, these positions being determined by the positions of the negatives on the flat. Thus, the flat must be stripped with great accuracy and care.

Equipment and Supplies

The following minimum tools, equipment, and supplies should be available and in good condition:

A frosted-glass stripping table, lighted from below.

80-pound (118 g/m²), double-coated goldenrod stock, cut to press-plate size.

Dispenser with colored litho tape.

Dispenser with transparent tape.

Stripping knife, or single-edge razor blades.

Steel T-square.

Steel straightedge (steel ruler) with beveled edges.

Steel triangles, 30-60 and 45 degrees.

Set of scribing tools.

Paper-cutting shears (scissors).

Black (India) drafting ink.

Drafter's ruling pen and 5″ dividers (a set of drafting tools is useful in the shop).

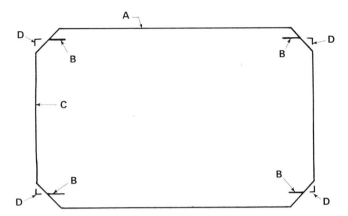

Fig. 12-4.   Sometimes the flat is wider than the plate. "A" is the edge of the flat; "B" shows printed guide lines. Prior to plate exposure, the flat is positioned so the head of the plate butts at "C", the sides line up at lines "B", and the corners then are at points D.

Chemco Photoproducts Company

Fig. 12-5.   Opaquing negative at medium size light table also used for stripping and layout.

Opaque solution.

Various sizes and shapes of artist's brushes.

Linen tester magnifying glass.

Steel square, to suit sizes of layouts.

Other tools, added as needed.

Foster Manufacturing Company

Fig. 12-6.   Light table, for layout and stripping.

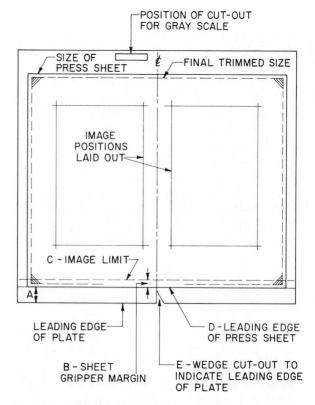

Fig. 12-7.   Laying out the flat.

Layout Table

The precision layout table, or line-up table, has a glass top. It is lighted from below and is equipped with movable horizontal straightedge (or T-square) and triangles.

Preparation for Stripping

Remove all traces of tape from the glass top of the stripping table with a razor blade. Wash the glass top with glass cleaner and dry thoroughly. Select the T-square you will use, and be sure to use this same T-square for all work on the same flat. (Another T-square may vary slightly in squareness.)

In using the T-square, work from only one edge of the table. Use triangles with the T-square to draw lines at angles to the T-square blade.

Laying Out the Flat

Place a sheet of goldenrod paper, cut to press-plate size, on the stripping table. One long edge of the sheet, which will be referred to as the gripper or feeding edge, should be parallel to the edge of the table nearest the stripper. This edge corresponds to the leading edge of the plate and of the paper as it is fed into the press. On small presses, such as a 10″ × 15″,

the lead edge is the short dimension, and can be placed at the left.

Line up the lower edge of the paper with the upper edge of the T-square. Fasten the paper to the glass top with pieces of tape, working from diagonal corners and smoothing the paper before taping it. Mark the flat in a corner with the number or name of the job to identify it.

Lay out the flat according to Figs. 12-7 and 12-9. Distance "A" represents that portion of the pressplate from the leading edge of the plate to the leading edge of the press sheet. Distance "B" represents that portion of the leading edge of the press sheet which is gripped by the press sheet grippers during the printing operation, and thus cannot receive an impression from the blanket.

The above distances vary from press to press, are subject to manufacturers' press modifications, and may vary according to the optional equipment of a specific model of press. Correct distances should be obtained from the individu-

OFFSET PRESSES — MAKES AND MODELS	Press Sheet Size				Max. Image Printing Area		(Locations of distances **A** and **B** below are shown in Figure 12-9. **A** is the press plate gripper area; **B** is the press sheet gripper bite.)															
							Pinbar Punched Plate				Straight Edge Plate				Slotted Hole Plate				Serrated End Plate			
	Max.		Min.				Size		A	B	Size		A	B	Size		A	B	Size		A	B
	W	L	W	L	W	L	W	L			W	L			W	L			W	L		

Fig. 12-8. Suggested layout for a wall chart of flat layout specifications.

al offset press manufacturer. Once obtained, the dimensions should be posted for ready reference on a wall chart such as shown in Fig. 12-8 along with a copy of Fig. 12-9 (offset plate area and dimensional terminology).

• **Note:** In all the following operations, remember that neither the press plate gripper area "A" nor the press sheet gripper margin "B" can carry an image. Therefore, when stripping in the negatives, avoid placing the image area of the negatives in either of these two areas.

Locate and draw a vertical centerline on the sheet. Label it "E" at the top.

Measure and lay out the length and width of the sheet of paper to be run. Width should be measured up from the line representing the leading edge of the press sheet. Measure and mark half the length on each side of the vertical centerline. Draw the outline of the press-size sheet of paper a little heavier than other lines.

If the printed press sheets are to have a final trim after printing, rule in the trim lines on the layout.

At this point, it will be helpful for the beginner to shade in the corners of the rectangle for the final trimmed size of the press sheet.

For each flat, lay out an oblong rectangle the size of a gray scale at the end of the plate (outside of the press sheet area). This should be cut

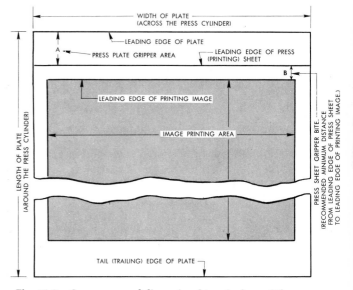

Fig. 12-9. Some area and dimensional terminology of the offset plate.

out later so the platemaker has a window in which to place the gray scale. See page 250 and Fig. 13-16 for use of the gray scale in properly exposing a plate.

Inside the finished sheet-size area, indicate the exact size and position of each of the *images* (not the entire negatives) which are to be included on the flat. Draw all lines with a sharp pencil. Extend the lines about ³/₈ inch beyond the corners of the rectangles, to assist in positioning the negatives on the flat. Be sure to use a scale with beveled edges. If the scale has a thick edge, hold it on edge to get accurate measurements.

If the images on some of the negatives do not have parallel or flush sides, it may be helpful to draw a centerline in each of those image rectangles on the flat to later match up the negatives, Fig. 12-14E.

Stripping-In the Negatives

The stripper generally works in "reverse" by positioning and fastening (taping) the film negatives to the flat with the emulsion side *up*.

Fig. 12-10. A film negative with image in unreadable or wrong-reading form.

Fig. 12-11. A film negative with a readable image.

Fig. 12-12. Correctly made negative will show transparent lines when scratched on the back with knife or needle.

In this position, the images on the negatives look like that in Fig. 12-10. The image is reversed fron right to left, and so it can be said that the image is unreadable (wrong-reading).

Determining the Emulsion Side

The back side of a film negative has a clear acetate base. The front side of the negative is coated with the blackened silver emulsion and is the side on which the image appears.

The stripper can easily determine the emulsion side of a negative. It is the duller of the two sides. Furthermore, if the emulsion side of a negative is scratched with the point of a knife or a razor blade, a transparent line or area is produced. In scratching, a portion of the emulsion is removed, exposing the clear acetate base of the film, Fig. 12-12.

The usual correctly made negative has a right-reading (readable) image as in Fig. 12-11. It reads normally from left to right when viewed from the base (back) side. The same correctly made negative appears *wrong-reading* (unreadable) as in Fig. 12-12 if viewed from the front or emulsion side.

• **Note:** We are disregarding, for the moment, that there are times when we intentionally make a negative which is wrong-reading (laterally reversed) when viewed from the base side (emulsion side down).

In stripping, the negatives are placed on the flat with the *emulsion side up* (in the *unreadable position*) so that later, when the flat is pressed against the coated plate during the plate exposure, the emulsion side of the negative will be tight against the plate's coating. If the negative were placed with the emulsion side *down* on the flat, when the flat were turned over and windows cut to expose the film, the emulsion would be scratched. This would require opaquing which could have been avoided. Also, during plate exposure, there would be, along the edge of the film, a space the thickness of the goldenrod paper. Since the opening would hold the film away from the plate coating, light rays could enter. The edge of the image being formed on the plate would be spread, or blurred. This creeping and spreading of the light rays is called *halation*.

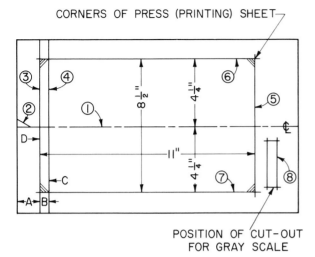

CORNERS OF PRESS (PRINTING) SHEET

POSITION OF CUT-OUT
FOR GRAY SCALE

Fig. 12-13. Layout of flat for 8½″ × 11″ sheet on typical duplicator size plate. Circled numerals indicate the consecutive order of ruling the lines on the layout.
A. Width of plate gripper area.
B. Width of sheet gripper area.
C. Image limit at leading edge of sheet.
D. Leading edge of press sheet.

Opaquing and Trimming

Handling the film by its edges to avoid scratches and fingerprints, lay the negative, emulsion side up, on the lighted stripping table. Using a brush, coat and opaque all pinholes, scratches, and other show-through defects on this emulsion side. This is needed only in the portion of the negative which will be exposed to the plate.

Some strippers prefer to opaque on the base (clear) side of the negatives, especially when ruling with the pen, cropping illustrations, or opaquing extensive areas. Errors in opaquing on the base side can be removed without damage to the emulsion. However, avoid opaquing any part of an image on the base side where, during plate exposure, the thickness of the film support may cause halation. Also, do not opaque film on the base side directly where you will be later cutting out the windows from the flat. Cutting through the goldenrod (or other "flat" material) will result in cutting a line through the opaque.

• **Note:** Before it is used to expose an offset plate, the flat should be checked on a lighted stripping table. Remedy any defects that need opaquing.

Trim the negatives to not less than ¼ inch from the images. The trimming need not be perfectly square, but be sure to leave at least ¼ inch for taping the negatives to the flat. Use either scissors, or a steel straightedge and a single-edge razor blade or knife. To protect the glass, cut on plastic sheeting.

Scribing Reference Marks

Reference lines are scribed into the emulsion of the negatives to aid in placing the negatives in accurate position on the layout.

Place the negative, emulsion side up, on the lighted stripping table. Lay a steel straightedge across the negative so the far side of the straightedge lines up with the top of the first line of type on the negative. With the edge of a razor blade or a sharp knife, scribe a line through the emulsion to the left and right of the top of the first line of type. Scribe at the edge of the negative (on the left, and then on the right) to within about ⅛ inch of the image. Do not scribe into the image.

Next, lay the straightedge along the left side of the image, and scribe a line through the emulsion from the top edge of the negative to within ⅛ inch of the image. This line, and the two described above, will give three reference lines on the negative with which to line it up with the marked-out position on the flat. See Fig. 12-14 views B through D.

• **Note:** Figure 12-14E shows how a center reference line is used to mount negatives along a vertical centerline.

Taping the Negatives

Place the negative (emulsion side up) over the area on the flat where it is to be fixed. The head of the type matter should be toward the marked-out head of the laid-out rectangle on the flat. Match the three reference lines of the negative with the corresponding reference

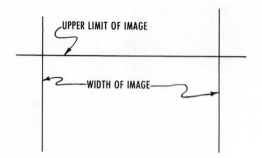

A. Lay out the position on flat which image will occupy.

D. Position negative on flat with aid of reference lines.

B. Scribe reference lines through emulsion.

E. If a vertical centerline is to be used to center images on the page, then scribe a center mark at the image center on the negative, as at "C", above. Align the negative at "A", "B", and "C", above.

C. Trim negative to within ¼" of image.

F. Stripping a negative. Tape negative in place.

G. Flat turned over and window cut out close to image.

Fig. 12-14. Stripping a negative.

Fig. 12-15. How to splice two negatives.

lines of the rectangle. Fasten the negative at the corners with little squares of red, amber, or black tape. If needed, fasten the negatives along the edges with additional pieces of tape, but use no more than is absolutely necessary. In any event, never tape the negative any closer to the image than $1/8$ inch. See Fig. 12-14F.

Cutting the Windows

Free the flat from the table top by cutting along the edges of the flat, through the tape at the corners of the flat. Turn the flat over and remove the goldenrod paper covering the images by cutting through the flat with a razor blade, or sharp knife. Be sure to cut only through the paper and *not through the negatives*. Make the cuts $1/16$ to $1/8$ inch outside the image areas, Fig. 12-14G.

Carefully scan the negative sections for any pinholes or scratches which might allow light to pass through. If any are found, opaque them.

If halftone negatives have been stripped into the flat, the opening in the flat is cut out. Then, by use of tape strips on all four sides, the halftone is framed (cropped) to the proper size. See Fig. 12-16.

A halftone may also be cropped by painting with opaque to the desired outline after the outline has been ruled with opaque in a ruling pen.

Scribing Lines on the Negatives

If the printed work is to include lines or borders which do not appear on the negatives, they may be provided by scribing, or scratching, them through the emulsion of the negatives.

Film-scribing tools may be used for scribing lines on negatives. Each tool head has two cutting edges. A complete set will enable one to scribe single or parallel lines of various weights and combinations. If scribing tools are unavailable, a lithographer's needle may be sharpened to the desired width. Be sure to produce a flat, chisel-shaped end.

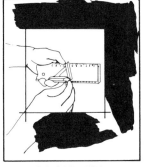

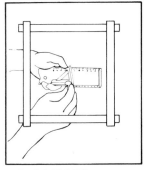

A. BY OPAQUING   B. BY TAPING

Fig. 12-16. Cropping negatives.

Roberts & Porter, Inc.

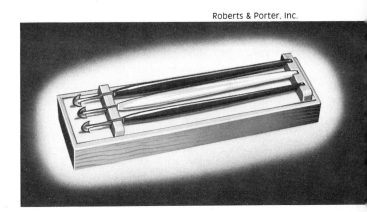

Fig. 12-17. Film scribing tools.

nuArc Company, Inc.

Fig. 12-18. Scriber, ruler, and cutter.

It is distinctly timesaving to intentionally omit rules in type composition. Negatives of the type proofs are made with only the type characters printed. A more uniform and neater job can be obtained by scribing the necessary rules or lines on the developed negatives.

Reference Marks Cut Into the Flats

Certain marks are provided on the flat to aid the platemaker, press operator, and papercutter. These marks are shown in Fig. 12-19.

Gripper Edge

The gripper edge of a flat is identified by a wedge-shaped piece cut from the edge of the flat, Fig. 12-19. One side of the wedge is cut along the centerline. The point of the wedge should not intrude far enough toward the image to print on the paper. The gripper mark *does* print on the plate, and tells the platemaker and press operator which edge of the flat is used in lining up the plate.

Cylinder Marks

A cylinder reference mark should be cut through on each side of the flat outside of the printing area. It should extend to the edge of the flat, removing a 1/64 inch sliver of paper from the flat. See Fig. 12-19. If each flat is provided with cylinder marks in the same locations, cor-

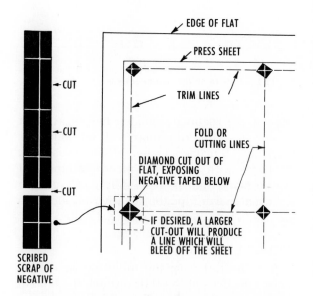

Fig. 12-20. Providing trim, fold, and cutting lines on flat.

responding to the position of the marks on the plate cylinder, successive plates may be registered and run with a minimum of plate shifting.

Trim, Fold, and Cut Marks

If trim, fold, and cut marks are desired on the printed sheets, a thin sliver of paper may be cut out of the flat so that a thin line will print on the paper. Or, a portion of the flat may be cut out and a piece of opaque negative can be taped in. Lines scribed on the negative emulsion will print on the paper. These marks indicate where to trim, fold, or cut the finished printed sheets. See Fig. 12-20.

Additional Layouts for Imposition

It is economical and timesaving to use a press sheet as large as can be accommodated on the press for the press run, and to print on that sheet as many images of the job as can be accommodated. Then, later, the job can be cut apart.

Figure 12-21 shows a layout for a job to be run "four-up," and which will be cut into the four pieces after printing. Notice that, in this job, a trim has been allowed on all sides of the press sheet.

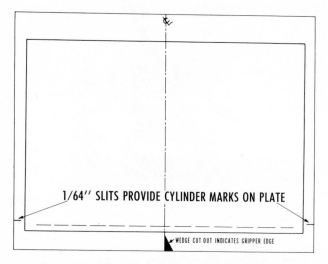

Fig. 12-19. Reference marks, gripper edge and cylinder.

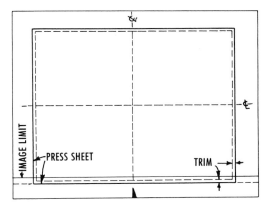

Fig. 12-21. Layout of flat for running a job four-up, allowing for trim after cutting.

Fig. 12-22. Flat layouts for four-page folder printed from two plates. Note that flats are laid out in reverse. When printed, page 1 will be a right-hand page and will be backed up by page 2.

Figure 12-22 shows the layout for printing a four-page folder (both sides of one sheet), using two plates. Notice that the work is done in reverse on the flats. When the flats are turned over for use in exposing the plates, the pages will be in normal order — page one will be a right-hand page, and will be backed-up by page two of the second plate.

Step-and-Repeat Work

Figure 12-23 shows how a job can be stripped up to expose one image a number of times on the same plate without duplicating the negatives for each unit area.

A register flat is laid out to include the number of unit areas required for the entire plate.

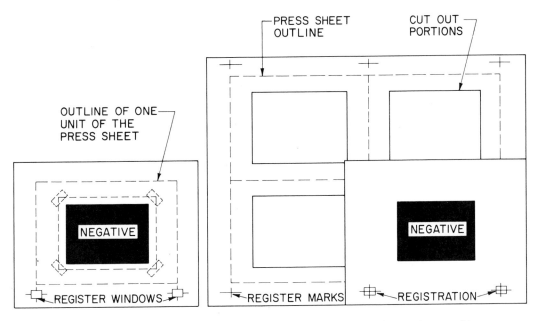

Fig. 12-23. Repeating exposures of one negative on a plate. Mask with negative taped in exact position is placed over the register flat for use in printing the first of four exposures on the plate.

Register cross marks are provided, as shown, in the nonprinting areas.

Another piece of goldenrod paper is placed over one of the unit areas on the flat. The layout for that area is traced onto this piece of goldenrod — which is now called the *mask*. The negatives for *one area* are now stripped into the mask, and the image window is cut out of the mask. Register windows are cut out of the mask as shown.

Portions of the flat, larger than the image areas of the mask, are cut out in each of the units on the flat.

In exposing the plate, the register flat is taped at diagonal corners to the plate. The mask is registered over the first of the units on the flat. To prevent the exposure light from striking them, the remaining openings in the flat are covered with other pieces of goldenrod paper. The process is repeated for each of the other areas on the flat. (See page 246 for additional information on step-and-repeat work.)

Combinations

Combination printing, in which lettering is superimposed over a halftone picture, can be achieved with the lettering appearing in positive (black) over the picture, or as reverse printing (open letters) on the picture area.

Positive Lettering

The photographer must furnish to the stripper a halftone negative of the desired illustration, plus a line negative of the desired lettering which is to appear over the illustration.

Two flats — the *main* flat and the *second* flat — are stripped up in register. The halftone negative is stripped on the main flat; the line negative is stripped on the second flat. Be sure to align the negative in exact position on the flat.

The halftone flat will be exposed to the plate, then removed. Then the line negative flat will be exposed in registered position over the plate. Upon development, the plate will carry a combination halftone and line illustration, with the lettering in black over the halftone picture.

It may take a little experimentation to arrive at a proper exposure time for the platemaking.

Reverse Lettering

The photographer should furnish the stripper with a halftone negative of the illustration, plus a line positive of the desired lettering.

The halftone negative is stripped up in the desired location on the flat and is then cropped. The flat is turned over and the window for the halftone negative is cut out of the flat. The line positive is stripped in place, in register, over the halftone negative. In this position, the emulsions of both the halftone negative and the line positive are *down*. The line positive is readable.

The platemaker has to make only one exposure with this combination flat to produce a combination image on the plate. Lettering on the halftone image will be open, or "white." The color of the paper will show through the halftone.

Stripping for Two or More Colors

If separate parts of the sheet are to be printed in two or more colors, the stripper can proceed to strip up all the negatives for the job on one flat, called the main flat. For example, on this flat, or on the layout for the flat, indicate in circled notations, the lines of type or type matter or illustrations that are to be printed in black and those that are to be printed in red. Mark register crosses in diagonal corners of this main flat and turn the flat over.

Over this main flat, place a second sheet of goldenrod. Trace register marks on this sheet, and expose the register cross by cutting out little windows at the center of the register marks. Cut windows out of this flat for each part that is to be printed in black. Mark this flat the "black" flat.

Place a third sheet of goldenrod over the main flat, and cut out the parts that are to be printed in red. Mark this flat the "red" flat. Use register marks as for the preceding flat.

The platemaker will tape the main flat to the plate, and then register the black flat to the main flat. After exposure and developing, the plate will bear the image for all the black printing.

For the red plate, the platemaker will remove the black flat and tape the red flat over the main flat. Exposure and development of the

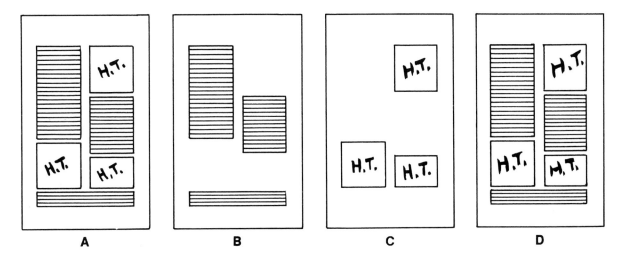

Fig. 12-24. Stripping line and halftone for one plate — two complementary or separate flats.
A. Layout showing desired positions of line work and continuous-tone photos (which are to appear as halftones).
B. Flat with line work negatives in position for first exposure of plate.
C. Flat with halftone negatives in position for second exposure of plate.
D. The developed plate has both line and halftone images, as per original layout.

plate will result in a plate which will print all parts that are to appear in red.

This method could be enlarged to include as many colors as desired, if a separate flat is cut for each of the colors. See also pages 189-191 in the chapter on color reproduction.

Line Work and Halftone Work on Same Plate

If the layout allows ample space between the line and halftone negative positions, there is little difficulty in stripping both on the one flat. When halftones must be stripped close to line matter, the following methods are useful:

Complementary Flats

Complementary flats (double printing) assumes that the line negatives and the halftone negatives are furnished separately to the stripper.

First, strip up all the line negatives on one flat. Using this flat as the master flat, register and tape a second goldenrod over the first flat. Strip the halftone negatives in register on the second flat. See Fig. 12-24.

The platemaker will make two exposures on the one plate (in register): first, the main exposure using the flat containing the line negatives; then, the second exposure using the flat containing the halftone negatives.

This method is useful when captions are required close to illustrations and when a longer or shorter exposure is to be given the halftone negatives during platemaking.

Stripping Halftones into Windows

The stripper may be furnished a large line negative containing one or more clear windows (transparent areas) into which halftone negatives or other artwork are to be inserted. In this case, it may be best for the stripper to cut out the openings and splice in the halftone negatives as inserts. Or, the stripper can attach the halftone negatives directly over the clear film openings with tape or thinned rubber cement.

Line and Halftone on One Negative

Sometimes a single negative will contain both line work and halftone work correctly spaced out in proper page format. This combination negative is treated as a single negative.

Stripping Positive

A flat consisting of *film positives* (a positive flat) is required when a positive-working offset plate is exposed. See page 248.

The positive flat may be composed of one or a number of individual film positives taped to a press-plate-size sheet of *transparent plastic*.

Or the flat may be a single press-plate-size film positive composed of a number of different positive images, or made up of one image repeated by stepping it off a number of times on that one sheet of film.

The Layout

To strip onto a film base (transparent plastic material), a sheet of layout material, larger than the press plate, is first taped to the surface of the stripping table. This layout material may be a sheet of white paper, a sheet of metal spray-painted white, or a sheet of plastic whose surface will readily accept India ink or pencil. (Since *film positives* are being stripped, there is no need for translucent layout material.)

Elements such as layout for the plate outline, image positions, and image and press sheet limits are ruled directly on this layout sheet. See Fig. 12-26.

• **Note:** If a certain job is repetitive, a standard layout can be reproduced as a film positive which can be fastened down on the stripping table.

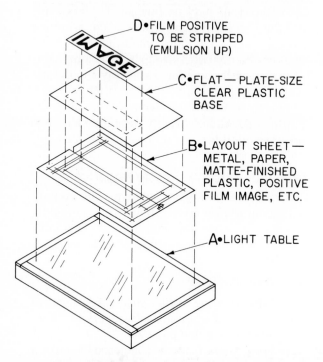

Fig. 12-25. **Basic procedure in positive stripping (stripping positive).**

D•FILM POSITIVE TO BE STRIPPED (EMULSION UP)

C•FLAT — PLATE-SIZE CLEAR PLASTIC BASE

B•LAYOUT SHEET — METAL, PAPER, MATTE-FINISHED PLASTIC, POSITIVE FILM IMAGE, ETC.

A•LIGHT TABLE

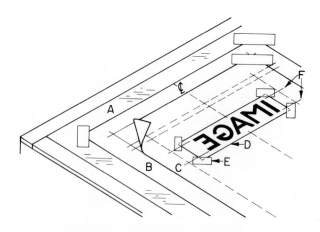

Fig. 12-26. **Schematic showing a flat which is stripped positive.**
A. **Light table surface**
B. **Master layout**
C. **Transparent flat**
D. **Film positive (emulsion down)**
E. **Transparent tape**
F. **Image position**
¢ **Centerline**

The Flat

Next, a press-plate-size sheet of transparent plastic (film base) is taped in register to the layout. The film positives are then taped, emulsion up, to this film base, using the layout underneath as a guide.

The flat is then removed from its support, placed over a lighted glass-top table, and inspected. Opaque any pin holes or defects in the images. Remove any dust and dirt with an antistatic brush and liquid film cleaner.

The following suggestions on stripping procedure will aid the beginner.

1. Always cut film edges at a 45° bevel so that the angle will help eliminate shadows during plate exposure.
2. In mounting the film positives, fasten with a thin, transparent cellulose tape, using as little as possible.
3. Check that all film positives on the one flat are of the same thickness (so exposure will be uniform over the entire plate).
4. Butt the joint, rather than overlap adjoining film positives.

Repeat Layouts

Means should be provided for easily and quickly making repeat or duplicate layouts. This saves time in making the layouts, and the similarity in duplication saves makeready time on the press. Five methods of producing duplicate layouts are described here:

1. *Purchase ready-made.* Masking sheets may be purchased cut to size and imprinted with the layout. Some layout sheets are also prepunched for pinregister system.
2. *Shop produced.* The desired layouts may be printed up in the shop as needed.
3. *Marked-up tapes on the glass top.* Two strips of tan-colored masking tape are fastened at right angles on the glass top of the stripping table, Fig. 12-27. Locations of often-used measurements are marked off on these tapes. In use, the masking sheet to be laid out is butted to the two tapes and is, itself, taped down. Using the lines on the tapes as starting points, rule vertical and horizontal lines on the flat.
4. *Master layout on acetate or other film.* See Fig. 12-28. A film positive is made of the layout, or the layout can be drawn in ink on a sheet of matte plastic (or any other transparent or translucent material). Fasten this layout to the stripping table. Then fasten the goldenrod squarely over this layout and trace the desired layout.
5. *Pin register system.* See next page.

Provision for Register

Close register on successive colors or passes through the press is aided by the provision of some method of register when the complementary flats are stripped up. Three registering methods are described below:

Register by Cutouts. After completing the stripping of the first color flat, place the second sheet (or additional sheets) of goldenrod squarely over the first sheet and tape it to the table. Now, through both flats, simultaneously cut either "butterflies" or x-shaped slits, Fig. 12-29. These crosses are cut in two diagonally opposite corners of the assembled flats in the trim area of the press sheet. Now, strip up the second flat. Repeat for additional flats.

Register Marks on Film. Two types of register marks on film are shown in Fig. 12-30. These

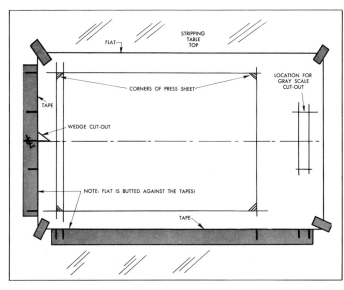

Fig. 12-27. Marked tapes aid in duplicate flat layout. Lines for additional elements may be added as desired.

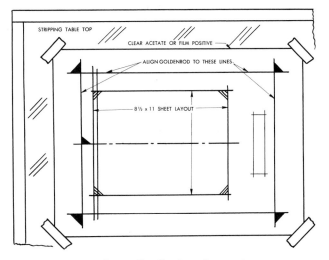

Fig. 12-28. Master layout (for flats) on clear acetate or on film positive.

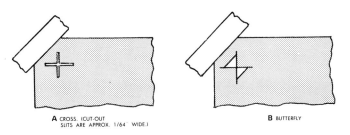

A CROSS. (CUT-OUT SLITS ARE APPROX. 1/64˝ WIDE.) B BUTTERFLY

Fig. 12-29. Register marks — cutouts in the flat.

are the crosses and the segmented circles. Make black-and-white drawings of these register marks and reproduce them in quantities on film. Film negatives are used for negative stripping and film positives are used for positive stripping.

These register marks are mounted in register in openings located in diagonally opposite corners of the flats. Note the rotation of register mark positions on successive printed sheets; that is, on the second press run or color, the register mark segment appears rotated 180°. All four runs produce a complete circle of printed segments.

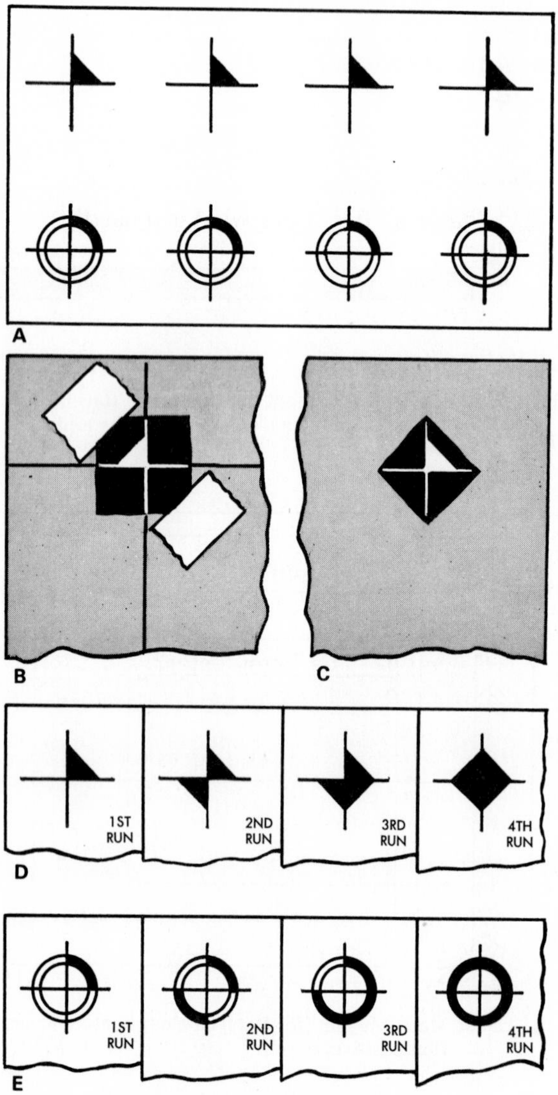

Register Pins. The use of register pins, or a pin register system, results in extremely accurate register. This is true if the flats and the plates are both punched accurately and identically and if the offset-press-plate cylinder is fitted with a matching pair of well-spaced and positioned pins on which the plates can be mounted for register.

The flats are first punched on a two- or three-hole gang punch. The first flat is then

Chemco Photoproducts Company

Fig. 12-31. "Protocol" master punch (for flats and plates).

Chemco Photoproducts Company

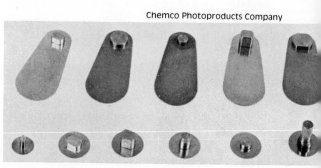

Fig. 12-32. "Protocol" register pins.

Fig. 12-30. Register marks — on film.
A. Drawings of two kinds of register marks. Use similar drawings as camera copy to make your own register marks on film.
B. Register mark (on film) taped in place on flat.
C. Appearance of register mark after flat is turned over and the window is cut out of the flat.
D. and E. Register marks as they appear on printed sheets after first, second, third, and fourth press runs (or colors).

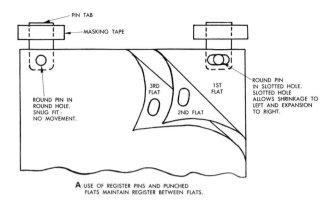

A USE OF REGISTER PINS AND PUNCHED FLATS MAINTAIN REGISTER BETWEEN FLATS.

B ROUND REGISTER PIN (WITH TAB).

Fig. 12-33. Use of register pins on stripping table.

placed in position on the stripping table, Fig. 12-33, and two register pins are fitted to the two holes of the flat. The tabs of the pins are then taped to the glass top of the stripping table. To achieve register after the first flat is stripped, the succeeding flats are simply fitted over the pins. Variations of pin register systems are shown in Fig. 12-34.

Questions

1. What is a "flat"? For what is it used?
2. What kind of paper is generally used for the flat?
3. At what point in the offset process does the last opportunity appear for introducing more or less space between elements in the printed job?
4. List the tools, equipment, and supplies generally used in stripping a flat.
5. Why are steel T-squares, triangles, and straightedges used in stripping a flat?
6. Why is it important to use a beveled-edge scale or rule for measuring and marking distances?
7. Of what use is a linen tester?
8. How does one clean the glass top of the stripping table?
9. Tell how to fasten the goldenrod paper squarely on the stripping table.
10. Why does the stripper work in "reverse"?
11. How is the emulsion side of a negative determined?
12. Why are the negatives placed emulsion side up on the flat?
13. What is "opaque solution"? How is it used?
14. Explain how to scribe reference marks on the negatives. Of what use are these reference marks?
15. Tell how to tape the negatives on the flat.
16. How are the negatives registered in position on the flat?
17. Describe how to cut the windows in the flat.
18. What reference marks are generally provided on the flat for the platemaker, press operator, and papercutter?
19. How can economies be effected by running large sheets on the press?

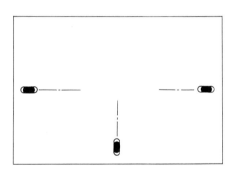

A. Three slotted holes; three elongated (oval) pins.

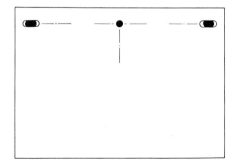

B. Two slotted and one round hole; two elongated (oval) pins and one round pin.

Fig. 12-34. Variations in pin register use.

20. What is meant by running a job "four-up"?
21. Outline the procedure for stripping positive (making a flat consisting of film positives).

Problems and Projects

1. Make out a requisition for a ream of goldenrod paper suitable for flats. Use current paper catalogs in the shop.
2. Make out a requisition, including prices, catalog numbers and correct terminology, for a list of equipment, tools and supplies for stripping flats.
3. Lay out and strip a flat, using your own negatives or those supplied by the instructor, for a single-negative job. Center the image on the sheet. Make this flat for the press specified by the instructor.
4. In cooperation with your instructor, plan a four-page folder for which you will make the layout, prepare the camera copy, make the negatives, and strip the flat. Make a dummy layout first.
5. Prepare layouts and perform stripping for jobs as required by the instructor. Include a job which must be cut apart and trimmed for padding, or one of several sheets which must be printed on both sides and then folded, assembled stapled, and trimmed.
6. Make up a quantity of register marks on film, both negative and positive.
7. Design and make a master layout on acetate or film for a job often produced in your shop.

New Terms

actinic light
beveled
combination printing
complementary flats
gripper edge
main flat
masking sheet
stripping negative
stripping positive
register
scribing
steel triangle
stock
straightedge
superimposed
unreadable

Chapter 13

Platemaking

An offset plate is a thin sheet of paper, plastic, or metal from whose surface the inked printing image is transferred to the offset blanket during the operation of the press.

Plate Characteristics

Plates differ in such factors as materials, styles of ends, coatings, areas, grain and so on.

Plate Surface Areas

The offset plate surface has two distinct and separate areas: (1) the clear area and (2) the image area. See Fig. 13-1.

The *clear area* of the plate bears no image. Because of its graining, or water-holding nature, this area will attract and hold a thin film of water (fountain solution, or dampening solution) on its surface, which repels any attempts by the ink rollers to deposit ink on it. This area also is known as the *nonprinting, nonimage, ink-repellent,* or *water-receptive area.*

The *image area* of the plate is actually the printing image. Since it has a slightly greasy nature, it repels the application of water, but *accepts* a film of applied ink. This area is also known as the *printing, image-bearing, ink-receptive,* or *water-repellent* area.

Surface Grain

The surface of an offset plate must be *grained* to make it water-receptive, Fig. 13-2. Graining may be done either chemically or mechanically. It results in minute pits or indentations on the plate surface. These depressions will readily retain small amounts of water or fountain solution.

In *chemical graining,* the metal plate is subjected to the controlled action of an etching acid or an anodizing solution.

3M Company

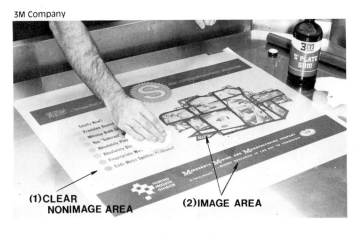

(1)CLEAR NONIMAGE AREA   (2)IMAGE AREA

Fig. 13-1.   An offset plate has two areas.

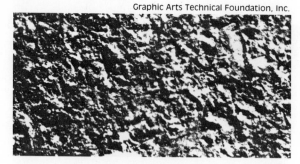

Fig. 13-2.   Grain of a mechanically grained metal offset plate, enlarged 50 times.

In *mechanical graining*, the metal plate is placed in the trough of a plate-graining machine where it is covered with an abrasive powder. Then a quantity of steel, glass, or wood marbles is placed in the trough, which is made to oscillate rapidly. The action of the marbles rolling over the abrasive causes the roughening or graining of the plate.

Other forms of mechanical graining are produced by *brush graining* (in which rotary brushes revolve against an abrasive powder on the surface of the plate) and by *sandblasting*.

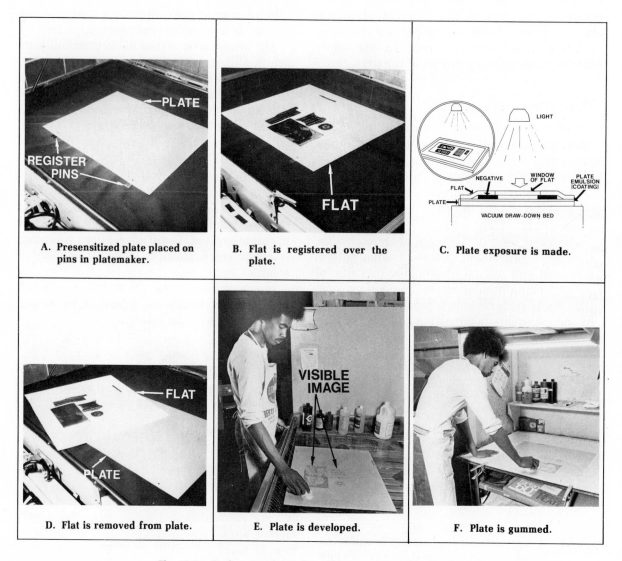

A. Presensitized plate placed on pins in platemaker.

B. Flat is registered over the plate.

C. Plate exposure is made.

D. Flat is removed from plate.

E. Plate is developed.

F. Plate is gummed.

Fig. 13-3.   Basic procedures in making a presensitized plate.

Paper and plastic plates and some metal plates are formed and treated during manufacture so that their surface retains an applied film of moisture. These are termed *grainless plates*.

Thickness and Form

Plates vary in thickness from about .005″ to .012″ for the smaller plates, to .020″ and above for the larger plates.

Most plates are sold cut to press size and, in smaller sizes, are available in four different styles of plate ends: straight; round-hole, or pin-bar punched; slotted, or oval hole; and serrated, or looped. See Fig. 13-4. The style of plate end needed depends upon the kind of plate clamps with which the press is equipped.

Plate material is used in roll form on some automated platemaking machines which expose the plate, develop it, and deliver it in cut form, ready for the press. See Figs. 13-5 and 13-23.

Usable Surfaces

Some photographic offset plates are sensitized so that they are usable on one side only. Many, however, have two usable surfaces.

Masters and Plates

In trade literature and catalogs, the term *master* is used interchangeably with the term *plate* to indicate an offset plate of metal or other material. However, "master" usually refers only to plates for the duplicator or smaller sizes of offset presses.

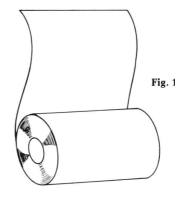

Fig. 13-5. **Master (plate) material in roll form for automated photo-direct camera processor.**

Material of Manufacture

Common offset plates are made of the following materials: paper (cellulose-base); plastic-impregnated or plastic-coated paper (sometimes called *plastic plates* or *paper plates*); acetate; aluminum; aluminum laminated on paper; plastic on steel; and copper on aluminum, chromium, or stainless steel.

The term *multimetal* refers to those plates consisting of two or three layers of metal (bimetal or tri-metal respectively).

General Care of Offset Plates

Since the printed result depends upon the condition of the offset plate, the following instructions should be rigidly observed.

Precautions with Unused Plates

Keep plates flat and wrapped in original containers in a cool, dry location. Handle sensitized plates in subdued light only; they should not be unduly exposed to room light or sunlight. Pick up plates by gripper ends, keeping fingers and moisture off the plate printing surface. Avoid scratching one plate with the corner of another.

Care of Developed Plates

Directly following the developing of a plate (or the placing of an image on a plate), the plate is generally *gummed*. That is, it is given a thin coating of gum arabic solution. This prevents deterioration of the clear area of the metal plate which might destroy the ability of this area to repel ink. Also, the gumming protects the clear areas from smudges of ink, grease, or

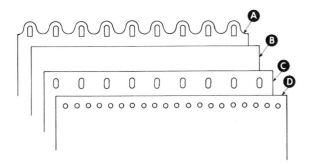

Fig. 13-4. **Styles of plate ends: (A) serrated, or looped; (B) straight; (C) slotted, or oval hole; and (D) pin-bar punched, or round-hole punched.**

dirt which might cause these areas to "scum" or pick up ink when running on the press.

A gummed plate may be used immediately, or its use may be delayed a number of days, since the gum coating serves as a preservative.

If a developed plate is to be stored for a considerable length of time, it should be both gummed and "put under," that is, coated with asphaltum. The asphaltum is nondrying and so maintains the image ink-receptive. If not given this coating, the developing ink on the image area might dry and thus not accept ink when placed on the press. This procedure also is advised if the plate is to print any color other than black. The gum and asphaltum coatings each can be removed when the plate is on the press, leaving the clean image to accept the colored ink. Presensitized plates have a durable lacquer coating and therefore do not usually require being put under. However, no harm is done, and almost any plate can be put under if desired.

Procedures for gumming, putting the plate under, and caring for the plate on the press are given below.

Gumming a Plate.   Wipe the plate surface with a water-wet sponge. Then, with a clean sponge or small pad, wet the entire plate surface with gum solution. Using a pad of clean, dry cheesecloth, or another pad, rub the gum briskly and evenly, up and down and across the plate, to a thin, hard finish, free of streaks. Fan the plate dry.

• **Note:** The plate may now be mounted on the press. However, if a plate is to be stored for a considerable length of time, a coating of asphaltum should be applied over the gum.

Putting the Plate Under (Asphaltum).   This process is used primarily for plates on which a soft developing ink has been used. After gumming, remove the developing ink from the image with a little press-cleaning solvent. Using a cheese-cloth pad, apply a thin coating of asphaltum to the plate. Rub this thin and dry.

Care on the Press.   Attach the plate on the plate cylinder of the press. When the press is ready to run, wash the gum (and asphaltum over the gum, if applied) from the plate with a clean sponge dipped in water.

If the press run is interrupted for more than a few seconds, a metal plate is likely to lose water, and it will oxidize. Gum the plate immediately.

• **Note:** Before gumming a plate on the press, turn the press *off*. To get at all parts of the plate, manually turn the press handwheel.

When ready to resume the press run, wash the gum off the plate with sponge and water.

At the end of the press run, "run down" the plate by running off a few sheets, with ink and dampener rollers in *off* position. This removes much of the image ink. Then gum the plate, remove it from the press, and store it for re-run. For extended storage, wash out the remaining image ink with solvent and apply asphaltum.

Gum Solution.   Formerly, gum solution (gum arabic solution) was prepared in the shop from dry gum arabic flakes. At present, the (liquid) gum solution is generally purchased ready to use.

A 14° Baumé gum solution is recommended for gumming a plate on the bench. An 8° to 10° Baumé gum solution is preferred for gumming a

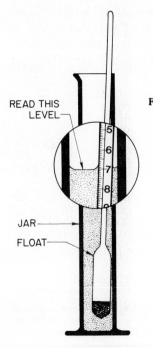

READ THIS
LEVEL

JAR

FLOAT

Fig. 13-6. Taking a reading with Baumé hydrometer and jar. This reading is 7° Baumé. Addition of water (distilled preferred) to a gum solution will lower its Baumé reading.

plate on the press. Adding water (preferably distilled) to a gum solution will lower its Baumé reading — for example, from 14° to 10° Baumé. Figure 13-6 shows how to use the Baumé hydrometer and jar to take a reading of a gum solution.

Care in Storage

Offset plates may be stored in shallow drawers (approximately 1″ high), in envelopes, or face-to-face. A more common method is to store them vertically, on hangers, in plate file cabinets, or on two rods.

Common Types of Offset Plates

The common types of offset plates presently in use include (among others):

1. Surface plates
   a. Direct image
   b. Presensitized
      1) Contact printed
         Negative working
         Positive working
      2) Projection printed
   c. Wipe-on
   d. Electrostatic
   e. Laser facsimile
2. Deep-etch plates
3. Relief plates

Figure 13-7 illustrates the relative image and nonimage heights of various types of plates.

Surface Plates

The image area of a surface plate is said to be *level with* the clear portion of the plate (although the inked image actually may be minutely above the surface of the nonprinting area), Fig. 13-7A. Surface plates are the most popularly used plates, especially with the smaller offset presses and duplicators.

Surface plates may be purchased as ready-cut, press-size plates or in continuous-roll form (as used on some automated platemaking machines). The base material may be paper, plastic-impregnated wood pulp, acetate, aluminum, or aluminum foil laminated to paper. They are available as *presensitized* plates with a light-sensitive coating on their surface; or they may

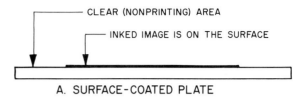

A. SURFACE-COATED PLATE

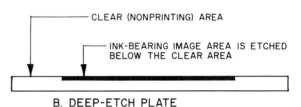

B. DEEP-ETCH PLATE

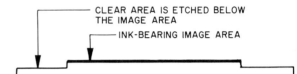

C. RELIEF OFFSET PLATE
(DRY OFFSET, SHALLOW RELIEF, LETTERSET, ETC)

Fig. 13-7. Relative image and non-image heights on some types of offset plates.

be purchased without this coating. The latter includes direct-image plates, plates to be coated in the shop, and plates intended for use with electrostatic, facsimile, and other platemaking methods.

Instructions for the preparation of a number of types of surface plates are provided later in this chapter.

Deep-Etch Plates

The printing (image) area of the deep-etch plate is chemically etched to a depth slightly below that of the nonprinting area. See Fig. 13-7B. The etched image (which carries the ink) in this metal plate has a greater ink-carrying capacity and a longer press life than the surface plate described above.

Relief Plates

Relief plates sometimes are referred to as *dry-offset*, *letterset*, *low relief*, or *shallow-relief* plates, in addition to being known by trade brands. During processing, the nonprinting areas of the plate are removed to a considerable depth below that of the printing areas. See Fig. 13-7C. Since relief plates are generally .016″ or more in thickness, the plate cylinder must sometimes be sufficiently undercut to accommodate the plate. Consequently, when a relief plate is run on the press, it requires only inking; the dampening operation is unnecessary.

Specialized and relatively expensive equipment is needed to produce these plates. For this reason, smaller plants usually have these relief plates made by a platemaking firm.

Plate Exposure Devices

Most general-purpose plates are light-sensitive and require the use of some type of exposure unit. This applies to both presensitized and shop-coated surface plates, as well as to deep-etch plates, relief plates, and multimetal plates. Even duplicator departments specializing in a utility class of work (using direct-image plates, transfer plates, electronic scanning, or electrostatic plates) probably will use some light-sensitive plates for jobs requiring top quality halftones. They should therefore have a plate-exposure device. Figures 13-3 and 13-8 give the basic procedure for exposing a plate to a flat. See also Figs. 13-9, 13-10, 13-12, and 13-14.

nuArc Company, Inc.

Fig. 13-9. Table-top vacuum frame and exposure light setup for contacting and platemaking.

Exposure Frames and Printers

Typically, the light-sensitive plate is placed in an exposure frame beneath (in direct contact with) the stripped-up flat. Positive contact is best insured by a vacuum pump which exhausts the air pressure under the plate. Thus, atmospheric pressure holds the plate snugly against the flat and the cover glass. It may take several minutes for the full vacuum to build up, but this method gives the most even contact. Even then, it is possible that halftone screens may not make full contact where openings were cut into the flat or where an extra layer of tape or film causes poor contact in nearby areas. More simple contact frames may use a foam rubber pad or an air bag to make this necessary contact.

Common light sources are a pulsed-xenon arc light or a mercury-vapor light bulb (the common suntan lamp). The pulsed-xenon light is essentially an electronic photoflash lamp which fires brilliantly many times a second. The bulb usually is coiled so as to provide almost a point-source light which helps to control image spread. When the light source is a

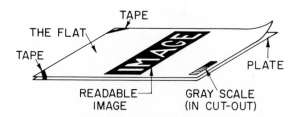

Fig. 13-8. Flat positioned for exposing a light-sensitive plate by contact printing.
1. Place the plate, sensitized side up, on the bed of the exposure frame or platemaker.
2. Register the flat over the plate with the image readable. Use register pins or tape corners of flat to the plate at the gripper edge.
3. Place a gray scale in cutout of flat so that it will print at trailing edge of plate.
4. Close glass lid and clamp shut.
5. Apply vacuum (if so equipped). Check for even contact and clean glass.
6. Make exposure.

nuArc Company, Inc.

Integrator
Digital Dial

Fig. 13-10. Flip-top platemaker, with back-to-back vacuum frames. This allows one side to be loaded while the other side is being exposed to the lights below; also common with frame on one side only.

part of the unit, it usually is called a *plate printer* (or platemaker). See Fig. 13-10.

For exposure, the frame is faced to the light which is positioned straight toward the frame. The distance from the light to the frame should be equal to the diagonal measurement of the printing frame. This distance may remain constant for all exposures.

The length of exposure is determined experimentally in the shop, and a careful record kept so that a plate may be successfully exposed with consistently good results.

Exposure Control. To provide a "measuring stick" so as to obtain consistent exposure and development of offset plates, it is advisable to use a platemaker's (film) *step gray scale*, Fig. 13-11, each time a plate is exposed. Also see pages 251 ff.

The gray scale should be placed along the gripper edge of the plate, and a corresponding window should be cut out of the flat so that the gray scale is not obscured. Thus, the gray scale will receive the same amount of exposure as the rest of the image.

Since the gray scale is made up of progressive areas or stages of increasing density, the darker areas which do not receive sufficient exposure will wash away during development of the plate. Those areas not so dense will produce an image on the plate.

Generally, if the gray scale image develops to a solid Step 6 for a negative working plate, it indicates a sufficiently exposed and satisfactorily developed plate. If steps on the gray scale above the seventh are retained in the development, it usually means that the image has spread enough to plug up (fill in) any halftones on the plate. If the plate contains only coarse line work, it probably can go as far as the eighth step without any plugging up.

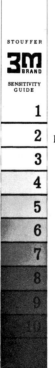

Fig. 13-11. Platemaker's ten-step (film) gray scale.

3M Company

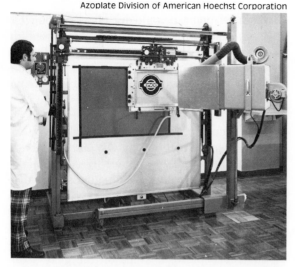

Fig. 13-12. Automatic photo-composing (step-and-repeat) machine. A single master image (negative or positive) can be programmed to be repeatedly exposed in a number of horizontal and vertical positions.

Photo-Direct Platemakers

The photo-direct platemakers Fig. 13-23, incorporate a camera which projects the reflected light directly from the original copy or paste-up to the fast emulsion on a plate (reducing or enlarging as needed).

Fig. 13-13. Model XT Anderson step-and-repeat machine.

Fig. 13-14. Example of step-and-repeat work.

Step-and-Repeat Work

Very often one image is repeated a number of times on a single, light-sensitive plate so that its entire capacity may be utilized. Letterheads, labels, cards, tags, and calendars are often printed many at a time in this fashion.

Instead of stripping up enough negatives for the entire plate, one (or a few) negatives are stripped up on a mask. This mask is then registered and exposed in a number of locations so as to cover the entire plate. Of course, during each exposure of one section of the plate, all other areas are masked, usually with goldenrod paper, to protect them from exposure. This type of work is known as *step-and-repeat work*.

A step-and-repeat platemaking machine is shown in Fig. 13-12. Figure 13-13 shows an exposure-frame printer specially made for step-and-repeat work. In use, a stripped-up mask, containing one or more negatives, is attached to the chase which is shown in the center of the bed. This chase is movable (back and forth or up and down) to any series of pre-set dimensions. For exposure, the frame is clamped, the vacuum is turned on, and then the frame is tilted vertically to face the exposure light.

Figure 13-14 shows a 77-on sheet produced by stepping a single negative 7 times on direct-duplicating film to produce a 7-on film negative. This 7-on negative was then stepped across the printer 11 times on the plate, producing a 77-on plate. All work could also be done on film for a single exposure on the plate.

Raden C Auto-Step Company

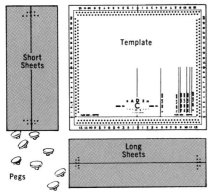

Fig. 13-15. Pin-register system for step-and-repeat work on a regular plate printer.

Figure 13-15 shows a template which has holes along its edge for pins or pegs. These are used to step the image using a regular plate printer. For example, for the butterflies in Fig. 13-14, the 7-on film negative would be located in one of the short sheets, and pegs would be placed in holes at the top and at the bottom of the template for 11 exposures across the plate. An 11-on film could also be used with a long sheet for 7 steps down the plate. Devices such as this can also be shop-constructed.

Surface Plates

Direct image, presensitized, wipe-on, electrostatic, and laser facsimile plates are discussed in depth here.

Direct-Image Plates

Direct-image plates (or *masters,* as they are more apt to be called) have no sensitized coating on their surface when purchased. They are available as press-size plates or in roll form. Base materials usually are paper, plastic-impregnated paper, or acetate (or, in some cases, aluminum or aluminum foil laminated to paper).

Imaging Methods

Since the direct-image plate is not sensitized, the image is placed on it by one or a combination of the following methods:

Hand Method. The image may be typed directly onto the direct-image plate, using a typewriter equipped with a special fabric, carbon, or plastic ribbon. Hand work also may be written, lettered, or drawn with pencil, pen or brush and ink, lithographic crayon, ball-point pen, ruling pen, or pantograph lettering device. In addition, typing can be done through carbon paper, or a rubber stamp can be used.

In each of the methods, the materials have a slightly greasy nature. For this reason, they are termed *reproducing* materials and are available from lithography dealers.

Mechanical Method. Letterpress forms (including type and relief plates) may be proofed directly onto direct-image plates. This may be achieved by using a letterpress proof press or a letterpress printing press; or by preprinting all, or part, of a form or image by letterpress or offset press. (The latter is called *printing a master from a master.*) A reproducing ink is used on the presses for this type of operation. (See litho catalogs.)

Guidelines which are to be imprinted or preprinted on a plate are placed there with nonreproducing ink or pencil. These lines will serve as guides for image placement on the plate.

Photo Method. Direct-image plates may be coated in the shop with diazo wipe-on solutions. This will make them light-sensitive, so that they may be exposed through negatives or positives. If so coated, they then are handled as presensitized plates. (See later pages of this chapter.)

• **Caution:** Since direct-image plates are especially sensitive to grease, handle them no more than necessary — and only by the clamping edges with *clean hands.* Keep unused plates boxed until ready for use.

Preserving Plates

Sometimes direct-image plates are discarded after one press run. However, if it is desired to preserve them for re-run, follow the procedure for gumming a plate as was given on page 242.

Typing a Direct-Image Plate

Keep sufficient space at top and bottom (leading and trailing ends) of the plate to allow for plate mounting and gripper margin. Some plates are preprinted with lines indicating the allowable typing space. If not, draw these lines lightly with nonreproducing pencil.

...riter with sharp, clean keys and ...er-resistant ribbon which will ...dark image. A one-time carbon or plastic ribbon is best in order to avoid the printed-fabric pattern of a cloth ribbon.

With manually operated typewriters, use firm, uniform strokes on the keys, but avoid punching through the surface of the plate. A sheet of acetate between the plate and typewriter platen will help prevent this. Punching through is especially noticeable with periods, which characteristically reproduce as hollow "donuts." Use of electric typewriters is advised so as to produce consistently uniform dense letters.

Make deletions with a special rubber eraser — first rubbed clean on paper. Erase just the greasy ink *lightly*. Do not scrub through the top surface of the plate. Large image areas may be eradicated with a special deletion fluid available from dealers.

Letterpress Impressions

Letterpress forms (type forms, relief plates, etc.) may be printed directly onto one or more direct-image plates on the proof press or other letterpress printing press. This saves photographing proofs of these forms. Use greasy-base (linseed-base lithographic) ink, and make provision for correct register of impression on the press. Before mounting the direct-image plate on the offset press, let the impression dry overnight, or dry it sufficiently with a drying lamp to cure the ink and prevent smearing.

Preprinting

To preprint all, or a part, of a form to be reproduced on direct-image plates, use an offset press or relief press and preprinting ink. Additions to the plate image, if desired, can be made later by typewriter or by other hand methods.

To preprint nonreproducing guide lines, use a *letterpress* and a nonreproducing water-soluble ink.

Presensitized Plates

Presensitized plates, when purchased, are already surface-coated with a light-sensitive material. To prepare the plate for press use, it is necessary only to expose the plate, process it briefly to bring out the image, and then mount it on the press. This requires from 5 to 15 minutes. Figure 13-3 illustrates the basic procedures in making a presensitized plate.

Contact-Exposed Presensitized Plates

Presensitized plates made for direct-contact exposure usually are coated with a relatively slow-speed diazo sensitizer. Most of the general-purpose plates used today are of the presensitized, contact-exposed, diazo-coated type.

Varieties of Presensitized Plates

The terms *negative-working plate* and *positive-working plate* are used to designate two kinds of light sensitivity in plates. Both of these yield a positive image upon final processing of the plate. See Fig. 12-3.

Negative-Working Plate

The negative-working plate is intended for exposure beneath a flat composed of film negatives, yielding a positive image on the plate when developed. Of course, if the flat contains any film positives, their corresponding images on the plate would emerge as "reverses" — clear image and dense background. The negative-working plate is probably the most common plate.

This type plate should be prepared in accordance with the directions of the manufacturer. General steps are as follows:

1. Expose the plate behind a flat composed of negatives.
2. Desensitize the plate.
3. Develop (lacquer) the plate.
4. Gum the plate.

The plate is now ready for the press or for storage.

Positive-Working Plate

The positive-working plate is intended for exposure beneath a flat composed of film positives or transparencies, yielding a *positive* image on the plate when developed. Whatever is transparent on the flat will appear as a clear area on the plate. Conversely, whatever is opaque will appear printed. Thus, should the flat contain any film negatives, their corresponding areas on the plate will appear with clear image and dense background.

Prior to exposure, if the film positives are not to cover the entire plate, a plate-size sheet of acetate should be interposed between the positives and the printing-frame glass. This will keep the plate coating from touching the glass.

Usually, the positives (and transparencies) are stripped to a plate-size sheet of acetate with clear transparent tape. After exposure, the image is evident (not latent), and may contain some unwanted marks or small areas. Edges and joints between film positives show as fine lines. These are painted out with a *staging* solution. During development, both the coating on the nonimage area and the staging solution are washed away. The resulting image then is intensified with lacquer, if needed, and the plate is gummed. Specific plate manufacturer's directions should be followed. The general steps are outlined below:

1. Expose plate to film positives or transparencies.
2. Stage out.
3. Develop.
4. Intensify with lacquer (if needed).
5. Gum.

The positive-working plate has several advantages:

1. Film positives can be obtained directly from phototype-composing equipment, and the resulting positives stripped directly into the flat.
2. Film positives are easier than negatives to superimpose in register when stripping several flats for surprinting and color runs.
3. Unscreened film positives can be contact-printed to Autoscreen film. This results in positive-screened negatives.
4. Hand art for posters can be painted or lettered on plate-size sheets of acetate, and these sheets exposed to the plates.
5. Regular film negatives can be used for reverses simply by stripping them into the flat.

Additive and Subtractive Lacquer Coatings

Thus far, only the traditional *additive type of coating* has been mentioned. With this type, the sensitized coating is exposed; during development, the nonimage areas are washed away; finally, the image is intensified by *adding* a lacquer to the printing area only. See Fig. 13-20. Carelessness may cause streaks or a weak lacquer coating which may wear off during the press run and result in less than the maximum possible life.

On plates with the *subtractive type of coatings,* the lacquer coating is applied in the factory over the entire plate. This provides a degree of consistency not possible with shop-applied coatings, and results in longer runs. After exposure (in the same manner as additive plates), the *lacquer coating is removed* (subtracted) along with the unwanted diazo sensitized coating from the nonprinting areas. See Fig. 13-21.

Wipe-On Sensitized Coatings

Although this section is concerned with *presensitized* plates, it should be pointed out that plates without any sensitized coating can be purchased. The diazo coating (as well as the added lacquer coating) then is applied in the shop. This type will be explained later in the chapter.

Base Material and Run Length

Manufacturers offer presensitized plates for short, medium, and long runs — meaning a possible expectation of perhaps 10,000 copies, 40,000 copies, and 100,000 copies respectively. In some cases, longer runs may be possible. Conversely, press problems may cause much shorter runs. To obtain the longer runs, heavier, more durable coatings and base materials are necessary. Some of these base materials include paper, aluminum foil laminated to paper (one side), foil laminated to paper on both sides, and sheet aluminum.

• **Precautions:** Store unexposed presensitized plates in a cool, dry area, away from light. Do not remove them from the original carton until ready for exposure. After removing a plate from the carton, refold the carton edges to protect against light.

Handle by plate-clamping edges only, in subdued light, keeping fingers off the surface.

Purchase only enough plates at one time as you can reasonably expect to use during the stated shelf life of the plates.

When processing plates, always follow manufacturer's instructions as to processes and chemicals.

Processing Presensitized Plates

Presensitized plates are made by a number of manufacturers. This section will give the specific processing procedures, as typical examples, for several types of the popular 3M brand of plates.[1]

Preliminary. Keep fingers off plate surfaces and handle only under yellow light before exposing. Store unused plates in a cool, dry place and observe the expiration date. The face side of the plate is indicated by the trademark in the upper right-hand corner.

Exposing

Expose the plates (preferably) in a vacuum frame with an ultra-violet light, such as black-light fluorescent tubes, pulsed-xenon arcs, or quartz-iodine lamps. If yellow room light is not provided, shield the unexposed plate from unnecessary white room light prior to exposure.

Include a platemaker's (film) gray scale in a cut-out portion of the flat along the gripper edge of the plate and outside the printing area. Expose to a solid Step 6, as shown in Fig. 13-16 (left column) which is the desired reading for all negative-working 3M plates, both additive and subtractive. For very short runs with "E" and "L" plates, the exposure may be shortened, and a solid Step 4 is satisfactory.

• **Note:** A solid Step 6 means that when the gray scale image is developed on the plate, the Step 6 is just as solid as Step 1.

---

[1] Illustrations and procedures are reproduced with the permission of Minnesota Mining and Mfg. Co.

3M Company

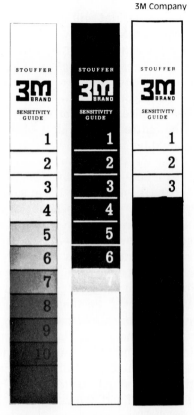

Fig. 13-16. Gray scale appearance. (Left) Platemaker's 10-step gray scale; (center) appearance of solid Step 6 exposure, as for a negative-working plate; (right) appearance of open Step 3, as for a positive-working plate.

For 3M positive-working plates, the gray-scale reading should be an *open* Step 3 or 4. See Fig. 13-16, right column. This means that Step 3 or 4 should be just as *open* as Step 1. If a positive-working plate does not develop satisfactorily, it is probably underexposed; and the gray scale should indicate this (open Step 1 or 2).

If you expose through more than one layer of film, increase the exposure time. One extra layer of film, even though it seems transparent, usually requires one-half step more exposure.

To check the exposure on a negative-working plate, expose the gray scale along with the flat onto the plate. Then develop the plate in the usual manner. Use the chart in Fig. 13-18 to adjust exposure time.

For an additive plate, such as the "E", "L", or "R" plate, after washing off the excess

Fig. 13-17. Gray scale image on gripper edge of plate.

3M Company

To increase original gray scale reading by:	1 Step	2 Steps	3 Steps	4 Steps
Multiply your original exposure time by:	1.4	2.0	2.8	4.0

To decrease original gray scale reading by:	1 Step	2 Steps	3 Steps	4 Steps
Multiply your original exposure time by:	0.7	0.5	0.36	0.25

Fig. 13-18. Charts to adjust plate exposure time if gray scale readings indicate under- or over-exposure.

developer, rub the gray scale image vigorously with the fingers while the plate is wet with water. Loosely bonded developer will rub off quickly.

For the "S" subtractive plates, add a small amount of 3M Brand Subtractive Developer to the gray scale image. Then, using the 3M developing pad, rub with brisk, circular motions, keeping the pad flat. This generally will remove two or three steps from the scale. Exposure time for a subtractive plate is approximately 1½ times that for an additive plate.

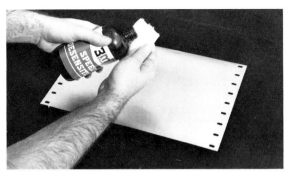

A. Method 1. For the fastest operation, use speed desensitizer to desensitize the plate, either immediately before or after mounting on the press. Wipe the desensitizer on the entire plate, using a cotton wipe. No developer is needed. For greater ease and efficiency, it is recommended that the plate be desensitized before it is mounted on the press.

B. Method 2. Apply one-step developer, using a soft, clean cellulose sponge about 2″ × 4″ × 4″. This desensitizes the background, develops the image, and gums the plate for storage. For very short runs, it is not necessary to develop to a deep-blue image.

C. Method 3. Best for maximum run. First apply "R" process gum to desensitize the plate. Then, use "R" developer to produce a visible image. The processing details are the same as for the "R" plates in 13-20A-F.

Fig. 13-19. Processing 3M "E" and small "L" plates — additive processing.

A. Step 1. Using a clean, soft cellulose sponge, wipe "R" process gum evenly over entire plate surface. Remove excess gum so that only a thin film is left on the plate.

D. Step 4. Flush off excess developer and inspect plate. Image should not be streaked or plugged, and should not be easily rubbed off with the fingers.

B. Step 2. Before gum dries, apply pool of "R" developer (red lacquer). Image area determines amount — too much causes slow rub-up and a pale-pink image. Rub a small "R" pad in a circular motion over entire surface.

E. Step 5. Squeegee plate dry. Caution: If the gum dried before the lacquer was rubbed smooth, or if the sponge used for lacquering has been used earlier with gum arabic, the result will be an image which rubs off easily.

C. Step 3. Continue rubbing until strong-red, uniform image appears. Try to maintain even pressure while rubbing. If developer starts to dry before image is a strong red, add small amount of water. Do not add more gum.

F. Step 6. Spread a small amount of "R" process gum with a small cellulose sponge. Polish the gum dry with a piece of soft, clean cheesecloth. Never use a fan to force the gum to dry.

Fig. 13-20. Processing 3M "R" plates — additive processing.

A. Step 1. Place plate on a cool surface, and moisten a developing pad with "S" (subtractive) developer. Use only the 3M pad, never moisten it with water, and replace it before it is badly worn.

B. Step 2. Pour the developer onto the center of the plate and distribute it over the entire surface with the developing pad. Wait a few seconds. Then rub off the blue coating, using firm, uniform pressure and circular motions. Keep the pad flat. Inspect the plate closely. If screens and halftones do not appear clean, add a little more developer and rub briskly. Squeegee off developer and flush immediately with water. Do not allow developer to dry.

C. Step 3. Keep developing pad clean. When necessary, scrape it with a clean, stiff rubber squeegee. Loose coating that clings to the developing pad reduces its ability to clean out the nonimage areas.

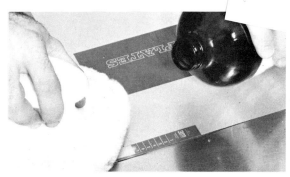

D. Step 4. Add developer and develop the gray scale. Then add more developer and rub briskly with pad flat to remove more steps. If exposure is right, a solid Step 6 will result. Squeegee off developer; flush with water.

E. Step 5. Rinse thoroughly with tap water; then squeegee. Flush excess developer with water from underneath the edges of the plate. Rub water over the plate with a clean wad of cheesecloth or disposable paper wipe. While rinsing, rub until developer has been completely removed with water. Tip plate to remove excess water; then lay plate down and check for uniform wetness. Rinse until the entire background (nonimage area) of the plate accepts water.

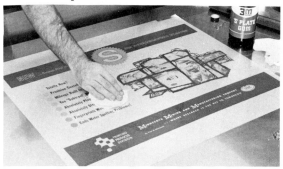

F. Step 6. Move plate to a dry area for gumming. Use only "S" (subtractive) gum. Pour a liberal amount on the plate and spread it over the entire surface with a clean sponge or wipe. Polish plate with a clean cheesecloth.

Fig. 13-21. Processing 3M "S" plates — subtractive processing.

Underexposure *can* affect plate mileage. To minimize image fade, cover an exposed but undeveloped plate with slipsheeting or masking paper. However, if the image does fade, this will not affect the developing or running characteristics of the plate.

"E" and Small "L" (Additive) Plates.   The "E" plate has aluminum foil laminated to one side of a strong paper backing, while the "L" plate has foil laminated to both sides of the paper. Both are recommended for short-run duplicating jobs.

Depending upon the type of work and the desired length of press run, either plate can be processed by one of the three methods described in Fig. 13-19.

"R" Plates (Sizes up to 48¾″ × 72″).   The "R" plate is an all-aluminum plate that is sensitized on both sides. It is recommended for medium runs (about 25,000 copies or more). Its processing is described in Fig. 13-20, steps 1-6.

"S" Plates.   The "S" plate is recommended for long runs up to 100,000 or more. It is a *subtractive* plate and is included here as an example of the procedure for *subtracting* rather than adding lacquer (in rub-up). The "S" plate is processed as shown in Fig. 13-21. After exposure, the subsequent processing of the plate removes the factory-applied lacquer from the nonimage areas.

Accidental water splashes may slow plate development if not wiped off immediately. Also, a worn developing pad can have the same effect. Remember to use "S" developer, *not water,* to moisten the developing pad. Scratches appearing during platemaking are caused by a dry or dirty developing pad or by dirty gumming cloths.

Only "S" gum should be used on an "S" plate — both in platemaking and in the pressroom. While 3M "S" gum can be used with other plates, other gum solutions, including standard gum arabic, must never be used on "S" plates.

Instructions for Use

Keep unused plates wrapped. Needless exposure to sunlight or to white fluorescent light may cause background toning in the subsequently exposed plate. It is also recommended that the plates be coated under either subdued or yellow light.[2]

Coating.   The wipe-on sensitizer is supplied in unit form, consisting of separate containers of diazo powder and a base solution. This packaging prevents deterioration, thereby giving a longer shelf life. When the sensitizer is mixed, it is usable for a period of at least ten days, if kept in a light-protected area. Store both the sensitizer unit and any mixed solution in a cool place.

To make a ready-to-use sensitizer solution, simply pour the entire container of diazo powder into the bottle of base solution, and shake until completely dissolved.

Additions, Deletions, and Repairs.

On "R" and "S" plates, broken lines can be repaired and minor additions (such as register marks) can be made. This is achieved by scratching the surface of the plate with a sharp needle or knife held at a slight angle and filling the scratch with printing ink.

Holes in solids which have not been coated with 3M Brand Image Guard can be repaired with 3M Brand Plate Tusche. Plates should be dry and free of gum before the tusche is applied to the plate surface with a cotton-tipped swab. The area tusched should turn a brown color in 20-40 seconds. Neutralize the area immediately with tap water (not etch). Then, dry the area with a disposable wipe and apply press ink by hand before gumming the plate. If the ink does not stick, reapply plate tusche for a second time. This step can be repeated as many times as necessary.

• **Note:** Tusche acts more rapidly on a warm surface. On the press, ink should be rubbed into the area before you drop the dampeners.

Deletions can be made with a clean, soft rubber eraser moistened with water or fountain solution. For large areas, a special deletion stop-out solution should be used. These deletion methods also are useful for "L" and "E" plates.

---

[2] Instructions reproduced by permission of Litho Chemical and Supply Co., Inc., suppliers of "Wipe-O" brand plates and related chemicals.

A #2 pencil may be used to make small additions and repairs to the "L" and "E" plates. Draw on a dry plate with sufficient pressure to indent (but not tear) the aluminum surface. Fill the indentation with press ink.

Photo-Direct Plates

Photo-direct (projection-speed) presensitized plates have a faster silver-halide coating and are used in an automatic or semiautomatic camera- or projector-type platemaker. (See Figs. 13-22 and 13-23.) Some of these platemakers use ready-cut plates; others use plate material in roll form.

In the photo-direct process, use of a negative intermediary is eliminated. Instead, the presensitized plates are loaded into the platemaker, the original copy material is placed in the copyboard, the platemaker is focused for size, etc., and the exposure is made. Light rays from the original copy material are reflected through a prism-lens arrangement to the plate inside the processing compartment of the platemaker. The plate is then automatically processed and delivered ready for use.

Since the photo-direct platemaker (processor) is its own camera, projecting the image directly onto the concealed plate, no darkroom is required for this entire sequence of platemaking. It is designed primarily for simplified techniques in duplicating work, rather than for use by commercial printers on more complex work.

Wipe-On Plates

The wipe-on (surface-coated offset) diazo plate is coated in the shop, prior to exposure. Briefly, the procedure consists of spreading a diazo sensitizer on a fine-grained aluminum plate, the surface of which has been chemically treated (after graining) to prevent oxidation and also to serve as a base for the coating. No whirler is used in the wipe-on coating procedure.

At present, brush-graining and sandblasting are two common methods of graining plates to be coated by the wipe-on process.

Select a fine-grain, photographic-grade, cellulose sponge as an applicator. Prepare it by saturating with water, and then wringing as

Itek Business Products

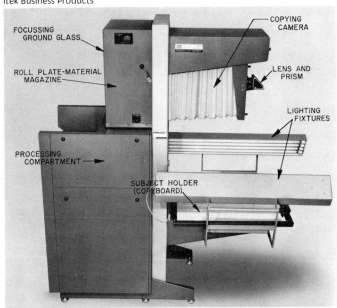

Fig. 13-22. Itek Project-A-Lith Platemaster unit for automatically making offset masters from copy.

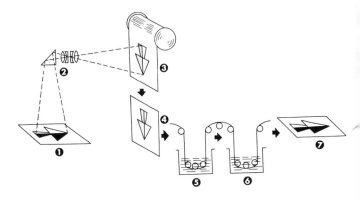

Fig. 13-23. Schematic showing offset plate being produced automatically by photo-direct (projection-speed) platemaker.
1. **Original copy on platemaker copyboard.**
2. **Prism and lens direct and "size" reflected image to plate material.**
3. **Latent image is formed on projection-speed silver-emulsion plate material.**
4. **Plate material is advanced and cut to length.**
5. **Activator-developer solution conditions the plate image to be ink-receptive and conditions the background area to be water-receptive.**
6. **Stop bath ends the plate developing.**
7. **Plate is ready for the press.**

Fig. 13-24. Automatic plate processor for presensitized negative-working subtractive plates. Uses only one chemical — a developer-finisher solution.

dry as possible. Pour a pool of the sensitizer solution on the center of the plate, and spread the solution over the entire plate surface with the sponge. Use straight strokes, first wiping horizontally across the plate until the entire plate area is covered, and then wiping vertically.

Turn over the sponge, and smooth the coating by repeating the above spreading method. Use only a light pressure, with a steady motion back and forth across the entire plate. At this point, the coating should be smooth and even. Eliminate any excess coating by repeating the horizontal and vertical strokes. Finally, fan the coating for at least one-half minute to dry it completely.

A slightly streaked appearance will not affect the finished plate or the printing, provided that the plate is covered completely with coating solution.

It is not necessary to rinse the sponge after coating each plate, but it is suggested that the sponge be rinsed at intervals.

Exposure. Expose wipe-on plates for approximately 60 seconds, using a NuArc Ultra Plus Mercury Vapor Flip-Top unit, Fig. 13-10.

When the plate is normally exposed and developed, a solid fifth to sixth step should be obtained, using a platemakers' sensitivity guide.

Developing and Lacquering. The plate is developed and the image lacquered in one operation. Wet a separate cellulose sponge and wring out the excess water. Shake the lacquer-developer thoroughly, and pour a sufficient pool in the center of the plate. Spread this over the entire surface, using firm pressure. The background areas will begin to develop immediately, and the image will accept the lacquer ingredients of the solution. Use a circular motion to rub up the image, applying more lacquer-developer, if necessary.

While rubbing up the image, squeeze the sponge over the center of the plate, forming a pool of excess water and lacquer-developer. Starting with the sponge in this pool, again go over the entire image area. With this technique, the free water will remove any residue of the developer phase of the solution from the image and will permit full coverage of the image by the lacquer phase.

Usually, there is a color intensity of the image during the last rubbing-up operation. When it appears that the background is fully developed and the image is rubbed up solidly, flush the plate well with water to remove dissolved coating and excess developer.

When the plate is clean, squeegee and apply gum etch, rubbing down dry. The gum etch has a grease-receptive ingredient which assures quick roll-up. (Do not apply asphaltum to the plate since it is not necessary, and the asphaltum would tend to penetrate the gum film.) The plate is now ready for the press.

On the Press. Remove gum with water sponge, and start the press run in the usual manner.

Deletions can be made with a rubber hone or regular slipstone, followed with plate etch or fountain solution.

If the plate has been subjected to scratches which print, apply Plate Kleen for one-half minute. This solution will remove the ink and will build up a new protective and hydrophilic (water-attractive) surface. Follow the same procedure if background toning is present.

THUR

Storage. For storage, the plate should be gummed with diluted gum solution (8° Bé), and washed out with asphaltum.

Additional notes: After coating, if the lacquer film of the plate coating is not perfect, apply a second coating of the sensitizer without washing off the first coating. Merely pour on a second application and re-wipe as above. If the plate is wet with rinse water, squeegee off the excess water before the lacquer-developer is applied a second time.

Automated Processing. Platemaking departments which process a considerable quantity of wipe-on plates use automated equipment to save time and to achieve uniform processing of the plates. Figure 13-25 illustrates a plate-coater in use; Fig. 13-26 shows automated equipment for exposing, developing, rinsing, gumming, and delivering the finished plate.

Electrostatic Plates

Electrostatic offset plates are prepared by a photoelectrostatic process.[3] In this process, an image (same-size, enlarged, or reduced) is produced on the plate from any original copy

[3] Often referred to formerly as *xerography* (zee-róg-ra-phy).

which may be typed, drawn, printed, or photographed. The preparation of the electrostatic plate is by use of an automatic electrostatic plate processor, such as is shown in Fig. 13-27.

The plate processor's magazine holds a quantity of unexposed plates which are cut to

Western Litho Plate & Supply Company

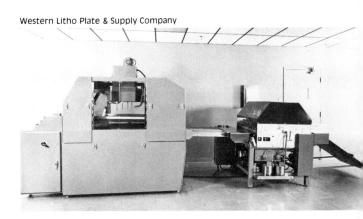

Fig. 13-26. Automated equipment for exposing, developing, rinsing, gumming, and drying wipe-on plates (left, "Lith-x-pozer"; right, "Lithoplater").

Itek Graphic Products

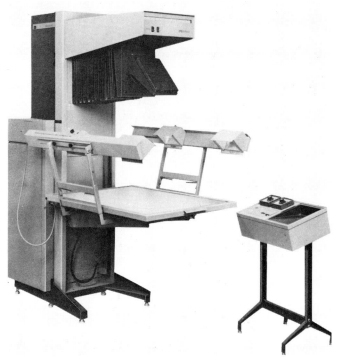

Fig. 13-27. Variable Focus Electrostatic Platemaker.

Western Litho Plate & Supply Company

Fig. 13-25. Coating a wipe-on plate with the "Lithocoater".

size or in roll form. These unexposed plates carry a light-sensitive zinc-oxide resin coating capable of accepting an electrostatic charge.

In use, the operator loads the paste-up (camera copy) on the copyboard; sets lens and copyholder distances for reproduction size; adjusts position of lights; sets lens aperture control for *f*/number and reproduction size; sets timer for length of exposure; and adjusts for the length of plate desired (if plate material is roll-fed).

When all is ready, pressing the start button causes the processor to carry the plate through four basic steps: *charging, exposure, developing,* and *fusing,* Fig. 13-28.

As the plate is carried through this first step, the entire plate surface is given an electrostatic charge. See Fig. 13-28A.

The processor's optical system then projects an image of the original copy onto the charged plate surface. The electrostatic charge is retained in the latent image area of the plate surface, Fig. 13-28B, but the charge is drained away from the exposed areas.

In the developing step, a charged developer (iron filings and toner) is applied to the surface,

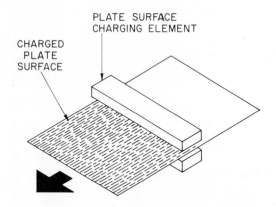

A. The entire plate surface coating is electrostatically charged.

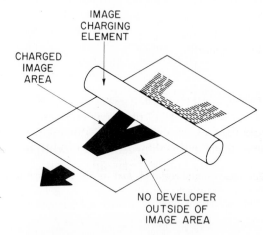

C. Applied developer adheres only to the charged image area.

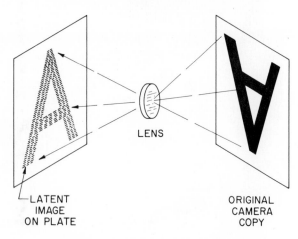

B. During camera exposure, the latent image retains the charge — exposed areas lose the charge.

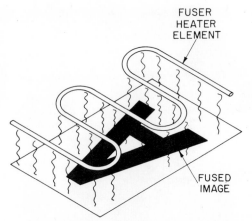

D. The image area is then fused by application of radiant heat.

Fig. 13-28. The basic principles of electrostatic platemaking.

adhering only to the charged image area. See Fig. 13-28C.

The "developed" image is then fused and made permanent by the application of radiated heat. See Fig. 13-28D.

After fusing, the plate coating is stripped from the nonimage area of the plate surface. The plate is then gummed and is ready for the press.

Metal electrostatic plates are commonly used by newspaper and commercial printers. Paper electrostatic plates (masters) are more frequently used on duplicators.

Laser Facsimile Surface Offset Plates

Figure 13-29 illustrates schematically in block form a laser facsimile[4] offset platemaking system. This basic system consists of two laser stations: the *page paste-up reading station,* and the *offset plate exposure station.*

The paste-up (or, *copy*) may be, for example, a full-page newspaper paste-up with line copy and with screened halftone prints. The offset plate used is one of several compatible conventional presensitized surface offset plates.

[4] *Facsimile* — (abbreviated: *fax*) — an exact copy of the original, usually in the same size.

In operation, the *reading laser* travels along the page paste-up, scanning narrow bands at right angles to the travel, much as the raster line scanning on a home television tube picture. The presence or absence of reflected light from the scanned image or from the copy background and from the location on the page causes the *sensor* to send an electronic signal to the *modulator.* In turn, the modulator, by digital signal, directs the *exposure laser* to place precisely controlled amounts of laser light on the plate's presensitized surface. This occurs line by line, in exact facsimile of the scanning of the original paste-up copy, until the entire plate is exposed.

The exposed plate is then automatically processed and is ready for the press. The entire operation, from paste-up to plate, may take about two minutes.

It should be pointed out, also, that in this system, both the reading and the exposure laser stations may be at the same locations. Signals may be sent by microwave or by telephone lines from the reading station to one or more satellite exposure stations. Each satellite station, as it receives the original signal from the reading station, produces facsimile plates.

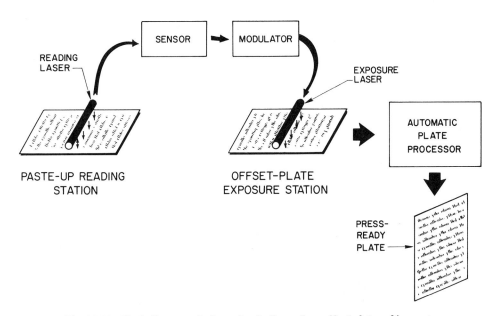

Fig. 13-29. Block diagram of a laser facsimile surface offset platemaking system.

All satellite stations will produce plates at the same time. This allows a publication to go to press simultaneously in several locations throughout the country or world without waiting for delivery of duplicate plates.

Since this process goes directly from paste-up to plate exposure, there is the elimination of the need for paste-up camera, film developing, negative opaquing, stripping, and negative-to-plate exposure.

Because the plate-exposure laser is controlled by digital signal, it is expected that future systems will go directly from input terminals (such as keyboard and OCR) to computer, to offset plate. This would also eliminate or minimize the need for phototypesetters.

Minor Surface Plate Corrections

Sometimes a developed surface plate reveals the need for repairing the image area or removing the unwanted spots before the plate is sent to the press.

Deletions

Immediately after developing a surface plate, and while it is still wet, inspect the entire plate. Determine whether there are any unwanted spots, lines, words, or other portions of the image. These can be removed by alternately wetting with water and gently rubbing with a rubber eraser, scotch hone, or snake slip. Too vigorous rubbing, or dry rubbing, may polish the rubbed area, robbing it of its grain and rendering that area nonreceptive to water.

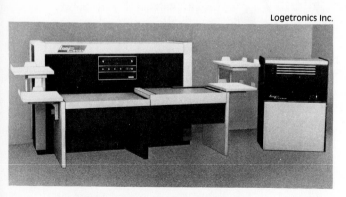

Logetronics Inc.

Fig. 13-30. LogEscan Laser Platemaker.

• **Note:** Deletions on paper plates should be made with only a rubber eraser, wetting either the eraser or the plate.

Should the grain of a metal plate be destroyed by too vigorous rubbing, it may be restored by rubbing the area with a water-dampened cotton swab on which has been sprinkled a little pumice.

If available, an air eraser (one which sprays compressed air and pumice) is an excellent device for making deletions. It does not disturb the grain structure of the plate surface.

Minor deletions may be made while the plate is on the press. Run down the image, stop the press, and gum the plate. Sponge off with water the area to be worked on. While the area is maintained wet with water, rub out the undesired work or defect with an eraser dipped in water or fountain solution or rub with a hone. Then gum the area again. Proceed to other areas on the plate, if necessary, and repeat.

Additions or Corrections

Lines may be added or repaired, and other parts of a broken image restored to a gummed metal plate, either on or off the press. This is achieved by scratching through the gum just deep enough into the metal surface to make it ink receptive. A lithographer's needle, sharpened or shaped on the end to suit the work, may be used. Finally, developing ink or printing ink should be rubbed into the scratches to complete the work.

Questions

1. Explain what is meant by "two separate areas" of an offset plate.
2. Why is a plate grained?
3. What is a master?
4. Of what materials are offset plates made?
5. Explain how a plate is gummed.
6. What is meant by "putting a plate under"?
7. Describe the care of a plate on the press.
8. Tell what is meant by a surface plate. Name the main types of surface plates.
9. Describe a relief plate. By what other names is this kind of plate known?
10. What is meant by "step-and-repeat" work? What are its advantages?

11. In platemaking, why is a step gray scale used?
12. Describe the various methods of placing an image on a direct-image plate.
13. What is a presensitized plate?
14. Explain the photo-electrostatic process of producing an image on a plate.
15. What is meant by the terms "negative-working" and "positive-working" plates?
16. What is the difference between subtractive and additive plates?
17. Explain photo-electrostatic.

Problems and Projects

1. Report on the manufacture of sheet aluminum.
2. Prepare a direct-image plate. Include typing and drawing by hand in the plate image.
3. Prepare a presensitized plate for the press.
4. Mix solutions for, and prepare, a wipe-on diazo surface plate.
5. Prepare a plate by the electrostatic process.
6. Make step-and-repeat exposures. Make these exposures on the platemaker in your shop.
7. Visit a plant to observe the laser facsimile platemaking process.
8. Prepare a report on why the name *Baumé* is associated with the measuring of liquid density.
9. Make a sketch showing how to "expose" a presensitized plate. Show the exposure light, the flat, and the plate.

New Terms

additive coating	insoluble
asphaltum	intermediary
cellulose-base	lacquer
charging	leading end
chase	medium run
diazo	modulator
facsimile	open step
fusing	positive-working
grain	reproducing materials
grainless plate	sandblasting
gum arabic	staging solution
hone	subdued
image-bearing	subtractive coating
ink-receptive	trailing end
ink-repellent	tusche

Chapter 14 # Offset Inks

Offset inks are compounded especially for use on offset presses. Never use letterpress inks or inks intended for *stone* lithography on offset presses.

Requirements

Offset ink must be able to withstand the reaction of the press fountain solution which it encounters on the dampened offset plate. Ideally, the ink should not emulsify (absorb any of the fountain solution); neither should the ink break down and *combine with* the fountain solution in the clear areas of the plate on the press. Either of these situations would tend to impair the body, color, or drying qualities of

the ink, weaken the plate image, or cause scumming (or ink-tinting) of the clear areas of the press plate and printed sheets.

The ink used on an offset press must be able to carry the full intended color and covering to the paper, despite the *film-splitting* action which occurs as the offset-press blanket picks up only a portion of the ink on the plate, and despite the necessary use of a comparatively soft rubber blanket in transferring the impression to the paper.

Composition

Most offset inks consist of a vehicle, pigments, and modifiers.

Vehicle is a heat-treated linseed oil, referred to as "lithographic varnish." It forms the body, or bulk, of the ink.

Pigments are the coloring materials. Offset inks usually employ pigments chemically manufactured from *coal tar*, a by-product in the manufacture of coke and fuel gas from coal. Pigments vary a great deal in cost. This difference is reflected in the prices of the ink colors.

Modifiers are added to control the drying, viscosity, length, tack, or other qualities of the ink. They even control the *odor* of the ink, as when wrappers are printed for such items as butter and bacon.

Manufacture

In addition to stock colors of ink, manufacturers will supply inks to match submitted color samples, as well as special inks for satisfactory

Interchemical Corporation

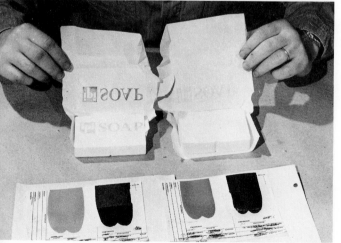

Fig. 14-1. Ink must be suited for the work. The two inks above looked alike, but the left example soaked through the wrapper, marring the soap.

printing on paper samples submitted. Advice on ink problems is generally available from the manufacturer's technical staff.

Preparing Ingredients. All ingredients for inkmaking are inspected, tested, and processed to meet the specifications of the laboratory technicians.

Mixing. For each batch to be mixed, a formula-controlled quantity of each necessary ingredient is carefully weighed out and sent to the *blade mixers*, which blend the ingredients together.

Grinding. After mixing, the ink is passed repeatedly through an *ink mill* where several smooth steel rollers grind the ingredients to the degree of fineness required.

Testing. Each finished batch of ink is tested by the laboratory, under actual printing conditions, to insure that it meets specifications.

Packaging. The final step before delivery is the packaging and labeling of the ink in convenient-size containers for the printer. Ink is packed in tubes, cans, and drums and is even delivered in tank-truck and tank-car loads.

Color Mixing of Inks

A supply of yellow, red, blue, orange, green, purple, white, and black will enable one to mix the usual colors needed.

Some color mixing (for small amounts of ink) may be done by the press operator who must

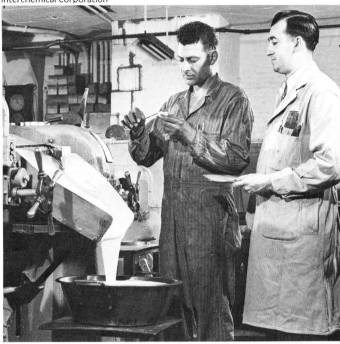

Interchemical Corporation

Fig. 14-3. Ink mill.

have a knowledge of the results of mixing primary colors to achieve another color, or getting a lighter or darker shade or tint of the ink on hand.

In general, the *stronger* colors should be added sparingly to the *weaker* colors, and then thoroughly blended until the desired color is reached. Notably, small amounts of colors such as green or blue will have a great effect on white. Cleanliness of the ink knife and the mixing slab are of primary importance. One should anticipate the amount of ink needed before mixing to the final color or shade.

For large amounts of colored ink, it is best to use stock colors of ink or to have the ink mixed to your specifications by the manufacturer. In this way, additional quantities and ink for reruns can always be matched. Inks for all process printing (four-color halftones) are best purchased ready-mixed for the job.

In addition to specifying the color or colors when ordering offset inks, be sure to give all information on the job to be run. This includes make of press; press operating speed; type of

Interchemical Corporation

Fig. 14-2. Ink mixer.

Fig. 14-4. Packaged ink.

stock to be used (and stock samples when possible); processing and/or converting requirements; and especially, end usage requirements such as light fastness, resistance to alkali, acid, alcohol, or grease.

Ink Terminology

In the language of the inkmaker, the following terms describe the various properties of offset inks:

Viscosity. This is the resistance to flow. If ink flows readily, it has a *low* viscosity. If it is heavy-bodied, it has a *high* viscosity. Of necessity, offset inks generally have a high viscosity.

Tack. It is a measure of stickiness. Too much tack in offset ink reduces its film-splitting ability, and thus its effectiveness.

Length. An ink may be *long* or *short*. Test it by tapping the ink with a corner of the ink knife and attempting to draw it out into a long string. A good offset ink is generally long.

Opacity. This is the hiding or covering quality of an ink. An opaque ink will show in its true color when printed over another color of a previous run.

Transparency. A transparent ink does not have great hiding power. It allows previously printed colors to show through clearly. Many times this show-through is desired.

Permanence or Fastness. Inks with this property maintain their color and do not fade even though exposed to sunlight for long periods. They are especially suitable for signs and posters.

Fugitive. A fugitive ink is one which tends to lose its color and fade when exposed for long periods to sunlight.

Resistant. A resistant ink is so constituted by the manufacturer to withstand the action of such factors as gases, chemicals, heat, and moisture.

Lakes. These are body colors. They are not particularly strong colors.

Toners. These are especially strong colors and highly concentrated. They are practically pure pigments ground in oil (linseed-oil varnish).

Job Black. This is a black ink which is used for the regular run of ordinary jobs.

Halftone Black. A finely ground ink especially suited for reproducing finely screened halftone work is called halftone black.

Metallic Inks. Aluminum or bronze powder mixed in a suitable vehicle to form metallic inks. Some color may be added. Such inks are difficult to run, and it is important that they be fresh.

Water Colors. These colors produce flat effects. They contain no varnish.

Heat Transfer Inks

Heat transfer inks are available in various colors for use on standard offset papers and presses. Heat transfer is a two-stage process of printing, usually onto synthetic fabrics, such as polyester. In this process, the artwork is first printed on paper in the desired colors. The printed sheet is then contacted, using pressure and heat, against the fabric. The heat causes the dyed artwork to evaporate (sublimate) and transfer to the fabric fibers where, upon penetration and cooling, the colors solidify and become *fast*.

Storing Inks

When an opened can of ink is to be stored, flatten the top surface of the ink and pour a little varnish over it. This coat of varnish will prevent air from forming a skin on the ink. If stored ink becomes thickened, mix in a little varnish to restore the consistency desired.

Questions

1. Are letterpress inks recommended for offset use?
2. What are the special requirements of offset inks?
3. What are the usual ingredients of offset inks?
4. Describe the function of each of the following: vehicle, pigment, modifiers.
5. Describe the ink-manufacturing process.
6. What is an ink mill?
7. Tell how small quantities of ink may be mixed in the shop when a certain color or tone is not available.
8. Define each of the following ink properties: opacity, transparency, length.
9. What is an opaque ink?
10. What is a transparent ink?
11. What is "long" ink?
12. How do you select from an ink catalog a good ink for posters which will be exposed to sunlight?

Problems and Projects

1. Consult an ink catalog, and select for the shop a suitable assortment of black and colored inks for general use. Include the colors necessary for mixing and obtaining the usual colors needed.
2. Prepare (mix) a quantity of ink for a job of the color specified by the instructor.
3. Locate a film on inkmaking, and arrange for a showing in your school or shop.
4. Write for an ink catalog for your shop. Get one which shows the colors of inks.

New Terms

blade mixer	metallic inks
coal tar	process printing
compounded	resistance
emulsify	film-splitting action
fugitive	tack
ink mill	toner
job black ink	varnish
lakes	viscosity

Chapter 15

Papers and Bindery Work

Fine paper stock will improve a printing job and avoid aggravating press trouble. It will also stand up well in the usage expected of the printed product.

Requirements

Good offset papers have the proper affinity for ink. They will not unduly absorb, nor repel, the ink. The surface of the paper must not soften under the action of the press dampening solution, lest it break down and give off coating particles. These particles may dirty the ink and cause a change in the pH (acidity) of the fountain solution.

The paper must have a truly even (flat) surface in order to reproduce faithfully every dot of a halftone illustration. The surface must be free of fuzz or lint. Its finish must set off to best advantage the quality of the artwork, photogra-

S. D. Warren Company

Fig. 15-1. **Hardwood chips for the digester. Note their size.**

phy, composition, and platemaking so that the finished printing will be a source of pride for both the printer and the customer.

Papermaking Pulps

All paper is made from pulp — the basic raw material reduced to fibers. Ingredients are also added for coloring and sizing or to provide other desirable characteristics.

Kinds of Pulps

Pulps in common use are:
1. Mechanically ground wood pulp
2. Old-paper pulp
3. Chemical wood pulp
4. Rag pulp
5. Cotton pulp

Mechanically ground wood pulp is produced by grinding the entire log (except for the bark), until it is reduced to tiny particles. Nothing is wasted, but the resulting pulp has short fibers and paper made from it has low tear-strength. Fugitive substances which are not removed cause later discoloration, weakening, and disintegration of the paper. This pulp is suited for handbills, newspapers, and other items which are not permanent.

Old-paper pulp is made by returning used paper to a pulp state by a chemical cooking process, and then removing the old ink. Again, the fibers are reduced in length, which makes for a weak paper. Inferior old-paper pulp is used for box boards and cheaper papers. However, a good grade of paper can be made from the better grades of used-paper pulp.

S. D. Warren Company

Fig. 15-2.   Digester.

S. D. Warren Company

Fig. 15-3.   Pulp after digesting, washing, and bleaching.

Chemical wood pulp is made by cooking wood chips in a digester to remove lignin, gums, resins, and other materials. This results in pure, long fibers which make a strong paper. Since about half the content of the original wood is eliminated in this process, the resulting paper is more expensive. Although this is a relatively new process, it is believed that paper made from chemical wood pulp is a *permanent* paper, since some of these papers over sixty years old are still in good condition.

Rag pulp and cotton pulp make a good or poor paper, depending upon the amount of laundering the original rags were subjected to and the amount of dye which has to be removed. New No. 1 white rags and new cotton make the finest pulps for permanent and strong bond paper, antique book paper, and cover stock.

Kimberly-Clark Corporation

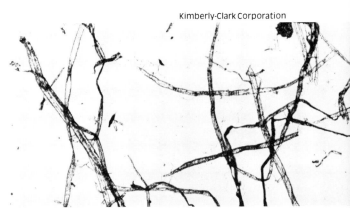

Fig. 15-4.   Magnified soft wood sulphite fibers.

Kimberly-Clark Corporation

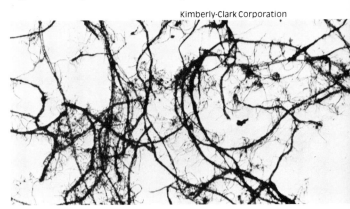

Fig. 15-5.   Magnified new cotton fibers.

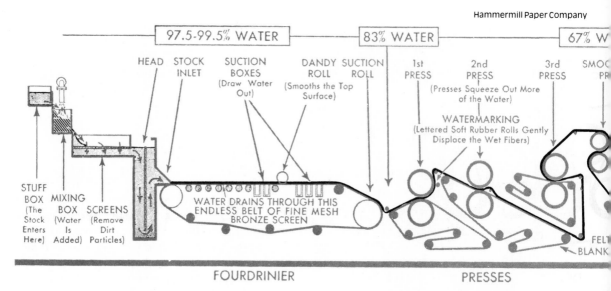

Fig. 15-6.   Diagram showing how paper is made on a modern Fourdrinier papermaking machine.

Papermaking

An outline of the usual steps in the making of paper is given below:

Reducing Materials to Fibers

Wood, old paper, cellulose, and rags are reduced to fibers as previously explained.

Beating

A many-bladed revolving drum on an oval-shaped tub beats the pulp each time the pulp is forced to travel beneath it. This roughens and frays the fibers so they may cling together better in the finished paper. Beating is controlled to provide the desired strength, opacity, surface, and bulk.

Fig. 15-7.   The beater.

Fig. 15-8.   The Jordan engine further refines the pulp.

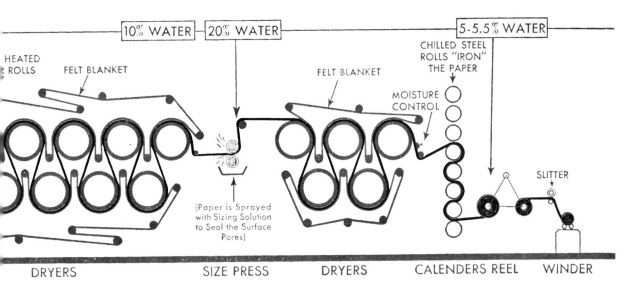

| 10% WATER | 20% WATER | | 5-5.5% WATER |

HEATED ROLLS   FELT BLANKET   FELT BLANKET

CHILLED STEEL ROLLS "IRON" THE PAPER

MOISTURE CONTROL

SLITTER

(Paper is Sprayed with Sizing Solution to Seal the Surface Pores)

DRYERS   SIZE PRESS   DRYERS   CALENDERS REEL   WINDER

Refining

A Jordan engine receives the pulp from the beater and gives it a further beating. This is the ultimate refinement of the pulp before it flows onto the paper machine.

Sizing

Pulps for lithographic printing papers receive generous quantities of sizing materials in manufacture. This prevents the finished paper from softening and shedding coating particles while on the offset press.

During press operation, the fountain solution tends to dampen the paper and weaken it. The pull of the ink on the offset press blanket may then tear off particles of weakened paper. These particles may get into the ink and the fountain, thus causing scumming on the press.

The addition of sizing prevents writing inks from blurring by keeping the ink on the surface. It also provides a binder to hold down the surface fibers which might tend to rise, making the surface fuzzy. A sized paper also keeps the offset ink on the surface, allowing the ink to retain its brilliance and density.

Rosin is used as a sizing, if the sizing is added while the pulp is in the beaters. If the sizing is sprayed on the surface after the paper is made, starch is used.

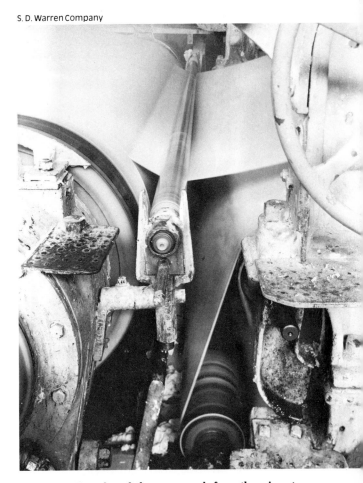

Fig. 15-9. Transfer of the paper web from the wire at left to the felts at right.

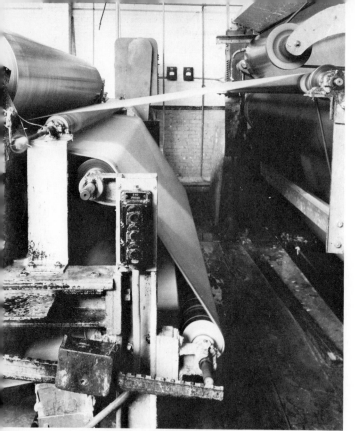

Fig. 15-10. Paper coming from the wet presses and starting through the smoothing press.

Loading

Clay, a natural earth product, is added to pulps which are intended for uncoated papers. This is done while the pulp is still in the beaters. Clay improves opacity, makes for a smooth surface, provides a better affinity for ink, and brightens the color of the paper.

Forming the Paper

After beating and loading, the pulp flows into the "stuff chest" (a vat) on the wet end of the papermaking machine.

In a highly water-diluted form, the pulp is flowed onto an endless, traveling wire screen. While traveling at high speed, the screen is shaken from side to side, meshing the fibers together, and draining off much of the water. At this time, the partially formed wet web of paper may be *watermarked* by a metal *dandy roller* which bears an etched design. The paper is then transferred to a felt blanket, which carries it through pressing and drying rolls to squeeze out the water and dry the paper. It is

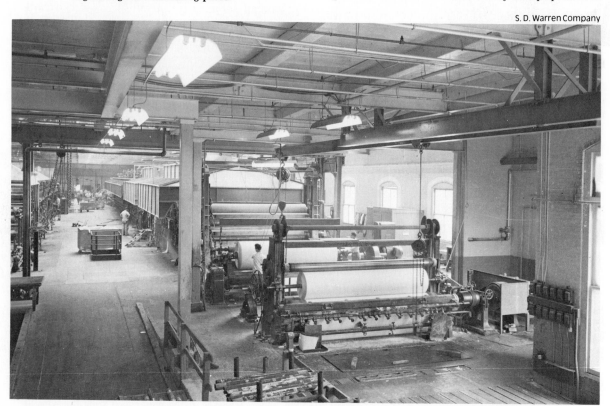

Fig. 15-11. Dry end of papermaking machine, showing paper being delivered and wound onto rolls.

then wound into rolls on the dry end of the papermaking machine, Fig. 5-11.

Calendering

Coated papers may be calendered after coating and drying. This is done in a separate machine, where the paper passes through a

Fig. 15-12. Slitters divide the web into rolls.

Fig. 15-13. Calendering.

series of calender rollers which press and polish the paper. See Fig. 15-13.

Packaging

Sheets are cut from the rolls, and trimmed; then inspected, counted, and wrapped. A wide variety of paper stock is also available in roll form for use on web presses (see Chapter 18) and on roll converters.

Some Common Paper Terms

Ream

A ream consists of 500 sheets of paper. Common papers are often packaged in this amount.

Package

Sheets in a package vary with thickness of sheets. For example, index bristol may be packaged in 100 sheets.

Piece

Full sheets of paper, as they come from a packaged ream, are cut into press-size or job-size pieces.

Sheet

Paper is purchased in full sheets and may be cut into job-sized pieces, but when it reaches

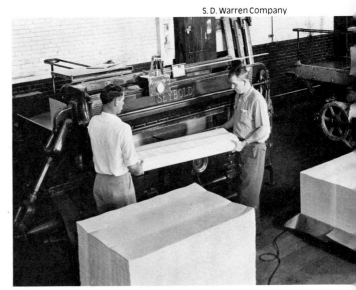

Fig. 15-14. Trimming the paper.

the press, the former pieces are again called *sheets*. Thus: "Cut 2000 pieces for the job," but, "Feed a sheet through the press."

Felt Side

The felt side is that surface which was next to the felt blanket on the papermaking machine. It is the better of the two sides (if distinguishable) of a sheet of paper. Use this side for printing, if there is a choice. The watermark is "readable" on the felt side of a sheet. Not all paper is watermarked, however.

Wire Side

The wire side is that surface which was next to the screen on the papermaking machine. The screen markings (pattern) can be distinguished,

Table 15-1
Paper Caliper (Thickness) Conversion Table

1 micrometer* = 0.001 millimeter
0.001″ = 25.4 micrometers

For practical purposes, the sums in the micrometers column have been rounded off to the nearest whole micrometer.

Inches	Micrometers	Typical Product (Approximate)
0.001	25	
0.002	51	
0.003	76	20-lb. Bond
0.004	102	
0.005	127	
0.006	152	
0.007	178	70-lb. Book
0.008	203	
0.009	229	110-lb. Index
0.010	254	
0.011	279	
0.012	305	140-lb. Index
0.013	330	
0.014	356	
0.015	381	
0.016	406	
0.017	432	
0.018	457	
0.019	483	
0.020	508	180-lb. Bristol (Pasted)

*Pronounced mī - crō - mē - ter.

on some papers, if a sheet is held horizontally toward the light. Also, when looking at the wire side, the watermark will appear reversed. If printing only one side of a sheet, do not use the wire side. Print on the felt side with the watermark right side up and readable left to right.

Lately, much newsprint is being produced on *twin-wire* machines. In this process, both sides of the paper are produced as a wire side. This eliminates the felt side of the paper which tends to release objectionable lint during printing. Less lint means better reproduction of halftones and better color reproduction in newspapers.

Caliper

The caliper (or thickness) of a sheet is measured in thousandths of an inch. This measurement in thousandths is sometimes called *points*, as in 10-point board when indicating a board of .010″ thickness or caliper.

- **Note:** See Table 15-1, for conversions of caliper measurements from U.S. Customary to metric.

To measure the caliper, cut or fold a sheet to form four thicknesses. Measure the thickness with a micrometer and divide by four. Twenty-pound bond paper will usually caliper from .0025″ to .0035″, or about three-thousandths of an inch thick.

Tables in paper catalogs indicate paper thickness in caliper — thousandths and ten-thousandths of an inch. This is useful information when the thickness of a book having a given number of pages must be calculated in advance.

- **Note:** *One sheet of paper* in a book is *one leaf*, printed on both sides to make *two pages*. The number of pages in a book divided by two equals the number of thicknesses of paper in that book.

Grain

The grain is determined by the direction of the fibers which make up the sheet. It runs either the long way or the short way of the sheet. Paper is stiffer *with* the grain than *across* the grain. Consequently, the grain should run

Table 15-2
Useful Paper Information*

Kind	General Uses	Basic Size (Inches)	Some Substance (or Basis Weights) (Pounds)	Some Other Sizes Commonly Made (Inches)
1. Bond	Letterheads, documents, office forms	17 x 22	9, 13, 16, 20, 24	17 x 28, 19 x 24, 22 x 34, 24 x 38
2. Onionskin	Makeready in pressroom, carbon copies, air mail	17 x 22	7, 8, 9, 10	17 x 26, 17 x 28, 19 x 24, 22 x 34
3. Writing or Flat	Price books, statements, booklets, broadsides	17 x 22	16, 20, 24	17 x 28, 19 x 24, 22 x 34, 24 x 38
4. Safety	Checks, drafts, notes	17 x 22	24	17 x 28, 19 x 24
5. Ledger	Accounting and machine bookkeeping	17 x 22	24, 28, 32, 36	17 x 28, 19 x 24, 22 x 34, 24 x 38
6. Index Bristol	Index cards, folders	25½ x 30½	90, 110, 140, 170	20½ x 24¾, 22½ x 28½
7. Card Bristol	Postcards, tickets	22½ x 28½	94	
8. Offset (Book)	Surface sized for general printing Surface sized book for books and halftones Calendered for halftones Enameled for best (finest) halftones	25 x 38	50, 60, 70 80, 90, 100	17½ x 22½, 19 x 25, 23 x 29, 28 x 42, and multiples
9. Opaque	Highly opaque for circulars with halftones	17 x 22	16, 20, 24, 28, 32	17½ x 22½, 23 x 29, 23 x 35
10. Cover	Covers. Enameled for covers with halftones	20 x 26	50, 60, 65, 80	23 x 35, 26 x 40
11. Label	Labels. Coated — for varnishing	25 x 38	50, 60, 70	

*For complete listings of papers in sheets and rolls, consult papermakers' catalogs.

vertically in a pamphlet, book, or show card. The paper (especially bristols and covers) makes a smoother and longer lasting fold if the fold runs *with* the grain. When purchasing paper, specify the direction of grain desired.

Grain Marking and Wrapper. The direction of grain may be stamped on the ream wrapper as "grain long" or "grain short." Sometimes the grain direction is indicated by underlining one of the dimensions on the label, such as: _17"_ × 22".

Testing Direction of Grain. If no label or wrapper markings are evident, the direction of grain may be tested in several ways:

1. *Bending.* Hold the sheet by one edge, letting the opposite edge sag under its own weight. Repeat with an adjacent edge. The test producing the greater sag indicates the grain is running in the same direction as the edge being held in your hands.
2. *Tearing.* Tear the paper halfway across from one edge. Repeat with an adjacent edge. The paper usually tears with a cleaner and more even tear *with* the grain.
3. *Folding.* Fold and crease sharply in one direction. Repeat at 90°. The sharper and cleaner fold (or crease) will be *with* the grain.
4. *Wetting.* Wet one side of a piece of paper (6" × 6", or so). Hold the paper flat on the palm with the wet side down. It will form a roll. The direction of grain is parallel to the axis of the roll.

Basis or Substance

The weight, in pounds, of 500 sheets of a basic size of a particular kind of paper is

Fig. 15-15. A Dual Label. In dual information on this label, the 22″ × 34″ sheet size is also stated as 559 mm × 864 mm; the grammage of 75 g/m² corresponds to 20-pound substance; and the total weight of this carton is shown as 120 pounds and also as 54.4 kilograms. (Also, note that the abbreviation gsm is sometimes used instead of g/m².)

known as its *basis weight* (or *substance*). For instance, the basic size of bond paper is 17″ × 22″. The label on a ream of 16-pound bond which is 17″ × 22″ would read "17 × 22 — 16" — 16 pounds per 500 sheets of 17″ × 22″, the basic size of bond paper. It might also read "17 × 22 — 16 32/M," indicating that the weight is 32 pounds per thousand sheets of that same 17″ × 22″ basic size. Basis weight (subtance) is related to the *thickness* of paper: 20-pound bond is thicker than 16-pound.

Weight

The weight indicates the actual number of pounds per ream. Thus, the designation on the label of a ream of 16-pound bond, 17″ × 28″ would read: "17 × 28 — 20.5 41/M Sub. 16." This means that, although the sheets in this ream of paper are of 16-pound substance (bond is always 17″ × 22″ basic size), the actual weight is 20.5 pounds per ream, and 41 pounds per thousand sheets. It weighs more per ream because the sheets are larger than the standard size.

Metric Dimensions and Weight of Paper

Most countries, except the United States, are now specifying paper dimensions (sheet sizes) and weights in metric units of measurement. Officially called the *International System of Units*, it is abbreviated as *SI* and is generally referred to as *the metric system.*

U.S. Use of Metric Paper Sizes

It is expected that at some time in the future the United States paper industry will make a full transition to the metric system. At the present time, however, only a *limited* change toward a metric system has been made. This is in the industry's use of a *dual label* in its packaging.

The dual label, Fig. 15-15, shows the sheet dimensions, substance (basis weight), and the total weight in two ways — *U.S. customary* units and *metric* units. Note in the illustration that the metric designations include (1) the sheet dimensions in *millimeters*; (2) the substance (basis weight) in *grams per square meter* (abbreviated g/m²), and often referred to as the *grammage*; and (3) sometimes the total weight in *kilograms*. These are further explained below.

Metric Sheet Dimensions

Metric sheet dimensions are stated in millimeters (mm). To convert from a dimension in inches to a dimension in millimeters, multiply inches by 25.4 mm and round off to the nearest whole millimeter. For example, to convert 8½″ × 11″ to millimeters, proceed as follows:

1. 8½″ × 25.4 = 215.9 mm = 216 mm (rounded off)

2. $11'' \times 25.4 = 279.4$ mm $= 279$ mm (rounded off)

Thus, the familiar $8\frac{1}{2}'' \times 11''$ becomes 216×279 mm.

Table 15-3 shows the metric equivalents of commonly used customary paper dimensions.

Grammage

In the metric system, the substance, or basis weight, of paper is stated as the *grammage*. Grammage is determined by weighing, in grams, a sheet of the paper measuring one square meter in area. Grammage is expressed in *grams per square meter*, and is abbreviated g/m^2 and *gms*.

To convert from substance in pounds to grams per square meter, multiply the substance by the constant 1406.5 and divide by the square inches in the basic sheet. For example: compute the grammage for $17'' \times 22''$—20 bond paper:

1. $17'' \times 22''$ is the basic size for bond paper.
2. Substance of this paper is 20 pounds.
3. $17'' \times 22'' = 374$ square inches.
4. 20 pounds (substance) $\times$ 1406.5 (constant) $= 28,130$.
5. $28,130 \div 374$ sq. inches $= 75.2$ g/m² rounded off $= 75$ g/m².

Thus, 20 pound (substance weight) bond has a grammage of 75, and may be referred to as 75

Table 15-3
Inch to Millimeter Conversion Table for Paper Dimensions
(Rounded off to nearest whole millimeter.)

Inches =	mm	Inches =	mm	Inches =	mm	Inches =	mm
6	152	$14\frac{1}{4}$	362	$22\frac{1}{2}$	572	$30\frac{3}{4}$	781
$6\frac{1}{4}$	159	$14\frac{1}{2}$	368	$22\frac{3}{4}$	578	31	787
$6\frac{1}{2}$	165	$14\frac{3}{4}$	375	23	584	$31\frac{1}{4}$	794
$6\frac{3}{4}$	171	15	381	$23\frac{1}{4}$	591	$31\frac{1}{2}$	800
7	178	$15\frac{1}{4}$	387	$23\frac{1}{2}$	597	$31\frac{3}{4}$	806
$7\frac{1}{4}$	184	$15\frac{1}{2}$	394	$23\frac{3}{4}$	603	32	813
$7\frac{1}{2}$	191	$15\frac{3}{4}$	400	24	610	$32\frac{1}{4}$	819
$7\frac{3}{4}$	197	16	406	$24\frac{1}{4}$	616	$32\frac{1}{2}$	826
8	203	$16\frac{1}{4}$	413	$24\frac{1}{2}$	622	$32\frac{3}{4}$	832
$8\frac{1}{4}$	210	$16\frac{1}{2}$	419	$24\frac{3}{4}$	629	33	838
$8\frac{1}{2}$	216	$16\frac{3}{4}$	425	25	635	$33\frac{1}{4}$	845
$8\frac{3}{4}$	222	17	432	$25\frac{1}{4}$	641	$33\frac{1}{2}$	851
9	229	$17\frac{1}{4}$	438	$25\frac{1}{2}$	648	$33\frac{3}{4}$	857
$9\frac{1}{4}$	235	$17\frac{1}{2}$	445	$25\frac{3}{4}$	654	34	864
$9\frac{1}{2}$	241	$17\frac{3}{4}$	451	26	660	$34\frac{1}{4}$	870
$9\frac{3}{4}$	248	18	457	$26\frac{1}{4}$	667	$34\frac{1}{2}$	876
10	254	$18\frac{1}{4}$	464	$26\frac{1}{2}$	673	$34\frac{3}{4}$	883
$10\frac{1}{4}$	260	$18\frac{1}{2}$	470	$26\frac{3}{4}$	679	35	889
$10\frac{1}{2}$	267	$18\frac{3}{4}$	476	27	686	$35\frac{1}{4}$	895
$10\frac{3}{4}$	273	19	483	$27\frac{1}{4}$	692	$35\frac{1}{2}$	902
11	279	$19\frac{1}{4}$	489	$27\frac{1}{2}$	699	$35\frac{3}{4}$	908
$11\frac{1}{4}$	286	$19\frac{1}{2}$	495	$27\frac{3}{4}$	705	36	914
$11\frac{1}{2}$	292	$19\frac{3}{4}$	502	28	711	$36\frac{1}{4}$	921
$11\frac{3}{4}$	298	20	508	$28\frac{1}{4}$	718	$36\frac{1}{2}$	927
12	305	$20\frac{1}{4}$	514	$28\frac{1}{2}$	724	$36\frac{3}{4}$	933
$12\frac{1}{4}$	311	$20\frac{1}{2}$	521	$28\frac{3}{4}$	730	37	940
$12\frac{1}{2}$	318	$20\frac{3}{4}$	527	29	737	$37\frac{1}{4}$	946
$12\frac{3}{4}$	324	21	533	$29\frac{1}{4}$	743	$37\frac{1}{2}$	953
13	330	$21\frac{1}{4}$	540	$29\frac{1}{2}$	749	$37\frac{3}{4}$	959
$13\frac{1}{4}$	337	$21\frac{1}{2}$	546	$29\frac{3}{4}$	756	38	965
$13\frac{1}{2}$	343	$21\frac{3}{4}$	552	30	762	*	
$13\frac{3}{4}$	349	22	559	$30\frac{1}{4}$	768		
14	356	$22\frac{1}{4}$	565	$30\frac{1}{2}$	775		

*To obtain other sizes — multiply inches $\times$ 25.4, and round off to nearest whole millimeter.

Table 15-4
Substance (Basis Weights) and Grammage

Basic Size						Grammage (grams per square meter or, g/m²)
Bond 17″ × 22″	Cover 20″ × 26″	Bristol 22½″ × 28½″	Index 25½″ × 28½″	Tag 24″ × 36″	Book 25″ × 38″	
x				x	20	30
9				x	x	34
x				x	24	36
11				x	x	41
x				x	30	44
13				30	33	49
x				x	35	52
15				x	x	56
x				x	40	59
16				x	x	60
x				40	x	65
x				x	45	67
x				x	50	74
20 →	→	→	→	→ (*)	→ (*)	→ 75
x				50	x	81
x				x	60	89
24				x	x	90
x				60	x	98
x				x	70	104
28				x	x	105
x	40			x	x	108
x	x			70	x	114
x	x			x	80	118
32	x			x	x	120
x	x			80	x	130
x	x	x		x	90	133
36	50	x		x	x	135
x	x	x		90	x	146
x	x	67		x	x	147
x	x	x		x	100	148
40	x	x	x	x	x	150
x	60	x	x	x	x	162
x	x	x	90	100	x	163
x	x	80	x	x	x	175
x	65	x	x	x	x	176
	70	x	x	x	120	178
	x	x	x	x	x	189
	x	90	x	x	x	197
	x	x	110	x	x	199
	x	x	x	125	x	203
	80	x	x	x		216
	x	x	x	x		218
	x	100	x	x		219
	x	x	x	150		244
	x	x	140	x		253
	x	x	x	x		262
	x	120	x	x		263
	100	x	x	x		270
	x	x	x	175		285
	x	x	x	x		306
	x	140	170	x		307
	x	x	x	200		325
	x	x	x	x		349
	x	160	x	x		351
	130	x	x	x		352
		180	x	x		395
		x	220	x		398
		x	x	250		407
		200	x	x		438

Left axis label: Substance (Basis Weight) — Pounds Per Ream of 500 Sheets

Example of Use: A sheet of bond paper (17″ X 22″ basic size) of substance 20 has a grammage of 75 g/m² (indicated by the arrows in the table, above.)

g/m². This may also be referred to as *75 gram paper*. Table 15-4 lists the grammage and substance equivalents for the more common basic sizes of paper stock.

Total Weight. The total (actual) weight of the ream, carton, or other quantity is shown in kilograms (kg); or, large quantities may be stated in metric tons.

$$1 \text{ kilogram} = 1000 \text{ grams};$$
$$1000 \text{ kilograms} = 1 \text{ metric ton}$$
$$\text{Pounds} \times 0.4536 = \text{kilograms}$$

Thus, 120 pounds × 0.4536 = 54.432, or 54 kilograms.

Caliper. Paper caliper, or thickness, is expressed in metrics as *micrometers*. It is abbreviated as ⟋ m. One micrometer is equal to one-thousandth of a millimeter or one-millionth of a meter. Refer again to Table 15-1 which shows conversions from micrometers to thousandths of an inch. For comparison, note that 20-pound bond paper, which measures about .003″ (three-thousandths of an inch) in caliper, has a metric measurement of about 76 micrometers.

Papercutting

For economy, paper should be bought in a size to fit the job or in a size that can be cut for the job without excessive waste. If paper is already on hand, try to plan the job to fit the size of the paper. Scrap or waste costs just as much per pound as the paper used.

In cutting paper, keep the blade sharp, and the cutter bed clean. Use a long-handled swab, faintly dampened with cedar oil, to brush off dust from the cutter blade and the bed. Dust may cause scumming on the press if it reaches the blanket.

If possible, "back trim" all sides of paper stock to eliminate cutter dust. That is, each side of the paper stock should be finally cut with the flat side of the blade toward the paper as the paper is positioned in the cutter.

Chandler & Price Company

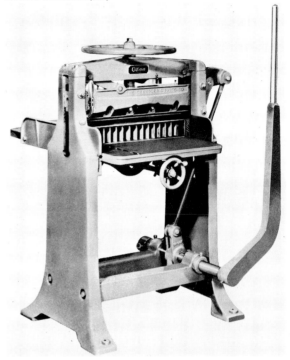

Fig. 15-16. Hand-lever paper cutter, floor model.

Challenge Machinery Company

Fig. 15-17. Challenge Champion 30½″ power paper cutter.

Figuring Number of Pieces from a Sheet

To find the number of 6″ × 10″ pieces that can be obtained from a sheet, 22½″ × 28½″,

...as shown below, cancelling up and down, first as in "A", then as in "B".

Solution A

$$\frac{22^{1}/_{2} \times 28^{1}/_{2}}{6 \times 10}$$

$$\frac{\overset{3}{22}^{1}/_{2} \times \overset{2}{28}^{1}/_{2}}{\underset{}{6} \times \underset{}{10}} = 6$$

Solution B

$$\frac{22^{1}/_{2} \times 28^{1}/_{2}}{10 \times 6}$$

$$\frac{\overset{2}{22}^{1}/_{2} \times \overset{4}{28}^{1}/_{2}}{\underset{}{10} \times \underset{}{6}} = 8$$

Solution B above results in eight pieces, two more than in A. Eight pieces, therefore, is the better answer. However, if there are large remainders when performing the division in the cancellations (as in the case of the above two solutions), it may be possible to draw the sizes of the pieces to be cut directly on the full sheet. This could result in a larger number of pieces per sheet. Study Fig. 15-18.

Figure 15-18 shows that nine 6" × 10" pieces can be obtained from the same 22½" × 28½" sheet — one additional piece per sheet. This would be a considerable saving if many sheets were to be cut.

The diagram method obviously is limited in use if it is required that the grain on all pieces run the same way. Note carefully in Fig. 15-18 that the first cut must, of necessity, be possible *as a straight line* across the entire width, or length, of the sheets — as line 'AB'.

It would be convenient, in the diagram shown to make all the cuts possible using the 10" setting on the cutter; then changing the setting to 6" for all the 6" cuts. If trim is needed on all four sides of the pieces, it should be allowed on the diagram where needed.

Carbonless Papers

Carbonless papers eliminate the need for inserting or using carbon paper between sheets in salesbooks, sheets of stationery, or where duplicate forms must be completed with pencil, ball-point pen, typewriter, or electronic data-processing equipment. Carbonless paper is available in sheets and rolls.

Self-Contained Carbonless Paper

Self-contained carbonless paper is coated with chemicals on one side only so as to yield an image on the paper surface when sharp pressure is applied. Another way of using imaging chemicals is to blend them with the paper fibers during manufacture. Under sharp pressure, this also will yield an image on the paper surface.

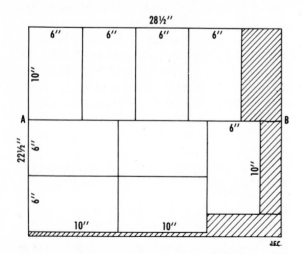

Fig. 15-18. Diagram method of figuring stock.

Fig. 15-19. Flat cutting operation on 84-inch cutter.

When an original and copies are typed or sets of business forms prepared, the original (first) sheet may be the usual bond or specialty stock. The remaining sheets in the set which will bear the printed form on the *carbonless-coated* surface are placed behind the original sheet (coated side to be printed toward the original), Fig. 15-20. Pressure of writing and typing on the original produces a duplicate image on the coated surface of each sheet beneath.

If offset printing of any nature is needed on the back side of self-contained carbonless paper prior to being assembled in sets for duplication, a light film of ink should be used rather than a heavy ink which would be absorbed into the paper. A heavy ink may seep through the chemical coating, rendering it useless. For this reason, most forms of this nature are printed on the back side in a light blue ink, giving information only and requiring no typewritten or handwritten entries.

Transfer Carbonless Paper

Transfer carbonless paper is a *two-coating* system. This means that two separate and dissimilar surfaces must be in contact before

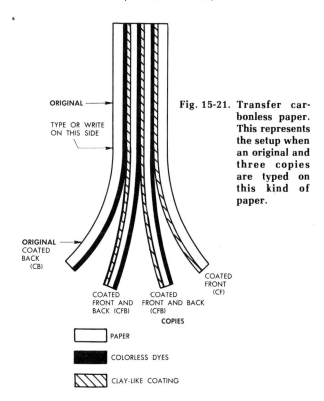

Fig. 15-21. **Transfer carbonless paper. This represents the setup when an original and three copies are typed on this kind of paper.**

applied pressure can produce images on the copy sheets beneath. See Fig. 15-21. In form sets, the original (the top sheet) contains a coating on the back only (designated "CB" for coating on back). The coating is of encapsulated, colored dye. The front surface is not coated. Intermediate sheets in the set contain a special clay coating on the front surface and the colorless dye coating on the back. These intermediate sheets are designated "CFB", indicating they are coated front and back. The last sheet of the form set is coated (with the clay coating) on the front side only and is designated "CF". Writing or typing on the first copy of the assembled set causes the dyes in any upper sheet to react with the clay coating on any mating sheet in order to produce an exact image.

Precautions with Carbonless Papers

If one is not careful, clamp pressure may cause images to form on carbonless paper when it is cut with a papercutter. To prevent

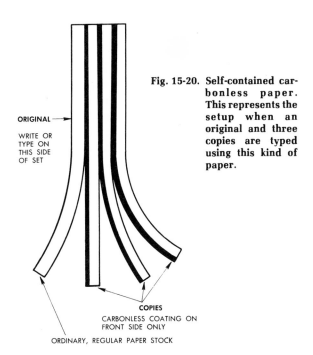

Fig. 15-20. **Self-contained carbonless paper. This represents the setup when an original and three copies are typed using this kind of paper.**

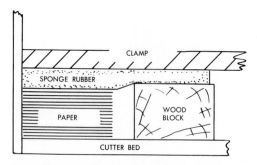

Fig. 15-22. Use a wood block and sponge rubber to avoid imaging by excessive pressure on carbonless paper.

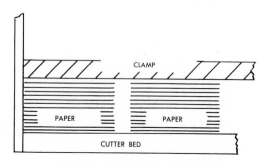

Fig. 15-23. Cut two or more lifts of carbonless paper at one time to reduce pressure and avoid unwanted imaging.

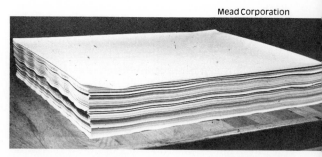

Mead Corporation

Fig. 15-24. Wavy edges of paper stack caused by variations in humidty.

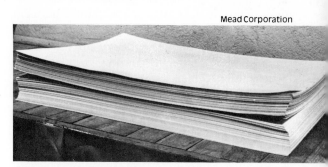

Mead Corporation

Fig. 15-25. Curl on paper stack caused by the variations in surrounding humidity.

this, block up with a wood block or sponge rubber (Fig. 15-22), or cut more than one lift at a time side by side (Fig. 15-23).

Keep paper in closed original containers when not in use. If sheets curl, "edge bend" each lift when you place it in the press feeder.

On the press, use reduced impression, a minimum of fountain solution, and reduced ink tack. Avoid undue pressure of such parts as feed rollers and guide rollers since it may cause *images* on the carbonless paper.

Controlling the Stretching and Shrinking of Paper

It is a fact that paper will tend to stretch when it absorbs moisture and will shrink when it loses moisture. This stretching and shrinking occurs *mostly across the grain* and *very little with the grain.* Consequently, when the paper is on the press, the paper grain should run *parallel with the cylinders* (the direction of least shrinkage or stretching). This fact should be remembered in specifying the direction of grain when ordering paper. Since large offset plates are wider in the direction parallel with the cylinders, most offset papers should be ordered *grain long.* The printer must often compromise and print short-grain stock so that the finished job has the proper grain direction.

Paper stock should be allowed to remain unprinted in the pressroom for *seasoning* until it reaches the same humidity or moisture content as the pressroom. If the paper is to be used for "register jobs," such as two or more colors, the top and sides of the stacks of paper should be covered between runs with polyethylene.

Paper usually has a 6% moisture content when it is shipped from the mill. If a relative humidity of 50 to 55% is maintained in the shop, day and night continuously, and the paper stock allowed to condition to this, shrink-

Mead Corporation

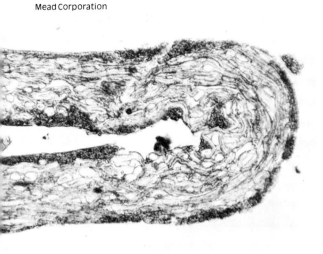

A. Sheet has proper moisture.

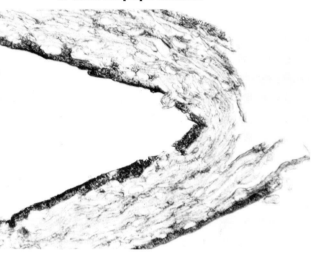

B. Sheet lacks enough moisture, is dry and brittle, and breaks on fold.

Fig. 15-26. Effects of moisture content in folding paper.

ing and stretching of the paper stock will be avoided or minimized, Figs. 15-24 through 15-26.

Bindery Operations

All work with sheets other than printing on them is classified as *bindery work*. This includes such operations as cutting, jogging, gathering sheets in sequence, folding, drilling or punching holes, padding, hand numbering, sewing, stapling, wire stitching, mechanical binding and wrapping, and labeling packages. Some of these are illustrated here.

Jogging

Jogging is the handling of sheets to make a neater, evenly piled stack. Usually it is necessary to *fan* a few sheets at a time (to get air between them) by holding one edge and flipping through them by moving the opposite edge back. Then the sheets are tapped on the edges until they are even. The operation is then repeated with the next few sheets. A mechanical jogger with a vibrating table makes this easier. See Fig. 15-27. A few sheets to be handled at once are called a *lift*. Sheets should not be jogged while ink is still wet.

Plastic Binding

Catalogs, manuals, and other items printed on single sheets may be bound conveniently into looseleaf books by using plastic bindings, Fig. 15-28. The sheets must be put in order and then punched, as shown in Fig. 15-29. There are special fingers on the binding machine which open the backing strip so that the punched sheets can be inserted, Fig. 15-30.

Illya Scheinker Inc.

Fig. 15-27. Jogger.

Fig. 15-28. Plastic binding.

Fig. 15-29. Punching sheets for plastic binding.

Fig. 15-30. Inserting punched sheets into binding.

Gathering

Putting individual sheets or pages in order is called *gathering*. It can be done by laying stacks of each page in order along the edge of a table, and picking one sheet from each stack while walking past them. Checking that the right number of pages has been gathered is called *collating*, although this term is often misused to also mean gathering. Staggered marks on the folded edge of a series of signatures (pages folded in a unit) which are used to check the order of the signatures are called *collating marks*. Figure 15-31 shows an eight-station gathering machine in-line with an electric punch for plastic binding.

Stapling and Stitching

Figure 15-32 shows a *stapler* which is loaded with U-shaped staples. The legs are available in various lengths to accommodate different thicknesses. If the machine makes its own staples from a coil of wire, it is known as a *wire stitcher*. Figure 15-32 shows the stapler set up for saddle-stitching — that is, placing a staple (from the back side) in the center fold of a pamphlet or signature. If the *saddle* of the machine is tipped up to form a small, flat table, stitches can be placed along the edge of the pamphlet. This is called *side-stitching*.

Punching and Drilling Holes

Figure 15-33 shows a paper drill that makes holes by means of a rotating, sharpened, hollow tube. Some versions have three heads so that three holes are drilled at once. Drills can ac-

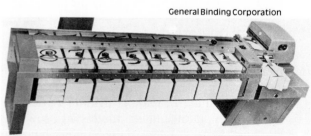

Fig. 15-31. Eight-station (pocket) collator, fitted with automatic electric punch for binding.

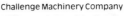
Challenge Machinery Company

Fig. 15-33. Paper drilling machine.

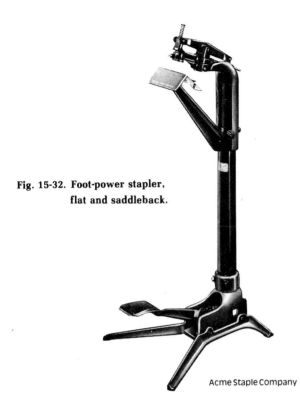
Fig. 15-32. Foot-power stapler, flat and saddleback.

Acme Staple Company

Challenge Machinery Company

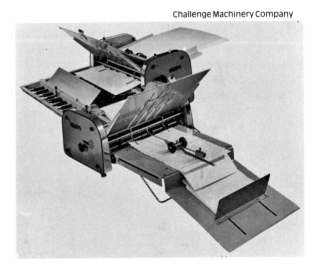
Fig. 15-34. A 17″ × 28″ folding machine.

commodate a lift of paper about ½″ high at a time.

Punches also make holes in paper. A punch has a solid rod-like piece which fits into a matching hole. Punches will take only a few sheets at a time.

Folding

Sheets may be folded easily by hand. Simply take the near edge of the sheet, place it evenly on the far edge, and crease down the fold smartly across the sheet. A wooden or bone folder makes creasing the sheet much easier. The back of a comb or a ruler also can be used. Figure 15-34 shows a folding machine which will make two successive folds in a sheet at right angles to each other, forming eight pages out of the flat sheet. It is known as a *buckle folder* due to the manner in which it buckles the bended sheet in forming the fold. This machine also will *score* (make a crease across the sheet for later folding), *slit* a sheet into two pieces, and *perforate* (cut a row of small slots across the sheet), either with or without folding.

Questions

1. What may be the disadvantages in using a poor grade of paper (not made or adapted) for offset printing?
2. What kinds of pulps are in use today for papermaking?
3. Describe the making of pulp for newsprint paper.
4. Describe the paper products made from old papers.
5. Describe each of the pulps produced by the chemical cooking of wood chips.
6. What kind of paper is made of rags?
7. Name the main steps in the process of papermaking.

8. Why is sizing important for offset papers? What sizing materials are added to the paper?

9. What does loading contribute to the paper?

10. Name the two *sides* of a sheet of paper. Which is the preferred side for printing?

11. What is meant by the *caliper* of a sheet of paper?

12. Describe four ways to test the grain direction of a sheet of paper.

13. How is the grain direction indicated on a wrapped ream or package of paper?

14. Explain the term *weight* as applied to paper.

15. What does 41/M mean on a ream of paper?

16. What is a *sheet* of paper? A *piece* of paper?

17. Make a list of the basic sizes of each of the papers listed in Table 15-2 on page 273.

18. In the metric system, what units are used to indicate sheet dimensions (sizes), substance (basis weight), actual (total) weight, and caliper?

19. Tell how grammage is determined.

20. What is meant by *CB*, *CBF*, and *CF* in reference to transfer carbonless paper?

Problems and Projects

1. Locate a film on papermaking. Write to the paper mill arranging for a showing of the film. Write a report on the film.

2. Make a display of papermaking materials. Try to secure samples of papermaking ingredients and pulps. Include samples of various kinds of papers and photographs of the processes involved.

3. If possible, arrange for a visit to a nearby paper mill. Follow the standard procedure for field trips for your school. Decide what you wish to see before making the trip. Write a report on the trip.

4. Determine the felt and wire sides of several kinds of paper in the shop. Can you find the wire side of a sheet of calendered stock? Of bond? Of index bristol?

5. Determine the direction of grain on several different kinds of paper stock in the shop, especially bristols and covers. Use all the methods for testing grain described for papers. Test the heavier stock by folding and bending.

6. At 35¢ per pound, determine the cost of:
   a. 3 reams 17″ × 22″—20 bond paper.
   b. 3000 sheets 17″ × 22″—20 bond paper.
   c. 6500 sheets 22″ × 34″—20 bond paper.

7. Convert the inch sizes for sheets, below, into millimeter sizes:
   a. 8½″ × 11″
   b. 6″ × 9″
   c. 17″ × 22″
   d. 20″ × 26″
   e. 25″ × 38″

8. Calipers below are stated in inches. What are their equivalents in micrometers?
   a. 0.003″
   b. 0.010″
   c. 0.020″

9. State the grammage of each of the paper stocks below:
   a. 24-pound bond.
   b. 50-pound cover.
   c. 50-pound book.

10. Figure how many pieces can be cut from the sheet sizes listed below. Use the formula method; if there is excessive waste, make a diagram to determine whether additional pieces can be obtained.

Piece Size	Sheet Size	Sheet Size
3″ × 5″	20½″ × 24¾″	22½″ × 28½″
5″ × 8″	17″ × 22″	17″ × 28″
8½″ × 11″	17″ × 22″	17″ × 28″
8″ × 10″	20″ × 26″	25″ × 38″

11. Make a wall display of dual labels.

New Terms

acidity	leaf
adjacent edge	lift
basis	pH
calendering	punch
caliper	ream
carbonless	saddle
collate	score
digester	signatures
drill	sizing
dual label	staple
felt side	stitch
gather	substance
grammage	twin-wire process
jog	watermark

Offset Press Fundamentals

Sheet-fed offset presses and duplicators all function in a similar manner. Different makes do vary in minor details of construction, operating controls, nomenclature of parts, arrangement of cylinders and rollers, and in the feeding, registration, and delivery of sheets.

The term *offset duplicators* generally is used to refer to some of the smaller offset-printing presses. In this book, the term *offset press*, in general, will include both presses and duplicators.[1] The same skills and understandings are required to do quality work with either type.

Operation and General Nomenclature

The reader is asked first to review the theory of offset printing (page 3) and to study carefully Figs. 16-1 and 16-2. Figure 16-2 illustrates, in schematic form, some basic components and nomenclature of a typical duplicator-size offset press. Note the six main systems or divisions: (1) the dampening system, (2) the inking system, (3) the main printing unit, (4) the feeder (usually vacuum operated), (5) the register board and sheet controls, and (6) the delivery system.

Dampening System

In the dampening system, the dampening rollers apply a film of dampening solution to the surface of the offset plate (master) which is wrapped around the plate cylinder. This dampening solution adheres only to the clear areas of the plate. The image areas repel the dampening solution.

Inking System

On the dampened plate, the ink rollers apply a film of ink which adheres only to the image portions of the plate. The ink is repelled by the dampened areas of the plate. This dampening and inking of the plate continues throughout

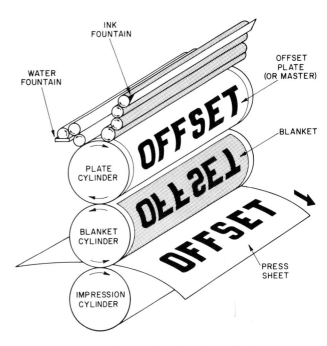

Fig. 16-1. Basic schematic drawing of an offset press.

---

[1] Press models referred to in this chapter are the products of the following firms: Multilith 1250 — AM International; Davidson Duplicators, ATF Chief 20 and 20A — American Type Founders Co., Inc.

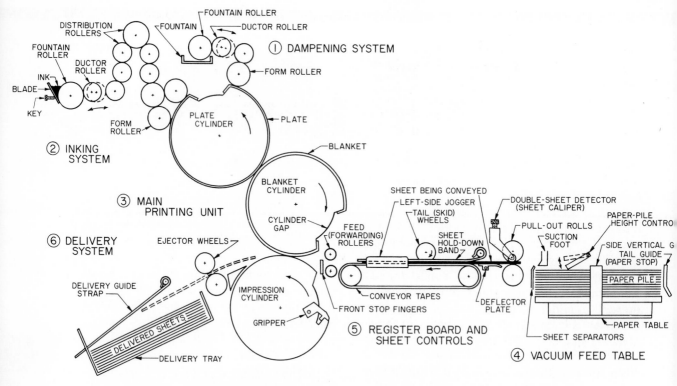

Fig. 16-2. Schematic cross section of a sheet-fed, single-color offset duplicator, with three main cylinders and conventional (separate) inking and dampening systems.

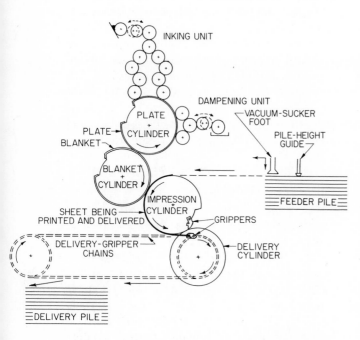

Fig. 16-3. Schematic cross section of a sheet-fed, single-color offset press with four-main-cylinder design, chain delivery, and conventional (separate) inking and dampening systems.

the press run (carefully controlled by the operator), thus maintaining the nonprinting areas of the plate clear and replenishing the ink on the plate image.

Main Printing Unit

In the main printing unit, the inked plate image is transferred to the surface of the blanket (on the blanket cylinder) when the plate cylinder and the blanket cylinder are brought into contact with each other. The blanket image is then printed on the sheet of paper as it passes (under pressure) between the blanket and impression cylinders.

Feeder Unit

Most feeders are air- and vacuum-operated. An air blast separates the top sheets causing them to float individually. The feed table maintains the paper pile at proper height so that the suction feet (suckers) can pick up the top sheet and pass it forward. Sheet separators hold back all but the top sheet, which is pulled off by the suction feet.

Register Board and Sheet Controls

Each sheet that is carried forward by the sucker feet is passed to the pullout rolls. It is then introduced to the caliper device, or multiple-sheet detector, which will pass only one sheet without tripping. The sheet is then conveyed down the register table (or board) until it reaches the front-stop fingers. Stopped at this point, it is jogged across the table to a predetermined register position.

Next, the front stop fingers drop down and the feed rolls propel the sheet forward into the impression cylinder grippers. The timing is adjusted so that the leading end of the sheet usually buckles slightly as it meets the gripper stops to insure positive positioning at the grippers. See insert "A" in view I of Fig. 16-4, pages 288 and 299. Then the impression cylinder grippers close on the sheet and carry it under impression (pressure) between the blanket and impression cylinders so that it receives the inked image from the blanket.

Delivery System

On duplicators, the printed sheet may be ejected simply into a delivery tray. If the press is so equipped, the sheet may be gripped by the chain delivery grippers which deliver the sheet into the receding stacker where it is jogged neatly, as in Fig. 16-3.

Paper Feeding to Delivery

In the paper feeding-to-delivery cycle, each individual sheet is lifted from the paper pile, passed down the delivery table, jogged into position, printed, and then delivered and stacked. This action is illustrated in schematic detail in Figs. 16-4, A through J.

Types of Inking and Dampening Systems

Several of the more common types of inking and dampening systems employed on offset presses are described below.

Conventional Inking and Dampening Systems

In conventional (separate) inking and dampening systems (Fig. 16-5), the ink and the damp-

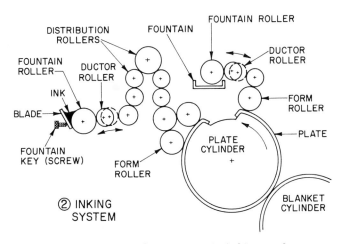

Fig. 16-5. Conventional (separate) inking-and-dampening system.

ening solutions originate in separate fountains and are applied to the offset-plate surface by separate form rollers.

Usually, the ink-form rollers and dampener-form rollers are driven by contact with the offset-plate surface. The fountain rollers are generally actuated by the offset-press mechanism. The ink and the fountain solutions are each fed to their roller trains by a ductor roller which rocks to-and-fro between, and in intermittent contact with, the fountain roller and the first roller in each of the roller trains.

Harris-Cottrell Continuous-Feed-Brush Dampening System

The Harris-Cottrell continuous-feed-brush dampening system employs a constant-speed nylon brush roller which runs in contact with a variable-speed fountain pan roller, Fig. 16-6. Interference by the fountain pan roller causes the brush roller bristles to flick a uniform spray of water to the water roller train and thus to the plate. The speed of the pan roller controls the amount of water. Because there is no contact between the brush roller and the vibrator roller, there can be no feedback of lint or ink from plate to fountain.

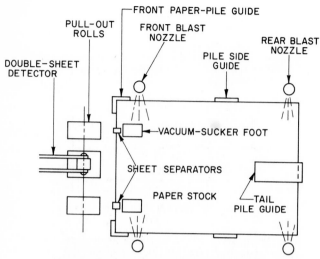

A. **Vacuum-feeder setup (top view). Paper pile is held in position by front, side, and tail pile guides. Front and rear blast nozzles direct streams of air to flutter the top sheets.**

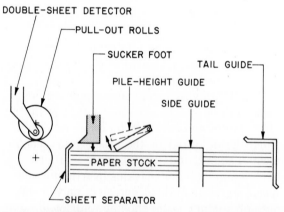

B. **Vacuum-feeder setup (side view). Sucker feet are in lowest position. Pile-height guide, rocking up and down, actuates mechanism to maintain pile height within lifting distance of sucker feet.**

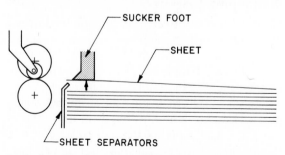

C. **Sucker foot has descended and has picked up one sheet. In its upward travel, sheet is dragged across tips of sheet separators (combs), which help to hold back other sheets.**

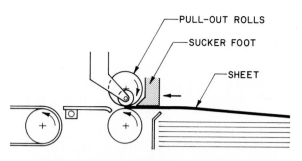

D. **Sucker foot has traveled forward, delivering sheet between revolving pull-out rolls.**

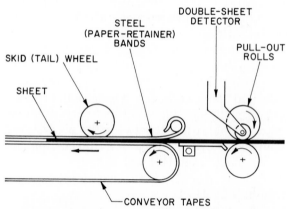

E. **Pull-out rolls have passed paper through double-sheet detector, and on to the conveyor tapes which propel sheet forward. Steel (paper-retainer) bands hold sheets to tapes. Skid (tail) wheels provide additional rotating pressure to traveling paper.**

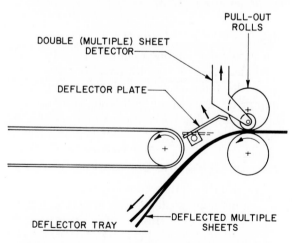

F. **The double-sheet detector is forced upward by the added thickness of any multiple sheets. This activates and opens the deflector plate, thus deflecting the double sheets downward into the deflector tray. Most larger presses simply have the feeder stop if detector trips.**

Fig. 16-4. Schematic detail of paper feeding-to-delivery system.

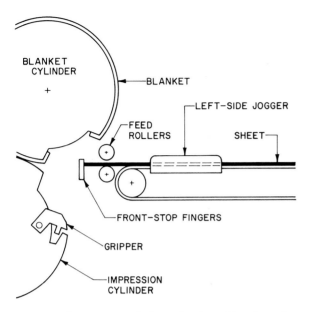

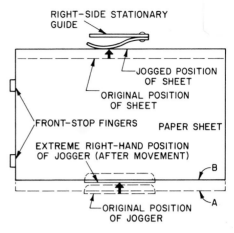

H. (View from above). The momentarily stopped sheet is jogged across the feed table (from "A" to "B") into registration position for printing. On some models, jogging side can be switched.

G. Having been conveyed down feeder table, sheet is stopped by the front-stop fingers and is ready to be jogged. Note that the impression-cylinder grippers have opened.

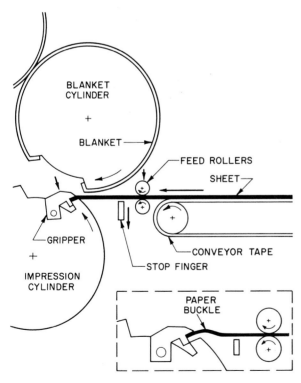

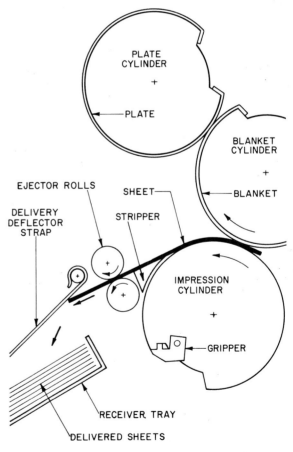

I. After sheet is jogged, stop fingers move downward, and feed rollers close on sheet, propelling it forward to grippers on the impression cylinder. Timing should be such that the sheet is buckled slightly (as at "A") as it meets the paper gripper stops, ensuring positive positioning at the grippers.

J. Impression-cylinder grippers have drawn sheet between blanket and impression cylinders where sheet has been printed. Grippers then open and strippers guide sheet between ejector rollers which propel the sheet into the tray.

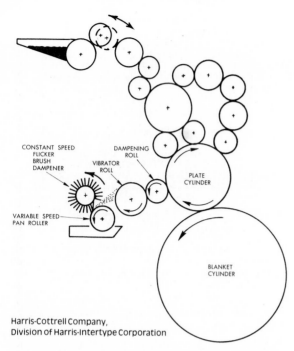

Harris-Cottrell Company,
Division of Harris-Intertype Corporation

**Fig. 16-6.   Continuous-feed flicker-brush dampening
system.**

MiehleMatic Dampening System

The MiehleMatic dampening system applies
a continuous and controlled film of water to the
plate through a series of four rollers completely independent of, and separate from, the inking system, Fig. 16-7. The *water form roller* (F)
and *vibrator roller* (V) are gear driven by the
plate cylinder and run at the same surface
speed as the plate cylinder. The *chrome pan
roller* (C) is driven separately by a variable-
speed motor. The *metering roller* (M) rides in
contact with the fountain roller and is driven at
the same surface speed as the fountain roller.

The arrangement of rollers in the Miehle-
Matic units shown in Fig. 16-7 are used for the
upper and lower units of a two-color press. See
also "Function of the Metering Roller," page 292.

Combined Inking and Dampening Systems

In combined inking and dampening systems,
the ink and the dampener solutions, although
originating in separate fountains, are both fed
through the same form roller[2] (or rollers) to the offset plate. See Fig. 16-8.

In this system, all the ink rollers first are
allowed to ink up. The fountain solution is then
added to the water fountain, and all the rollers
are allowed to operate. A controlled film of

---

[2] The term "form roller" refers to any roller in either the
inking or dampening systems which contacts the offset
plate during operation of the press.

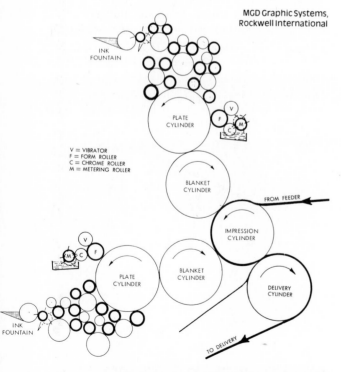

**Fig. 16-7.   Roller, cylinder, and sheet flow diagram for
Miehle 38″ two-color offset press equipped
with MiehleMatic dampeners.**

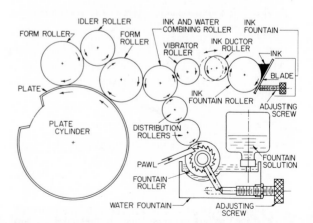

**Fig. 16-8.   Simflo combined inking-and-dampening
system.**

dampener solution is transferred to the surface of one of the ink-train rollers, usually an ink-vibrator roller or an ink-form roller. The ink-form roller thus carries a film of ink *in addition to* a film of fine droplets of fountain solution *on* the ink film.

When the form roller contacts the premoistened offset plate surface, the hydrophilic/oleophilic (water-attracting/grease-attracting) properties of the plate cause the fountain solution to be attracted to the clear areas of the plate, and the ink to be attracted to the image areas of the plate. Adjustment controls on the fountains are provided to maintain proper ink-and-water balance for printing.

A slight *emulsification*[3] of the ink occurs when the fountain solution is applied over the ink film on the rollers, but the amount is not objectionable. In fact, some ink emulsification takes place in the conventional system as well.

Didde-Glaser Dampening System

In the Didde-Glaser (DG) dampening system, the dampening solution is gravity fed from a reservoir to the pump block. See Fig. 16-9. Nine miniature diaphragm pumps transmit the solution to the spray bar mounted across the offset tower. Just enough pressure is used to emit the solution in a fine spray from the nine spray nozzles. The spray, directed toward the ink vibrator, is squeezed into the vibrator-form roller nip and delivered as a solution-ink film to the form rollers and the plate.

A. B. Dick Aquamatic Dampening System

The A. B. Dick Aquamatic dampening system is a combined ink-water system with ductor-type ink feed and ductor-type water feed, Fig. 16-10. Fountain solution is fed to one of the ink form rollers and thus to the plate.

Dahlgren Dampening System

The Dahlgren dampening system, Fig. 16-11, contains three rollers. Two of the rollers, a *chrome transfer roller* and a *metering roller*,

[3] *Emulsification* (emulsifying), in presswork, generally indicates that some fountain solution is working into, and mixing with, the ink so that its substance is diluted somewhat.

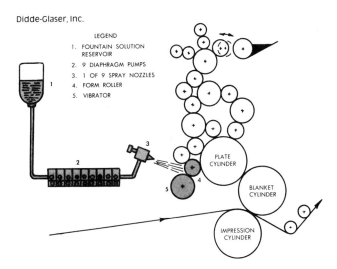

Didde-Glaser, Inc.

LEGEND
1. FOUNTAIN SOLUTION RESERVOIR
2. 9 DIAPHRAGM PUMPS
3. 1 OF 9 SPRAY NOZZLES
4. FORM ROLLER
5. VIBRATOR

Fig. 16-9.   Didde-Glaser (D-G) dampening system.

are gear interconnected and driven by an independent variable-speed motor. The third, a *form roller*, is driven by the offset press ink vibrator roller and thus rotates at the same surface speed as the plate cylinder.

The pan roller, which can be either the transfer or metering roller, picks up fountain solution. The solution passes into the metering roller-transfer roller nip where pressure between the metering and transfer roller surfaces meters the moisture into a thin, uniform film. This film is transferred from the transfer roller surface to the surface of the form roller, and then to the offset plate surface.

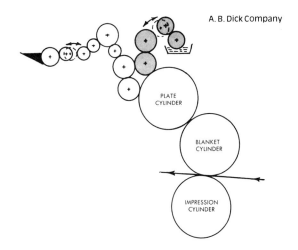

A. B. Dick Company

Fig. 16-10. A. B. Dick arrangement of ink-water (Aquamatic) system and cylinders.

MGD Graphic Systems, Rockwell International

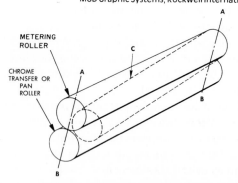

Fig. 16-12. Metering roll two-way adjustment. AB line: varying the parallel pressure of metering roller against the pan roller varies the overall water feed. C line: skewing varies feed at center and end (or ends).

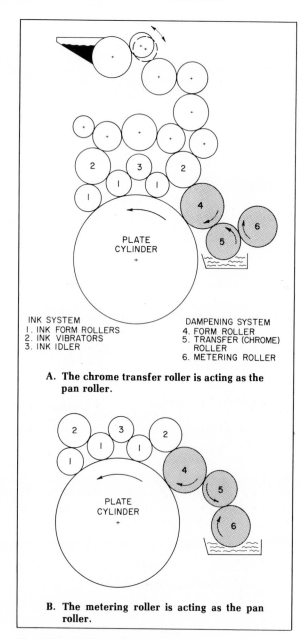

A. The chrome transfer roller is acting as the pan roller.

B. The metering roller is acting as the pan roller.

Fig. 16-11. Dahlgren dampening system.

Function of the Metering Roller

The MiehleMatic and the Dahlgren dampening systems each employ a metering roller which functions in a similar manner. In each case, the metering roller is driven at the same surface speed as the chrome transfer roller in contact with it. In some installations the chrome trans-

fer roller acts as the pan roller; in others, the metering roller is employed as the pan roller. See Fig. 16-11.

Parallel adjustment of the metering roller, Fig. 16-12, away from or toward the chrome transfer roller varies the thickness of solution film passing through the *nip* (point of contact between the two rollers).

Skewing the metering roller position "C" in Fig. 16-12 out of parallel with the pan roller allows for a variation of solution application *across* the plate (without using water stops).

With end pressures equal, skewing increases the pressure at the center. This gives less water at the center and more at the ends. By tightening or loosening either end of the metering rolls, water distribution may be made greater to one side or the other.

Main Cylinder Arrangements

Several common arrangements of cylinders on sheet-fed offset presses are described and illustrated on the following pages.

Three-Main-Cylinder Design

The three-main-cylinder design employs the *plate, blanket,* and *impression* cylinders. Refer again to Fig. 16-2.

The offset plate is mounted on the plate cylinder. The plate image is transferred to the blanket surface which, in turn, transfers the image to the paper passing between the blanket and impression cylinders.

After it is printed, the paper is propelled forward by ejector wheels and the squeeze-thrust of the blanket and impression cylinders, to be deposited in the delivery pile or receiver.

The inked plate image must deposit additional ink in *exactly* the same places on the blanket image during successive revolutions of the cylinders. To insure this, both the plate and blanket cylinders must be virtually identical in diameter, their bearers (full diameter surface at each end) must be in contact, and they must be gear-driven to prevent slipping. See Fig. 16-35.

Four-Main-Cylinder Design

In addition to the plate, blanket, and impression cylinders, a fourth cylinder may be used. This is the *delivery* (or transfer) cylinder. It is located beneath the impression cylinder and carries the gripper-equipped chains which control the printed sheet as it leaves the impression and blanket cylinders, starting it toward the delivery end of the press. Refer again to Fig. 16-3.

Two-Main-Cylinder Design

In the two-main-cylinder design, the double-sized upper cylinder contains two segments — the plate segment and the impression segment. The smaller lower cylinder (the blanket drum) carries the blanket. See Fig. 16-13.

The blanket drum is exactly half the circumference of the upper cylinder. Thus, for each single revolution of the upper cylinder, the blanket revolves twice. On the first revolution, the blanket contacts the plate segment. On the second revolution, the blanket contacts (presses against) the impression segment.

When the plate segment and the blanket drum are opposite, the inked image of the plate contacts the rubber blanket. At this time, the image is transferred from the plate to the blanket, Fig. 16-14.

As the duplicator continues to revolve and the plate segment returns to the dampening unit for replenishing, the blanket drum with its inked image begins its second revolution.

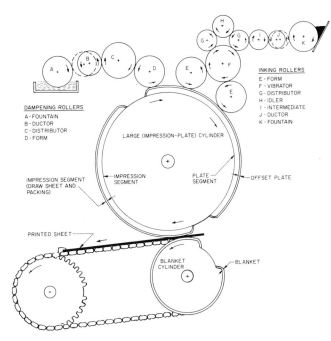

Fig. 16-13. **Two-main-cylinder design used on Davidson Duplicators.**

Davidson Division — American Type Founders Company, Inc.

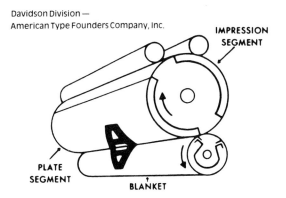

Fig. 16-14. **Plate-to-blanket image transfer.**

Davidson Division — American Type Founders Company, Inc.

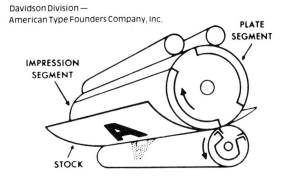

Fig. 16-15. **Image offset from blanket to sheet.**

Just as the leading edge of the impression segment would contact the leading edge of the blanket, a sheet of paper arrives and passes between the cylinders. The impression segment exerts a downward pressure, *offsetting* the blanket image onto the sheet, Fig. 16-15. The printed sheet is then carried face upwards to the delivery end of the machine.

Additional Main-Cylinder Arrangements

Several additional main-cylinder arrangements as used on offset presses are shown in Fig. 16-16. Others are described in Chapter 18.

In the following descriptions, a *press unit* may be considered as a stand-alone, complete section of a press for an operation such as printing, perforating, or folding. On a multicolor press, such as a blanket-to-blanket perfecting press, each printing unit may consist of one or more *printing couples.* A *printing couple* consists of all components necessary to print one color on one side of the sheet — dampening system, inking system, plate cylinder, and blanket cylinder. Two printing couples of a unit may share a common-impression cylinder, or may print blanket-to-blanket.

Perfecting Press. A perfecting press prints on both sides of the sheet in one pass through the press. View A of Fig. 16-16 shows a blanket-to-blanket perfecting press. The blanket cylinders serve as impression cylinders for each other. Perfecting can also be done by using a press which has two single-color printing units and "flops" or turns the sheets over automatically between printing units See pages 349 and 350.

Multicolor Press. Figure 16-16B shows a sheet being printed in two colors on the same side by use of a two-unit press. Press manufacturers offer presses with more units and printing couples for additonal colors and additional operations, such as numbering and perforating.

Common-Impression-Cylinder Press. In Fig. 16-16C, the one common-impression cylinder serves as the impression cylinder for the two printing couples. Each couple prints one color (total of two colors) on the same side of the sheet in one pass through the press.

Some Feeder and Delivery Features

The following feeder and delivery features are found on duplicator-style and on other sheet-fed presses.

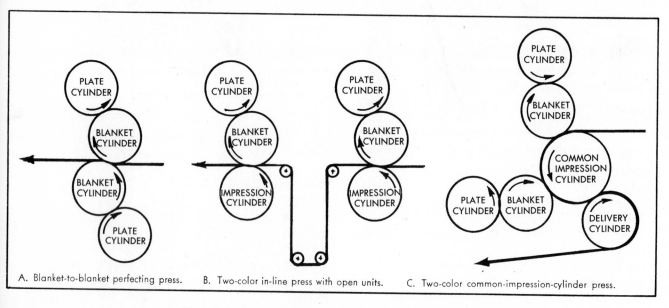

A. Blanket-to-blanket perfecting press.   B. Two-color in-line press with open units.   C. Two-color common-impression-cylinder press.

Fig. 16-16. Additional main cylinder arrangements on offset presses.

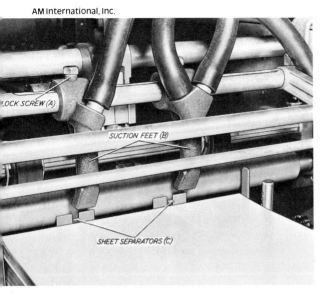

Fig. 16-19. Ejector mechanism and delivery tray with automatic jogger — Multilith 1250.

Fig. 16-17. Suction (vacuum) paper feeder — Multilith 1250.

Fig. 16-20. Chain delivery with receding stacker — Multilith 1850.

Fig. 16-18. Friction paper feed — Multilith 85.

Suction (Vacuum) Paper Feed. Sucker feet pick up the sheet of paper stock from the feeder pile by vacuum and pass it down the register table, or board, Fig. 16-17. See also "Paper Feeding to Delivery," page 287.

Friction Paper Feed. Rubber-covered, rotating wheels, in contact with the paper stock on the feeder table, propel the top sheet forward into the printing unit. See Fig. 16-18.

Ejector Mechanism. The printed sheet, emerging from between the blanket and impression cylinders, is guided and propelled, in part, by ejector rolls (wheels) riding on the ejector ring shaft, Fig. 16-19. The rolls are positioned just outside the rings so that the sheet is cupped upward at the center. This helps to keep the fore edge from buckling under as it is pushed out.

Chain Delivery. The chain delivery uses gripper bars mounted across two endless chains which revolve between the delivery cylinder and the delivery end of the press. See Figs. 16-3, 16-13, and 16-20.

The gripper bars, traveling around the delivery cylinder, grip the fore edge of the printed sheet when it is released from the impression-cylinder grippers and carry the sheet to, and deposit it in, the delivery pile. This positive delivery is better than the simpler ejector rolls for large sheets, thin paper, or high speeds.

Receiver (Delivery) Tray.   On presses without chain delivery, the printed sheets are merely ejected or dropped into a tray arrangement. In the tray, they may or may not be jogged into a neat pile. Capacity of the tray is about 500 sheets. Refer again to Fig. 16-19.

Receding Stacker.   Chain-delivered, printed sheets are released into the stacker and are jogged automatically. The stacker also recedes (lowers itself) automatically to accommodate a large quantity of printed sheets, as shown in Fig. 16-20. The stacker platform may be equipped with wheels so that the printed sheets may be moved without rehandling (which may smudge the ink).

The stacker also may be equipped with an anti-offset spray which shoots a fine powder

mist over each freshly printed sheet. This prevents smudging and transfer of wet ink to the back side of the next sheet above. This undesirable offsetting from one sheet to another is often called *set-off* to distinguish it from the *offset* process. See page 362.

The Dampening System

During the press operation, the dampening system feeds a controlled amount of fountain solution (dampener solution or water) from the fountain to the surface of the offset plate. See Fig. 16-21.

Description

The capped bottle of prepared fountain solution is placed into its recess in the water fountain. After the bottle is capped, it should be inverted to check that no water is leaking from it. A valve in the bottle cap allows the fountain solution to escape and rise to its proper level in the fountain.

The fountain roller is partially submerged along its length in the fountain solution. As it rotates, the roller carries on its surface a film of the fountain solution. Its rotation is activated by a pawl-and-ratchet arrangement. By adjustment of the stroke of the pawl, more or less solution can be fed.

A ductor roller, rocking to-and-fro, transfers the solution from the fountain roller to the dampener (rider, or oscillating) roller. The rider roller, oscillating (vibrating) from end-to-end as it revolves, equalizes the coverage of fountain solution along its length. Finally, it transfers the fountain solution to the form roller and thence to the plate.

Commonly, the form roller and the ductor roller are encased in either a molleton (towel-like) cover or a paper (cellulose-base) cover. See also "Combined Inking and Dampening Systems," page 303.

Controls

A knob on one end of the fountain roller can be turned by hand when it is desired to add large amounts of water quickly.

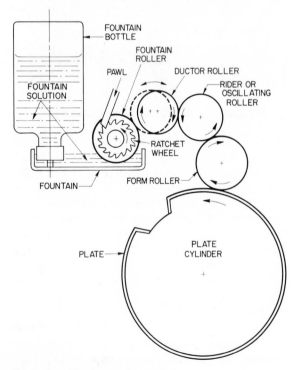

Fig. 16-21.   The dampening system.

A ratchet-control lever may be set to provide the desired speed of rotation of the fountain roller during the press run.

A ductor-contact lever may be set to stop the action of the ductor roller when it is desired to discontinue the flow of fountain solution to the form roller during press operation.

A form-roller control lever is used to lift the form roller from the plate or to drop it into contact with the plate.

Generally, a night-latch lever is provided to lift the rollers away from each other when press operation is stopped for any length of time. This prevents the formation of flat spots along the length of the rollers.

Rollers

Dampening system rollers may be solid metal or solid rubber, or they may be covered. Covered rollers increase the water-carrying capacity of the roller surface.

Fountain rollers generally are knurled solid metal, while ductor and form rollers generally are covered. Distributor rollers may be any of the three varieties.

• **Note:** Combined ink-and-water systems may have *all* solid-rubber rollers.

Metal dampening rollers occasionally should be scoured with pumice and water. Complete the cleaning by etching rollers to resist ink attraction.

Molleton Covers

Molleton-covered dampening rollers should be clean, the molleton evenly applied, and the rollers properly *set* (pressure setting) to deliver an even, continuous supply of moisture to the plate. These rollers must be able to hold the floating scum or tint that collects on the face of all plates and prevent this scum from reaching the blanket and press sheet. The condition of the molleton covers, rather than their age or length of press service, should determine whether or not they need attention. Careful, constant care of dampening rollers is very necessary for quality work.

Dirty rollers should be removed from the press and washed first with solvent, then with detergent and water. If they are excessively greasy or dirty, the covering should be replaced.

Washed molleton rollers should be replaced in the press so that they run in the same direction as previously. This will maintain the established twist of their fibers. A dab of paint or other mark on the operator's side of the roller core end will insure their correct installation each time.

Installing

Molleton covers may be purchased ready-cut for your press, in tubular or wrap-around strip form or in continuous rolls of tubular material. For installation, the instructions supplied with the covers should be followed. In general, the following instructions apply to installation of tubular molleton covers:

Cut a length of molleton about two or three inches longer than the roller. Work the molleton over the roller end, being sure that any seam in the cover is not over a seam in the undercover. Slip the molleton a few inches along the roller as smoothly as possible, allowing $3/8$" of the molleton to overhang the shoulder of the roller. Sew a drawcord in the end of the overhang. Pull tight and knot this end.

Begin to stretch the remaining molleton along the length of the roller. Slightly moistened hands or rubber gloves will help you get some "grab" on the molleton surface. Keep forcing the molleton along smoothly and tightly, starting near the first drawcord end. Uneven stretching may result in unequal diameters along the length. By gradually working the molleton along, it will lay smoothly the entire length, past the remaining shoulder.

Cut the molleton $3/8$" past the shoulder, and sew a draw cord in this second end. Tie and knot this second drawcord. With a damp sponge, smooth the finished roller in the direction of the nap. This helps it set smoothly and evenly.

Fiber Covers

A dampening-roller sleeve of preformed synthetic fiber (a product of the 3M Company) may be used instead of cloth and paper dampening covers. Its seamless fiber design eliminates lint and the bulge of seams, and results in uniformity across the plate. The sleeves are designed to be used with a matching dampening roller to insure maximum performance.

3M Company

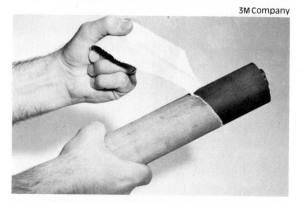

A. Step 1 — Tear old sleeve from roller.

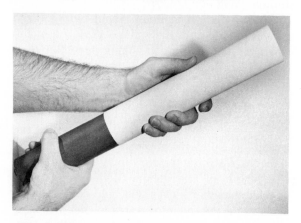

B. Step 2 — Slip seamless sleeve onto roller.

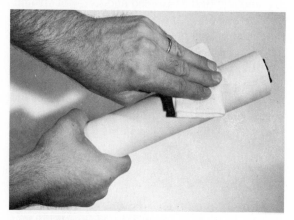

C. Step 3 — Install dampening sleeve.

Fig. 16-22. Installing dampening sleeve.

Installation. Installation of the 3M sleeve is performed in the three simple steps below:

1. *Tear off the old sleeve.* When the sleeve needs changing, remove the dampening roller from the press, and peel off the moist, dirty sleeve, Fig. 16-22A. Clean the roller with a mild solvent, removing all ink or grease.

2. *Slip on the new sleeve,* Fig. 16-22B. It should overhang evenly on both ends of the dampening roller. Since these sleeves are very sensitive to moisture, they should not be removed from the package until ready for use.

3. *Moisten the sleeve,* Fig. 16-22C. Wet the sleeve thoroughly with running tap water or with a water-soaked pad. The sleeve will shrink skintight onto the dampening roller in 60 seconds. A run-in period is not required, nor is it necessary to reset the dampening-roller pressure after each sleeve change. However, the dampening roller should be replaced as it was before removal.

Checking Pressure. Pressure of the dampening roller to the plate should be checked after installation and, if necessary, readjusted, using a 0.005″ gauge. See "Dampener-Roller Pressure Settings," below.

Cleaning and Care. Before starting the press run each day and before recommencing a press run after a shut-down of 30 minutes or longer, dampen the sleeve thoroughly with fountain solution. Failure to do this may cause ink to be transferred to the sleeve.

When the sleeve becomes dirty or when going from a dark ink to a light ink, clean the roller sleeve with mild solvent, followed by fountain solution.

Dampener-Roller Pressure Settings

Newly installed dampener covers may settle due to water and "roll-in" squeeze. They should be set for proper pressure first after they are installed, then after they have been run-in for a while against a plate on the press, and finally at a later time during the day. This pressure check also should be made on all presses each morning before the press run.

Specific press manufacturer's instructions should be followed for plate packing (if used),

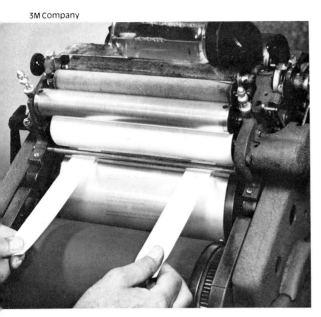

Fig. 16-23. **Checking pressure of dampening roller to plate.**

order of procedure, rollers to be checked, and pressure recommended. In general, the following procedure may be used to check dampening-roller settings:

1. Prepare dampening system for operation. Test for dampness of form roller. Allow form roller to run-in against plate on plate cylinder for a minute or two. Then lift the form roller and *stop the press*. Skill in testing the form roller for dampness comes with practice. Some operators test with the knuckle of a clenched finger. Ask your instructor to show you the preferred method of testing the dampness of the form roller.

2. *With the press stopped*, place two strips of 20-pound bond paper (or 0.005"-thick acetate gauges) between the form roller and the plate, one strip near each end, as shown in Fig. 16-23. Drop the form roller to *on* position.

3. With one hand holding each test strip, pull toward your body with slow, uniform tension. You should feel a slight drag on both strips. If one strip pulls easier than the other or if there is too much (or too little) drag on both, adjust the roller on one end, or both, as indicated by the test procedure.

When pressures are satisfactory — still with the *press stopped*, drop the form roller to the plate and lift it. Do this quickly! If you inspect the plate carefully, you should see a *dampened* line across its surface.

Water (Fountain) Stops. One or more water stops may be installed to bear against the fountain roller and thus limit the amount of fountain solution fed to areas of the plate where a lesser amount of solution is desired. Figure 16-24A shows the roller-type water stop used to bear against covered fountain rollers. Figure 16-24B

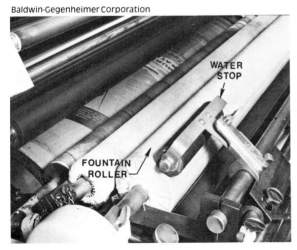

A. **Roller Type.**

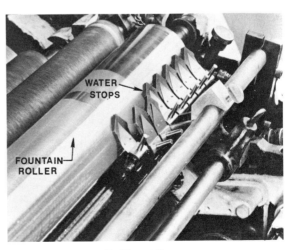

B. **Finger Type.**

Fig. 16-24. **Water (fountain) stops.**

shows the flexible finger-type water stops for riding against bare metal rollers.

Fountain Solution

The function of the offset press fountain (dampening) solution is to furnish a mildly acidic wetting agent to the offset plate surface during the press run so as to keep the clear (nonprinting) areas of the plate free of ink. This solution sometimes is referred to as the *water* or *dampener* solution.

Preparing the Solution

Fountain solution generally is purchased in concentrated form and prepared as directed on the container. It is also well to check the plate manufacturer's recommendations and instructions for the particular plate being used.

Sometimes a quantity of gum arabic is added to the fountain solution. It is a mild etch and is slow to evaporate. These two qualities tend to keep nonprinting areas of the plate free of ink.

In making up the fountain solution, add the concentrate (acid constituent) in small amounts to the total volume of water required, and test for *pH*. The pH is the degree of alkalinity or acidity, as explained below. If needed, add more of the acid constituent and test again. Continue until the desired pH is reached.

pH Values

The chemical term *pH* means the *degree of alkalinity or acidity* of a solution. The pH of a solution is expressed as a numerical value (reading), as shown on the scale in Fig. 16-25. A solution which has a pH value of 7.0 is regarded as neutral — neither acid nor alkaline. As the

readings decrease from 7 toward 0, they are increasingly acid. As they increase from 7 to 14, they are increasingly alkaline.

A fountain solution at pH 4.6 is recommended when running aluminum plates.

Test for pH of the fountain solution frequently during the press run, as it may change due to contact with the fountain metal, the rollers, the ink, or the paper. When the fountain solution has too high a pH value (low acidity), the nonprinting areas of the plate tend to pick up ink. This is called *scumming*. City water with high chlorine or mineral content may cause this. When the fountain solution has too low a pH value (high acidity), the image areas will not pick up the ink properly.

Determining the pH of the Solution

The pH of fountain solutions and platemaking solutions may be tested by use of lithographic pH test papers, as shown and explained in Fig. 16-26 A through C. The specific pH value is printed above each color on the dispenser chart. The pH can be measured directly by use of a meter, as in Fig. 16-27. Strengthen or weaken the solution if a change in the pH reading of the solution being tested is desired.

• **Note:** Only distilled water is neutral. Tap water has additives and therefore should be tested for pH.

Alcohol in Fountain Solutions

The addition of alcohol to the fountain solution is advised by manufacturers of continuous-flow (continuous-feed) dampening systems such as Dahlgren and MiehleMatic. This is also recommended for use on some presses using conventional, (intermittent or ductor-type)

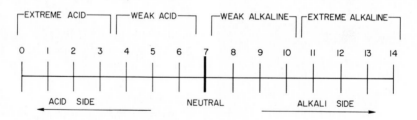

Fig. 16-25. pH Scale.

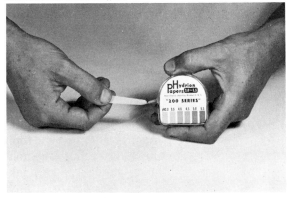

A. Step 1 — Draw out and tear off 2" strip of lithographic test paper.

B. Step 2 — Dip test paper into solution or water fountain.

C. Step 3 — Match wet color of test paper with color standard on dispenser.

Fig. 16-26. Steps in testing pH.

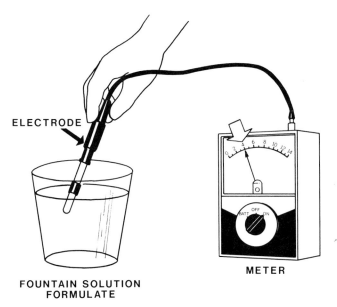

Fig. 16-27. Measuring pH with a direct-reading meter.

dampening systems, especially where a bare-rubber dampener is used. The alcohol recommended is 99% pure (anhydrous) isopropyl alcohol (Isopropanol) and is generally not to exceed 25% by volume in the fountain solution. The user should follow the equipment manufacturer's specific recommendations for proportions and procedure for mixing the fountain solution.

Alcohol serves the following functions in the fountain solution: (1) It lowers the surface tension of the water so that a finer film of water is fed to the plate by the dampener roller; and (2) the alcohol causes faster evaporation of moisture from the offset plate and the ink rollers, leading to drier printed sheets and less emulsification of ink.

The Inking System

The inking system provides a metered flow of well-distributed ink from the ink fountain to the offset plate during the operation of the press. See Fig. 16-28.

Description

As the fountain roller revolves, a film of ink is drawn from the fountain, from between the

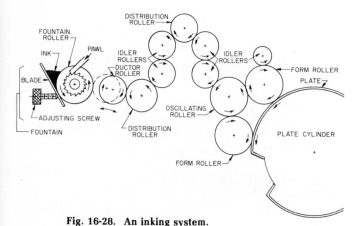

Fig. 16-28. An inking system.

AM International, Inc.

Fig. 16-29. Ink fountain, fountain adjusting keys, ink-feed control lever, and ink rollers — Multilith 1250.

fountain blade and the fountain roller. This adheres to the surface of the fountain roller. The ductor roller, rocking to-and-fro as it revolves, transfers this ink to the train of ink rollers, and from there to the form rollers, which deposit the ink on the offset-plate image.

Controls

Note in Fig. 16-29 that a series of adjusting screws, or fountain keys (B), along the length of the fountain serve to move the fountain blade either in toward, or away from, the fountain roller (A). This provides easy control over the thickness of the film of ink which the fountain roller may draw from the fountain.

The ink coverage supplied to specific areas across the offset plate may be varied by adjusting the proper screws. It is important to make "tapered" adjustments with the keys. For example, if one or more screws are opened, say one-quarter turn, then the adjoining screws should be opened one-eighth turn. The blade is steel — not rubber!

A pawl-and-ratchet arrangement, adjustable for length of stroke (lever C), drives the fountain roller. It also governs the rotational speed of that roller.

The ductor roller is usually provided with an ON-OFF lever to stop the addition of ink to the ink train while the press is operating.

The ON-OFF lever of the form roller brings these rollers into contact with, or away from, the offset plate.

The ink in the fountain tends to form into a ball, or roll, when not agitated. See Fig. 16-30. It then tends to back away from the fountain roller, causing uneven ink distribution and laydown.

Ink agitation may be accomplished at intervals by running an ink knife to-and-fro longitudinally through the ink in the fountain, mixing it, and laying it against the nip of the blade and roller. Agitation may also be performed automatically by equipping the fountain with an ink

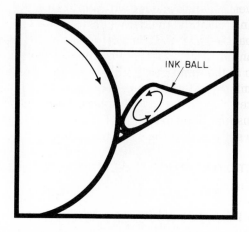

Fig. 16-30. If ink is not agitated, it will ball up or back away from the ink fountain.

Baldwin-Gegenheimer Corporation

Fig. 16-31. Ink agitator installed on ink fountain.

The Printing Machinery Company

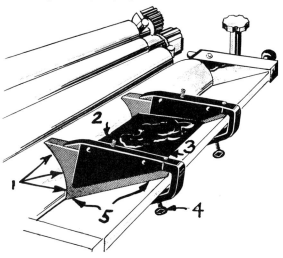

Fig. 16-32. Ink fountain dividers used to reduce the size (length) of the ink fountain. Synthetic rubber center blade (1 and 5) assures close contact with ink roll and fountain blade; adjusting screw (4) holds divider in position; ink (2 and 3).

AM International, Inc.

Fig. 16-33. Checking ink form roller-to-plate contact on Multilith 1250. Ink stripe should be of uniform width — from $1/8''$ to $3/16''$ wide — clear across the plate.

agitator (rotary ink beater) which travels back-and-forth along the ink fountain, Fig. 16-31.

A night-latch lever is provided to lift the oscillating roller (and perhaps others) out of contact with the form rollers during extended shutdowns. This prevents the formation of flat spots on the rollers.

Ink Fountain Dividers

Ink fountain dividers may be installed as shown in Fig. 16-32 in order to reduce the size (length) of the ink fountain when narrower-than-maximum-size sheets are being run. This saves ink and reduces wash-up time.

Ink fountain dividers can also be used to separate inks of different colors in the same fountain. This enables two or more colors to be run at the same time with the one fountain. Circumferential grooves can be cut into the surfaces of (a spare set of) rollers. These indentations limit the spreading of the ink film beyond the set width of the fountain dividers.

Combined Inking-and-Dampening System

See page 287.

Ink-Form-Roller Pressure Settings

With the ink unit prepared and an old plate (or a gummed plate) on the press, test the con-

tact of the form roller to the plate *while the press is stopped!*

Drop the form rollers in full contact with the plate, and lift them off. There should be an inked line of uniform width clear across the plate — about $1/8''$ in width, although $3/16''$ is sometimes preferred. See Fig. 16-34A. Turn the hand-

A. Uniform, parallel line: rollers and setting are correct.

B. Uniform tapered line: rollers correct, but unequal pressure settings at roller ends.

C. Uneven line: end pressure settings may be correct, but indication is that rollers need resurfacing or regrinding.

Fig. 16-34. Roller stripe test indicates condition and setting of ink form rollers.

wheel to see the inked test lines on the plate. Perform this test at several places along the plate.

If needed, adjust the roller settings, first for parallel (uniform) width across the plate and then to obtain the desired width. If the inking system has two form rollers, complete all adjustments on one before working on the second. A uniformly *tapered* line across the plate (Fig. 16-34B) indicates unequal pressure settings for the roller ends. An *uneven* line indicates that the roller is unevenly worn and should be reground or replaced. See Fig. 16-34C.

Specific press manufacturer's instructions should be followed for plate packing (if used) prior to testing, order of procedure, rollers to be checked, and width of line recommended.

Care of Ink Rollers

Rollers that are properly cared for will add to the quality of the printed job. They will cause less trouble on the press and will give maximum service.

Composition of Rollers

Offset press rollers commonly are made of natural rubber, synthetic rubber, or compounded or vulcanized vegetable oils.

Setting

Proper setting of the rollers minimizes friction and its resulting roller troubles. In general, the form rollers are set parallel to the plate cylinder, and are set for the clearance specified by the press manufacturer. When composition rollers are used, the setting should be checked occasionally during the run, as it may vary.

Resurfacing

Rubber and vulcanized-oil rollers may be reground and buffed by the roller manufacturers. This procedure will give a fresh surface and years of additional use.

Washing Up

Proper wash-up will prolong the life of rollers. An accumulation of dried ink on the rollers should be avoided. Wash lengthwise of the roller, and avoid using too much pressure. Wash more frequently when using tacky inks or inks with driers or reducers. Avoid strong solvents. See "Solvents," page 369.

For a *complete periodic washup*, a warm-water bath with Lava soap is recommended. Place the roller in warm water, and wash with Lava soap and cloth pad lengthwise of the roller. Be sure to rinse all traces of soap from the roller when finished.

Storing Rollers

All rollers should be carefully cleaned before being put away. Composition rollers should be covered with a thin film of oil to seal them against changing weather conditions. Rubber and vulcanized-oil rollers need no special preparation other than the cleaning. All rollers should be stored in cabinets, rather than on open racks where they might be injured or might pick up dirt. A vertical rack is preferred, as horizontal racking may produce sags in the rollers unless they are rotated frequently. Regardless of how rollers are stored, they must have free air circulation.

American Type Founders Company, Inc.

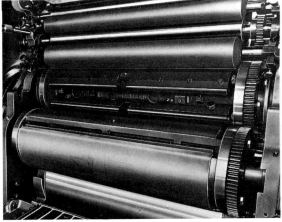

Fig. 16-35. Gear-driven cylinders — Chief 20A offset press.

AM International, Inc.

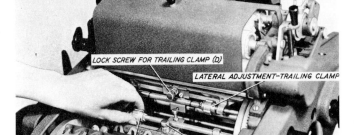

Fig. 16-36. Plate (master) lateral adjustment — Multilith 1250.

The Plate Cylinder

The smooth-metal plate cylinder has a longitudinal gap fitted with plate-clamping devices. These clamps may be for plates which have straight, pin-hole, slotted-hole (oval), or looped (serrated) ends.

On many presses, the style of plate clamp may be changed as necessary. Some plate-cylinder clamps are adjustable laterally (from side-to-side) to "twist" the plate slightly and compensate for an image which is not placed squarely on the plate. See Fig. 16-36. If the lead clamp is moved to one side in twisting a plate, then the trail clamp must be moved a corresponding amount to the opposite side. Plate images that are badly tilted require a plate re-make.

AM International, Inc.

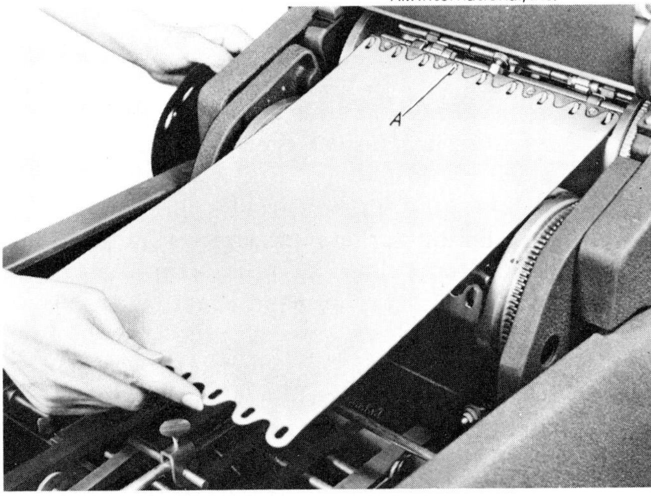

Fig. 16-37. Attaching serrated (slotted) master — lead end — on Multilith 1250. Note hooks "A" on plateholding device.

Installing an Offset Plate

Check *to be sure* that power is OFF. Handle the plate carefully to avoid scratching one plate with the corner of another. Clean the back of the plate and the plate cylinder. Wipe off the blanket. Check that the plate image is square.

If the plate differs from the one just previously run, measure the thickness with micrometer calipers. A difference in thickness may call for new pressure checks on dampeners and ink-form rollers, plus a change in the total thickness of packing sheets.

If the plate cylinder calls for packing, see page 312.

Installing a Plate on a Duplicator. For the duplicators, engage the leading end of the plate on (or in) the lead clamp, Fig. 16-37. Holding the free end of the plate in the right hand, turn the handwheel and draw the plate evenly around

Fig. 16-38. Attaching serrated (slotted) master — trailing end — on Multilith 1250.

the cylinder, engaging the plate with the tail clamp, Fig. 16-38.

Spring pressure is adequate for paper plates. Metal plates require that the plate-clamp drawdown screw be tightened, but not so much that the plate is torn.

Before installation, the ends of metal plates should be preformed (bent somewhat) with a plate-bending jig. See Fig. 16-39.

Installing a Plate on Presses Larger than Duplicators. Set the press impression ON. Check that ink rollers and water rollers are in OFF position. In paper-feeding mechanisms with an automatic trip, the impression may be thrown off when the cylinders are rotated. This is because no paper is being fed while the plate is being installed. This problem may be avoided by placing a sheet of paper under the paper feeding mechanism or otherwise arranging it so that the impression remains stable. Bend the ends of the plate with the plate-bending jig.

Attach the leading end of the plate to the leading edge of the cylinder, catching $\frac{1}{4}$" to $\frac{1}{2}$" of the leading edges of the packing sheets beyond the bend of the cylinder. The plate should be centered on the cylinder with the image facing the operator, Fig. 16-40.

Turn the cylinder (against the pressure of the blanket cylinder) to draw the plate and its packing smoothly over the cylinder. Engage the tail end of the plate in the tail clamp of the cylinder, taking care not to tighten excessively and thus tear the plate, Fig. 16-41.

Rearrange the automatic trip on the press so it will again function (with no paper going through).

If it is necessary to twist the plate for register, refer to the press manufacturer's instructions.

Fig. 16-40. Installing plate on cylinder — ATF Chief 20 press.

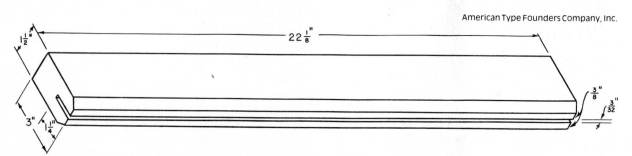

Fig. 16-39. Plate-bending jig — ATF Chief 20 press.

American Type Founders Company, Inc.

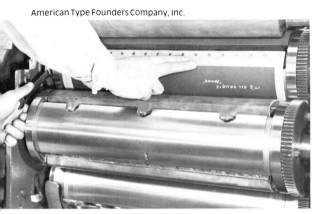

Fig. 16-41. Fastening plate on cylinder — ATF Chief 20 press.

Removing an Offset Plate

At the end of a press run, run a few extra sheets through the press with impression ON, and ink and water rollers OFF. This "runs down" the plate image (removes excess ink). Now *stop the press.*

Moisten a sponge with gum arabic solution[4] and wipe over the plate surface, turning the press handwheel so the entire plate can be reached. Wipe smooth and dry with a cheese-cloth pad.

Release the tail end of the plate first, turning the press backward by hand. Then release the leading (gripper) edge. Prepare the plate for storage. See page 243.

The Blanket Cylinder

Two blanket-clamping devices in the blanket-cylinder gap are provided for attaching the blanket to its cylinder. One is the lead clamp, shown in Fig. 16-42, and the other the trailing clamp, Fig. 16-43. The screw arrangement on the trailing clamp permits drawing the blanket tightly around the cylinder. Some presses have tightening screws which are used to adjust blanket tension, as in Fig. 16-46. See also "Pressure Settings," page 309, and "Undercut-Cylinder and Packing," page 312.

---

[4] A diluted gum arabic solution of 8° to 10° Baumé is recommended for gumming a plate while it is on the press. For gumming a plate on the bench, a 14° Baumé gum arabic solution is recommended.

AM International, Inc.

Fig. 16-42. Attaching blanket to lead clamp — Multilith 1250. (A) Blanket; (B) lead clamp.

AM International, Inc.

Fig. 16-43. Attaching blanket to trailing clamp — Multilith 1250. (A) Trailing clamp; (B) lock nut; (C) tightening screw.

The Blanket

The blanket is made of a rubber-covered fabric. This relatively soft surface receives the inked image from the plate and transfers it to the printing paper which is pressed against the

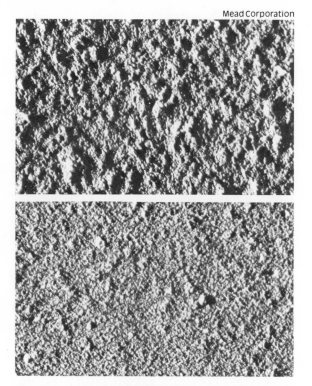

Fig. 16-44. 25X magnification shows the different surface smoothness of typical commercially available blankets.

blanket by the impression cylinder. Since the impression cylinder is an unyielding steel surface, the character and quality of the impression depend upon the blanket surface.

Preparing a New Blanket

Clean the powder from a new blanket by washing with press wash; scour with pumice if necessary. Inspect the surface for nicks and other imperfections. Low spots in the blanket prevent image transfer. These can be repaired by pasting one or more layers of tissue on the back side under the low spot.

Measure the thickness of the blanket with a micrometer caliper. Record this measurement for future use in packing the blanket cylinder with this particular blanket.

If necessary, lay the blanket on a clean, covered surface, and mark the two edges which will be parallel with the blanket cylinder. Mark and punch the holes, and attach the mounting bars, as required.

Powder the surface of the blanket with a mixture of sulphur and French chalk or prepared blanket dusting powder.

Installing a New Blanket

If called for in the press manufacturer's instructions, add packing sheets beneath the blanket. See also "Cylinder Undercut and Packing," page 312.

The forward edge of the blanket *and* the forward edges of the packing sheets should be fastened to the blanket cylinder. Follow the instruction manual for your particular press. Fastening the packing at the forward edge will keep it from creeping during operation of the press. If clamping screws are used, tighten all equally.

Turn the press over *by hand* to feed the blanket to the cylinder. Be sure the packing is fed smoothly with the blanket, Fig. 16-45. Attach the free end of the blanket to the cylinder. If tightening screws are used, tighten each equally. See Fig. 16-46. Avoid stretching the blanket "dead" as this produces a hard, poor printing surface.

After a short run, a new blanket is apt to stretch and should be slightly retightened.

Care of Blankets

The life of the blanket and the quality of the printing can both be improved by following these suggestions:

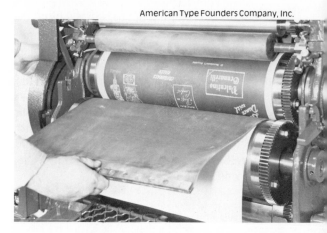

Fig. 16-45. Installing blanket on blanket cylinder — ATF Chief 20 press.

Fig. 16-46. Adjusting blanket tension — ATF Chief 20 press.

1. When the press is to be idle for several days, release the tension on the blanket.
2. Check and correct the thickness of the packing occasionally to eliminate surface friction.
3. Keep the blanket clean and powdered with sulphur and French chalk when not in use.
4. Wash the blanket with water to remove gum solution or accumulation.
5. Dissolve any dried ink on the blanket with press solvent, whether on the surface, edges, or back. For the best presswork, keep the blanket absolutely clean. Do not let fluids dry on the blanket. *Wipe* the blanket clean and dry.
6. Keep the blanket away from heat, and especially away from direct rays of the sun.
7. Never use gasoline or combinations of turpentine and gasoline.
8. Level any low spot on the blanket by pasting one or more patches of tissue or onionskin *under* the area, using Sphinx or pressroom paste.
9. When the blanket is too tacky to receive a good impression, treat it with carbon disulfide and sulphur powder.
10. When the blanket is too glazed to receive a good impression, scour the surface with pumice and solvent. Treat with a mixture of equal parts of powdered sulphur and soapstone (French chalk).

11. When the blanket is to be stored for a time, wash the surface thoroughly with press solvent and caustic soda or pumice. Powder it well with a half-and-half mixture of sulphur and French chalk. To protect the blanket, roll it so the printing surface is on the inside.
12. To prolong the life of the blanket, give it a rest occasionally. It is well to have extra blankets and to rotate them periodically. Blankets might be used progressively. That is, a new blanket could be used for the most exacting kind of work, and when it becomes somewhat worn, it could be used for the general run of line work.

The Impression Cylinder

A set of grippers in the leading edge of the impression-cylinder gap grips the forwarded sheet of paper and carries it between the impression cylinder and the blanket cylinder. This transfers the blanket image to the paper. See Fig. 16-47. These grippers should *not* be adjusted to compensate for a tipped plate image.

Pressure Checks (Settings)

In general, a number of pressure checks must be made of rollers and cylinders each day before the press is run. These checks also should

Fig. 16-47. Impression-cylinder gripper fingers — Multilith 1250. (A) Stop plates; (B) grippers.

...hen blanket, rollers, or roller cover-...
...placed; when troubles develop with the plate image; or when a plate or printing paper of different thickness is to be used. Specific press manufacturer's instructions should be followed. General instructions for sequence and procedure are given below. See also Fig. 16-48.

1. *Dampener form roller-to-plate.* See page 298.
2. *Ink form roller-to-plate.* See page 303.
3. *Plate cylinder-to-blanket cylinder.* With a properly mounted, packed, and gummed plate on the press, start the press. See page 312 for plate packing. Keep dampener form rollers in OFF position. Drop ink rollers to ON position, and allow the gummed plate to ink up over its entire surface. Now, *stop the press,* lifting the ink rollers to OFF position.

   Bring the plate cylinder *fully* in contact with the blanket cylinder. Then take the plate cylinder *out* of contact. Perform this test several times in different locations on the blanket.

Uniformly inked lines, about $\frac{1}{8}''$ to $\frac{3}{16}''$ wide, should appear across the blanket. See Fig. 16-49. If not, an adjustment must be made, first for *parallel,* then for *overall* pressure, if needed.

Some presses require a packing (using sheets of paper) beneath the blanket to arrive at proper printing pressure or to compensate for differences in thickness of blankets. See page 312 and appropriate press manual.

A second test can be made. Start the press with dampeners OFF, drop the ink rollers to ON, and ink up (roll up) the plate completely. With the press still in operation, allow the blanket to ink up *completely.* Any area of the blanket which will not "roll up" indicates a low spot. See page 308 for underlaying a low spot.

4. *Impression adjustment (squeeze).* Your press may have a compensating adjustment, or spring-loaded impression, which will provide self-adjustment for variations in stock thickness. Otherwise, the pressure between the blanket cylinder and the impression cyl-

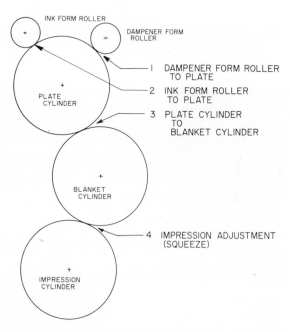

Fig. 16-48. Sequence and location of pressure checks (settings).

Fig. 16-49. Plate cylinder to blanket cylinder (master to blanket) ink band pressure test — Multilith 1250. (B) Master inked completely; and (C) ink band $\frac{1}{8}''$ to $\frac{3}{16}''$ wide.

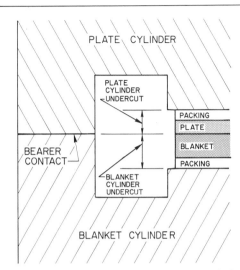

A. Enlarged cross-section view of encircled area "A". The plate and blanket cylinder bodies are undercut to a smaller diameter than their bearers. The plate and blanket cylinder undercuts provide accommodation for the plate and blanket and their packing sheets when the bearers are in correct rolling contact.

B. Enlarged cross-section view of encircled area "B". The impression cylinder body is not undercut. However, its bearers are undercut to allow for impression adjustment between it and the blanket cylinder.

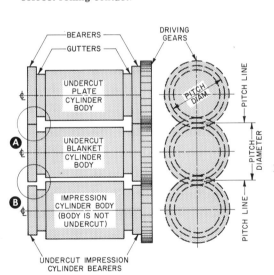

Fig. 16-50. Meshing gears provide postive drive without slipping. Plate and blanket cylinder bearers are the same diameter as the pitch diameter of the gears. Encircled portion "A" is enlarged in view A, and encircled portion "B" is enlarged in view B.

inder should be adjusted to provide the correct "squeeze" for each different thickness of stock being run. Your press manufacturer's instructions should be followed. Two methods of testing are explained below.

a. *Ink-band test.* With a plate on the plate cylinder, start the press. Drop dampeners and then ink-form rollers, inking up the plate image in the usual manner. Bring the blanket cylinder into contact with the plate cylinder, then back away, thus obtaining an inked image on the blanket. *Stop the press first lifting the ink rollers and dampeners.*

Rotate the handwheel until the blanket image is over the solid part of the impression cylinder. Insert a sheet of the printing paper between the blanket and the impression cylinders. Bring the blanket cylinder into contact with the impression cylinder; then bring it away. A $^3/_{16}$"-wide, uniformly inked band of the image should appear across the paper. Adjust, if needed, first for parallel, then for width of the band. (Fig. 16-49).

> • **Note:** This band test may be performed also by contacting the printing paper with a blanket that has been completely covered with ink.

b. *Test strips.* With the press *stopped,* insert two 2" × 8" test strips of the printing stock between the blanket and the impression cylinders, one strip near each end. Adjust for *parallel* impression until a pull on each strip indicates the strips are held firmly between the cylinders. Always begin this test from a setting *greater than* the thickness of the stock to be run.

In general, to obtain a *uniform drag* on the two test strips, 0.003" more squeeze should be added, either by adjustment or by addition of packing sheets.

Cylinder Undercut and Packing

On the larger presses, the plate, blanket, and impression cylinders are driven by meshing gears, Figs. 16-45 and 16-50. This insures that the cylinders rotate without slipping. Midpoint between a pair of meshing gears is the pitch line. The pitch diameter on a gear is from pitch line to pitch line, as shown in Fig. 16-50.

Bearers. The bearers are the narrow bands at the ends of the press cylinders. On the plate and blanket cylinders, the bearers are the same diameter as the pitch diameter of the driving gears, as shown in Fig. 16-50.

Plate and Blanket Cylinders. The bodies of the plate and blanket cylinders are each *undercut.* That is, they are made smaller in diameter than the bearers on those cylinders. See *A* in Fig. 16-50 and view A. When properly adjusted, the bearers maintain these two cylinders parallel to each other and at the correct "rolling off" level.

The amount that the cylinders are undercut below the surface of the bearers is usually

stamped somewhere in the cylinder gutters. These figures indicate in thousandths of an inch how much the cylinder body is undercut in *radius* below the bearers.

The undercutting accommodates the plate and blanket, and allows for adding the packing sheets beneath the plate and the blanket, as in view B of Fig. 16-50. This also helps compensate for variations in thickness of plates and blankets, thus maintaining these two cylinders virtually equal in diameter. If one were larger, this would tend to change the image length during transfer, as explained below.

Squeeze. Usually, the total thickness of the packing sheets plus the thicknesses of the blanket and the plate should equal 0.003" *more* than the combined undercut of the plate and blanket cylinders. This excess is called the *squeeze.* During the printing operation, when the bearers are in proper rolling contact with each other, this squeeze is absorbed primarily by the resiliency, or give, of the blanket.

Example in Cylinder Packing. (Refer to Fig. 16-50, view A and to Table 16-1.) Measurements below are illustrative only. In your work, substitute the actual figures for your press.

A 0.071" undercut blanket cylinder has added packing sheets totaling 0.008" and a blanket 0.065" thick. Together, these equal 0.002" more than the blanket cylinder undercut.

Similarly, 0.007" of packing sheets has been added to the 0.006" plate, totaling 0.001" more than the 0.012" undercut of the plate cylinder. These two excesses of packing total 0.003" — the recommended squeeze.

Impression Cylinder. The impression cylinder body is *not undercut.* However, its bearers are undercut below the impression cylinder body surface, as shown in view B of Fig. 16-50. This undercut is more than sufficient to allow the blanket cylinder to be adjusted toward or away from the impression cylinder so as to compensate for the thickness of stock to be run, even though some packing may have been removed from beneath the blanket.

Normally, 0.002" to 0.004" squeeze is required between the blanket and impression cylinders in order to obtain a satisfactory image transfer from blanket to paper.

Table 16-1
Computation of Amount of Squeeze in a
Typical Cylinder Packing Instance

		Inches		
A. Plate thickness	0.006			
B. Plate packing	+ 0.007			
Plate, plus packing		0.013		
C. Plate cylinder undercut		– 0.012		
Plate cylinder squeeze (excess)			0.001″	
D. Blanket thickness	0.065			
E. Blanket packing	+ 0.008			
Blanket, plus packing		0.073		
F. Blanket cylinder undercut		– 0.071		
Blanket cylinder squeeze (excess)			+ 0.002″	
Total squeeze (excess)			0.003″	

Changing the Printing Length

When a job is to be run through the press a second time, sometimes the paper has shrunk or stretched after the first run. To compensate for this stretching or shrinking on the second run, certain adjustments can be made. The image for the second press run can be *shortened* to effect register by transferring some of the packing from the blanket cylinder to the plate cylinder. The image can be *lengthened* by transferring some packing from the plate cylinder to the blanket cylinder.

• **Note:** Remember, if packing is added to one cylinder, the same thickness of packing should be removed from the other cylinder.

Only minor changes in register should be attempted in the manner described above. This is because greatly different cylinder diameters may cause undue plate-image wear and slurs. Also see "Controlling the Stretching and Shrinking of Paper," page 280.

Baldwin-Gegenheimer Corporation

Chemco Photoproducts Company

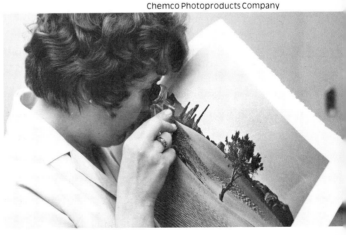

Fig. 16-51. Packing gage used for measuring the height of the plate and the blanket in relation to the press bearer.

Fig. 16-52. Press operator checking dot quality on press sheet.

Questions

1. Name the basic parts of an offset press. Briefly describe the function of each.
2. Explain in detail what happens to the paper stock from the time it is picked out of the feeder pile until it is delivered into the receiver or delivery unit.
3. Describe the operation of both the *conventional* (separate) and the *combined* inking-and-dampening systems.
4. Which of the following inking and dampening systems are of the separate type and which are of the combined type? Miehle-Matic, Harris-Cottrell Brush-Dampening, Simflo, Didde-Glaser Spray, 1250 Multilith, A. B. Dick Aquamatic, Dahlgren.
5. How does the four-main-cylinder design of offset press differ from the three-main-cylinder design?
6. Explain the theory of operation of the two-main-cylinder design of offset press.
7. Why are coverings used for dampener form rollers? Name two kinds.
8. Explain how to check the setting (pressure) of the dampener form roller (or rollers).
9. Explain the term *pH*. How is it measured?
10. Tell how to prepare fountain solution from the concentrate. What is the recommended pH value of fountain solution to be used with aluminum plates?
11. Explain how to control the amount of ink that is fed to any area across the width of the plate.
12. Describe the test for proper pressure setting of ink form rollers.
13. How should ink rollers be stored?
14. Tell how to prepare and install a new blanket.
15. How should gum be removed from the blanket?
16. Describe the installation of a plate on a duplicator. On a large press.
17. What does *running down* a plate mean? Describe how this is done.
18. How is an offset plate removed from the press?
19. Describe how to check the pressure of the plate cylinder to blanket cylinder.
20. Describe one method of checking the impression adjustment.
21. What is meant by a cylinder *undercut*? Why is the undercut provided?

Problems and Projects

1. For each of the different presses in your shop, make a schematic drawing of the roller systems, cylinder arrangement, and paper feeding-to-delivery components.
2. While your instructor demonstrates, observe the action and function of each of the press components.
3. Study thoroughly the press operator's manual for each of the presses suggested by your instructor.
4. Assist your instructor in applying new dampener covers.
5. Under your instructor's supervision, make the dampening-system pressure checks on the press assigned to you.
6. Under the direction of your instructor, prepare and install a new blanket. Test and correct for any low spots.
7. Under the direction of your instructor, install and remove an offset plate.
8. Assist your instructor in performing complete pressure checks on an offset press.
9. Assist your instructor in determining and installing proper packing for blanket and plate cylinders for a specific situation.

New Terms

alkalinity	oleophilic
bearers	pawl-and-ratchet
blanket drum	plate segment
delivery cylinder	press unit
ductor roller	printing couple
duplicator	register board
emulsification	rider roller
feeder	set-off
French chalk	sheet controls
hydrophilic	skewing
impression segment	slurs
metering roller	squeeze
micrometer	stacker
mineral spirits	thrust

Offset Presswork Operations

Chapter 17

For optimum results, it is most desirable that a qualified instructor demonstrate and teach the operation of the press. The instructions in this chapter apply, in general, to most duplicators and presses.[1]

Preliminary Preparation

No press should be operated by anyone until that person has been thoroughly instructed in its safe operation, can demonstrate a complete understanding of its operation, and is specifically designated to operate that press. No unauthorized persons should help the operator or experiment with the press.

In addition, no adjustments to the press should be attempted until the student has personally received proper instruction and is judged competent by the instructor. The student should not hesitate to ask questions or to seek assistance or further instruction.

Press Instruction Manuals

Operators' instruction manuals for the particular presses in the shop should be on hand and available to students.

Personal Dress

Tie back long hair. Remove coats and sweaters. Roll shirt sleeves *above* the elbows. Remove or tuck in neckties. Remove jewelry such as rings and bracelets. Do not wear gloves

[1] All photographs in this chapter courtesy AM International, Inc.

or loose aprons. Tuck shirttails into slacks. Do not carry wiping cloths in pockets.

Items Needed

While the exact needs will vary with the situation, note the following items as suggestions.

10-quart enamel pail (half-filled with tepid water).

Cellulose sponge, approximately $2'' \times 4'' \times 4''$ (for sponging the plate on the press).

Shallow bowl, about $4''$ or $5''$ diameter, with about $1''$ of $8°$ or $10°$ Baumé gum solution (for gumming the plate on the press). Use $14°$ Baumé gum for gumming the plate on the bench.

Cheesecloth pads, about $4''$ square.

Cotton wipes, about $4''$ square.

Clean cotton wiping cloths.

Oil can with spout (hand oiler) filled with solvent. Label it "Solvent" and use only for this purpose.

Pint- or quart-size safety can, filled with solvent.

- **Note:** See "Solvents," page 369.

Ink knife, square end (or putty knife).

Screwdriver, Allen wrenches, open-end wrenches, socket wrenches, and pliers to fit commonly adjusted screws and nuts on the press being used. A tool panel is a handy way to keep tools accessible.

Roller-storage rack.

Cleaner sheets.

Roller-cleaning device.

Magnifier (tripod-base, linen-tester, or pocket-clip type).

315

Dampener gauges (acetate or paper strips, 0.005" thick × 1" wide × 8" or more long).
Paper micrometers and blanket gage.
Newspaper sheets, cut half-page size.

In addition to the above, it helps to have on hand chemicals and supplies for storing and preserving specific plates.

A worktable should be provided for the press operator's use.

The proper fountain solution and ink supply should be available, according to the plates that are being run and the specifications for the inks to be used.

Visual Inspection

Remove the fabric press covering. Examine the press carefully to see that all component parts are in place and that all settings and controls are in OFF position.

Install any fountains and rollers which may have been removed the previous day. First remove any protective gum coating (if so treated).

Remove any paper dust or lint from the feeder and register table.

Wipe off any dust from the blanket, cylinders, and rollers with a cloth that is dampened in solvent.

Press Hand Check

As an additional check to be certain there is no interference, turn the press by means of the handwheel for a revolution or two.

Press Power Check

If all is clear, turn on the power, allowing the press to revolve for a few times. Check that all parts are functioning correctly. If the speed selector is at other than the slowest speed, set it at this speed *while the press is operating.* Do not adjust the speed setting while the press is stopped.

Lubrication

Lubricate the press daily before operation *while the press is stopped!* Never attempt to lubricate a moving press.

Study the manufacturer's lubrication chart and locate each oil hole, grease fitting, and point of lubrication. These should be marked with red paint to make them prominent.

Begin at one point on the press and work your way around, filling each hole with the type of oil recommended by the press manufacturer, or use a good non-detergent oil of grade No. 20 S.A.E. Wipe off the excess with a clean cloth. If any oil holes are on parts which rotate during operation, turn the press by hand so that these holes are on top, and then oil them. In this way, the oil will have a chance to work down to the bearing surfaces.

Once a week, lubricate the delivery and feeder drive chains with penetrating oil or a mixture of equal parts of kerosene and a non-detergent No. 20 S.A.E. motor oil. Use gear grease compound on all gears. Oil the motors sparingly at this weekly lubrication. If the motors have grease fittings, add grease twice yearly or every 1000 hours.

Occasionally, during the day when the press is stopped, check the main bearings. They should never be very warm. Lubricate if needed.

Check the recommended oil level in the vacuum-blower pump jars weekly, Fig. 17-1. This is generally a non-detergent No. 10 S.A.E. oil. Clean the air inlet holes.

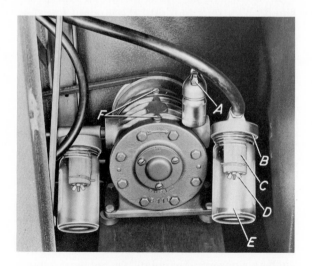

Fig. 17-1. Vacuum-blower pump. (A) Oil filler cap, (B) gasket, (C) filter elements, (D) wing nut, (E) glass jar, and (F) pump bearing oil holes (Multilith 1250).

Check Specifications

Check the job specifications. Do you have the correct ink? Is the correct paper stock at hand, and is it cut to the correct size? Are the plates ready? What other "specs" are called for? If in doubt, consult your instructor.

Setting Up for Operation

Assuming the preliminary preparation of the press as described above has been done, set up for operation as follows.

Prepare the Ink Unit

Install the ink fountain and all rollers which may have been removed. If an ink-fountain liner is used, install it now. See Fig. 17-2.

Estimate how much ink is needed. It is better to start with too little ink on the rollers than too much. More can easily be added.

Turn the handwheel (or adjust press) so that the ink ductor roller is out of contact with the fountain roller.

Place the ink in the bottom of the fountain, forcing it from the tube and rotating the fountain roller by hand. Adjust keys (or fountain screws) so that an even film of ink is all along the fountain roller.

If the ink is in a can, first use the ink knife to scrape and discard any scum from the top. Then, with a rotary motion, pick up the ink with the knife, removing an even layer from the top of the ink in the can. Hold this glob down in the fountain against the roller, and turn the roller by hand so that it picks off the ink from the knife. Add more ink, if needed, in a different location. With the knife, work the ink along the length of the fountain.

Turn the night latch of the ink form roller to the OFF position, so that these rollers are in contact with other ink unit rollers, ready to operate.

Set the ink ductor roller ON, and turn the ratchet control for the ink fountain to FULL ON position. Do not set the form rollers to ON.

Turn on the press, and when sufficient ink is on the rollers (just barely enough to begin to "hiss"), shut off the press. Set the ratchet control for the fountain roller to the usual running

Fig. 17-2. Installing ink-fountain liner. (A) Liner, (B) blade assembly, (C) fountain roller (Multilith 1250).

position, as determined by experience (usually a little less than the middle setting).

Prepare the Water Unit

Install the water fountain, fountain roller, and all other water (dampening) system rollers which may have been removed.

Fill the fountain bottle with the recommended solution. Invert the bottle to make sure no solution leaks out from between the cap and the bottle. Place the bottle in its recess in the fountain. Allow the solution to reach its level.

If there is a night latch for the dampener roller, turn it to OFF. This drops the rollers into operating position. The form roller remains OFF, not contacting the plate.

Start the press, allowing the rollers to pick up moisture. Help the moisture along by operating the fountain roller knob by hand. Some operators drip a little fountain solution on the oscillating roller from the corner of a sponge.

The dampener ductor roller may be predampened as follows: With the press stopped, turn the handwheel to bring the ductor roller into contact with the fountain roller. Turn the fountain roller knob by hand, thus quickly transferring fountain solution from the fountain roller to the ductor roller, until the ductor roller is sufficiently dampened.

Stop the press when the form rollers are sufficiently damp, as determined from experience. Some operators extend a clenched fist, touching the form roller with the knuckle of one finger as the press revolves. Have your instructor show you. *Never use a finger tip!*

Set the ratchet control for the fountain roller at its *normal* setting.

Install the Plate

When performing pressure checks, use either the gummed plate to be used on the job or a test plate of the same thickness as the plate for the job.

Follow instructions given on page 305.

Perform the Pressure Checks

Perform the pressure checks in this order:

1. Dampener form roller to plate. See page 298.
2. Ink form roller to plate. See page 303.
3. Plate cylinder to blanket cylinder. See page 310.
4. Impression adjustment, or squeeze. See page 310.

Prepare the Feeder, Sheet Controls and Delivery

Setting up for the *paper cycle* (feeder, sheet controls, and delivery) is greatly simplified if all jobs are laid out on the flat so that the *printing sheet* (not necessarily the image) is always centered on the flat from left to right. The leading edge of the sheet should always be the same distance down from the leading edge of the flat.

Feeder Setup. A typical vacuum feeder is shown in Figs. 17-3 and 17-4. The setup is as follows:

1. Cut a piece of heavy cardboard or binder's board $1/8''$ shorter and narrower than the stock to be run. Place this on the paper supports, Fig. 17-3.
2. Take a sheet of the paper stock to be run and fold it in the center. Place it on the feeder platform so that the crease is $1/8''$ to the *left* of the center mark of the scale, Fig. 17-4.
3. Secure the left pile (magazine) guide $1/32''$ from the paper, Fig. 17-4.
4. "Wind" or fan the paper in small lifts, and jog it neatly against the front and left pile guides, Fig. 17-5.

Fig. 17-3. Vacuum feeder and paper magazine (Multilith 1250).

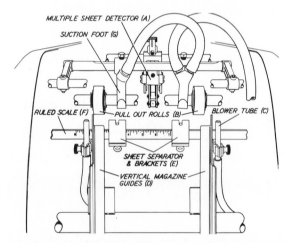

Fig. 17-4. Vacuum feeder and paper magazine, showing relative positioning of units (Multilith 1250).

Fig. 17-5. Loading the paper magazine (Multilith 1250).

Do not turn over any lift of paper unless you are instructed to do so. This is done sometimes if the paper tends to curl upward, or for backing up sheets (printing on the other side). Ordinarily, paper is cut and fed so that the felt side (usually the better side) is up. Also, any watermark on the paper should be right side up and readable when the front (face) side of the sheets are printed. (See Chapter 15 for more information on paper.)

5. Position and secure the right pile guide against the paper pile. This should not be a snug fit.

6. Turn the press handwheel until the sucker feet are at their lowest point of travel. Raise the paper pile so that the top sheet is $1/4''$ below the sucker feet.

7. Position and secure the tail guide against the tail end of the paper pile so that it will not be struck by the rising paper platform when the last few sheets are fed.

8. Position the sheet separator combs so they will provide a "combing" action to the vaccum-lifted sheet. Then position the vacuum feet directly above the sheet separators, Fig. 17-6.

9. Turn on the air pump. Adjust the blast to flutter the top few sheets, so the top sheet can be picked up by the sucker feet. Both blast and suction are increased as needed for heavier weights of stock.

10. After positioning the sucker feet at their lowest point, check the vacuum. The amount of suction should be just enough to lift one sheet and hold it. Usually, this need not be changed.

11. Adjust the pile-height governor so it just touches the top sheet when the sucker feet are at their lowest position and the top sheet is about $1/4''$ below the sucker feet. See Fig. 17-7. Check it by lowering the pile a bit to see if it will return to the proper height.

Conveyor Board and Sheet Controls. The conveyor board and sheet controls include the pullout roll and wheels, the sheet caliper (double-sheet detector), the conveyor tapes, the riders (steel balls or metal bands), front stops, side jogger, stationary side guide, and forwarding rollers. (See Figs. 17-8 through 17-10).

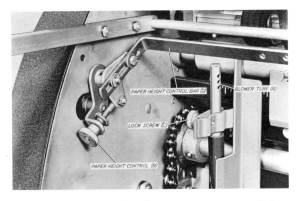

Fig. 17-7. Paper-pile-height (governor) control bar (Multilith 1250).

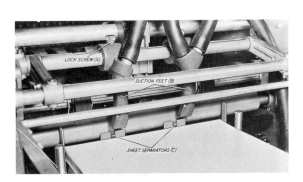

Fig. 17-6. Positioning of suction feet and sheet separators (Combs) (Multilith 1250).

Fig. 17-8. Multiple-sheet detector (Multilith 1250).

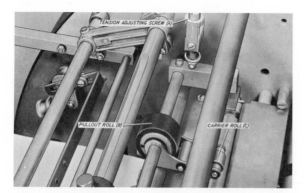

Fig. 17-9. Pullout rolls — left side shown (Multilith 1250).

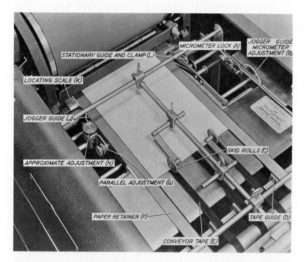

Fig. 17-10. Conveyor board (register table) (Multilith 1250).

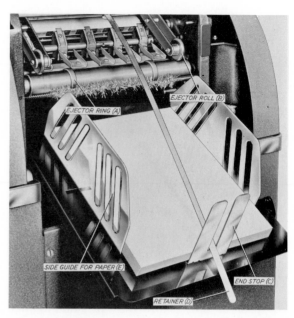

Fig. 17-11. Ejector mechanism and paper receiver (Multilith 1250).

1. Cut a strip of paper from the stock to be run (about 2″ × 11″), and fold it about 4″ from the end. Holding the strip by the fold, insert it into the sheet caliper under the detector roll (part C of Fig. 17-8), so that the single thickness passes but the double thickness trips the mechanism (press running, feed vacuum on).
2. Adjust the pullout rolls, Fig. 17-9 for light, equal traction, using two paper test strips — one for each wheel.
3. Move the register board side guides out to the left and right, Fig. 17-10. Run a sheet down the board to the front stop fingers, and stop the press.

4. Turn the handwheel until the left side guide (jogger) is in its extreme position towards the far side of the press. Loosen and move the left side guide over to just touch the sheet. Then move it ⅛″ *more,* and secure it in position. During press operation, this ⅛″ lateral movement is the jogging action.
5. Bring the right side guide (stationary guide) just to the right-hand edge of the paper. Secure in place.

   If the stationary guide has a leaf spring, bring the guide over to the paper, then ¹⁄₃₂″ *more,* compressing the spring slightly. Secure in place.
6. Check that the conveyor tapes are equidistant across the table under the paper. Position the hold-downs (rider balls or steel bands) over the two outside tapes.
7. Set the rider wheels (speed or "skid" wheels) so that they are just off the trailing end of the sheet as the sheet meets the front guides (stop fingers) and in jogging position.

Delivery. Set the delivery tray, jogger, or stacker for maximum width. See Fig. 17-11.

Feed a sheet through. Turn the press by hand until the jogger is in closed position. Set the jogger, tray, or stacker to this sheet position.

Feeding Test Sheets

After the press has been set up and *before* the run is started, one or more test sheets should be run to determine whether any adjustments are necessary to obtain the most satisfactory results. No press run should be started until the test sheets are approved by the instructor or by the supervisor.

With a proper press setup, feed a test sheet as follows:

1. Using sponge and water, wash off preservative from plate surface, or simply dampen the unpreserved plate. (Other plate dampening solution may be used if the plate manufacturer so recommends.)
2. Turn on press motor.
3. Drop dampener form rollers, and allow press to turn several revolutions. *Do not stop press.*
4. Drop ink form rollers, allowing plate image several revolutions to *roll up* (ink up).
5. Bring plate in contact with blanket.
6. Turn on blowers, and check for blast.
7. Turn on feeder, adjust suction, and allow a sheet or two to be fed.
8. Shut off feeder.
9. Break contact between plate and blanket.
10. Lift ink form rollers.
11. Lift dampener form rollers.
12. Stop the press.
13. Gum the plate if a metal plate. Remember to sponge off the gum when recommencing operation.

Inspection of Test Sheet

Test sheets should be carefully inspected. Some of the important points to check are:

1. Is the ink coverage correct — not too heavy or not too light?
2. Is the ink coverage consistent across the sheet?
3. Are the clear areas free of ink?
4. Is the entire image printing?

5. Is the image square on the sheet?
6. Is the image correctly placed laterally?
7. Is the image correctly placed vertically?
8. Is the overall impression satisfactory — not too light and not too heavy?
9. In the halftones, are highlight dots visible and shadow dots unplugged?

Adjustments

If the answer to any of the above questions is *no*, then adjustments must be made for these printing deficiencies. Instructions for correcting some of these are described below. Corrections for other operating troubles are discussed in Chapter 19.

The operator should remain alert so as to detect printing troubles as they occur. This will avoid unnecessary waste of paper and time. Also, in making adjustments, as many corrections as possible should be made at one time.

Obtaining Ink and Water Balance. Ideally, the printed image should be dense and the nonprinting areas clear.

Initially, start the run with a thin supply of image ink. Increase the supply gradually to obtain the desired density. Adjust the ink-fountain keys so that there is a uniform inking of the image across the sheet.

If the clear areas tend to *scum* (show tones in the clear areas, Fig. 19-3), cut back some ink and increase the flow of water a bit. Then increase the ink gradually. Water level should be just enough to prevent scumming.

If the image is too light, increase the ink supply by small degrees. If the increase causes scum, add more water.

Obtaining proper ink and water balance is a matter of experience in using *just enough* moisture with the proper amount of ink to obtain a dense image. Too much initial moisture will invite the use of excess ink, leading to "mud" and troubles. See Chapter 19.

Correcting Image Position on Sheet. The test sheet may show that the image on the sheet must be moved laterally (to the left or right), vertically (up or down), or, possibly, straightened from a cocked position.

Whenever a position adjustment is made to a plate or plate cylinder, the image must be washed from the blanket. This is because on most presses, the next test impression will be in a different place on the blanket. See blanket washing instructions, page 324.

1. *Lateral Adjustment.* To move the image to the left of right on the printed sheet, reset the side jogger and the stationary guide on the feed board, Fig. 17-10. If necessary, make a minute adjustment of the jogger guide micrometer adjustment wheel. Large adjustments require repositioning the feed pile.

2. *Cocked Image.* To straighten a cocked image (if not excessively crooked), adjust the leading and trailing plate clamp lateral adjusting screws, if the press is so equipped. Refer again to Fig. 16-36.

    For straight-edge plates, release the plate from the trailing clamp and loosen and twist

A. Pictorial view.

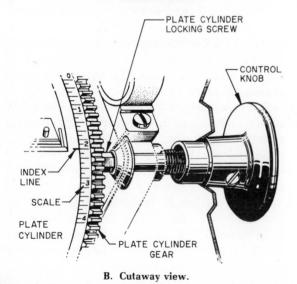

B. Cutaway view.

Fig. 17-12. Vertical positioning control (Multilith 1250).

at the lead clamp. Tighten the plate again at the lead and trailing ends.

For a badly cocked image, have the plate remade.

3. *Vertical Adjustment.* To make a vertical adjustment on some presses, move the plate around the plate cylinder by loosening the tension on the set of plate clamp screws at one end of the plate. Then tighten the plate clamp screws at the opposite end of the plate.

On many presses, the plate cylinder or the impression cylinder may be moved independently of its driving gears so that, when moved, the plate image will print on the blanket either up or down from its previous location. See Fig. 17-12A and B. To make a vertical adjustment on this type of press, first turn the press *off*. Then locate and engage the vertical positioning control onto the plate cylinder lock screw. While it is still engaged, loosen the screw and rock the handwheel up or down to move the plate cylinder in relation to the plate cylinder gear. See circled area in Fig. 17-12A. Retighten the plate cylinder lock screw.

Impression. The impression check (impression cylinder to blanket cylinder, page 310) should be performed prior to the running of the test sheets. Too little impression will result in too-light an image and, perhaps, missing highlight dots. Too heavy an impression will result in a "squashed-out" image — a spreading of individual highlight dots and a filling-in of halftone shadow areas and fine reverses.

On some presses, the impression is adjusted by means of a micrometer lever or handscrew, which moves the impression cylinder closer to or away from the blanket cylinder.

Refer to appropriate press manuals for details for your specific press. Your instructor will demonstrate the proper procedure to follow for the presses in your shop.

Operating the Press

During the operation of the press, stop the press if something goes amiss which you cannot readily and understandably cope with. Ask for your instructor's help. Considerable paper can be wasted while you experiment.

If, for any reason, the press is stopped for more than a few seconds (while running a metal plate), gum the plate immediately. Sponge off with water before restarting the run.

Before the Run

Ask yourself these important questions before starting the run:

1. Am I authorized to operate this press and make this run?
2. Am I observing all personal safety precautions? (Pages 315, 366-374.)
3. Are all supplies and equipment on hand? (Page 315.)
4. Do I have the proper plate, paper stock, and ink, as checked against the job specifications?
5. Have I inspected the press — visually; by turning over by hand; with power on?
6. Has the press been lubricated?

Preparation

Is the press prepared for operation?

1. Ink unit prepared?
2. Water unit prepared?
3. Plate installed?
4. All pressure checks completed?
5. Paper feeding and delivery system setup okay?
6. Test sheets okayed?

When press is fully prepared, set the counter to zero (all 9's, then trip once).

Operation

Usually, plates are already gummed when they arrive at the press. With the plate mounted and *the press stopped,* remove the gum from the plate with a sponge dipped in water. Be careful to wipe the entire plate, including the edges.

The usual procedure in the operation of the press follows:

To begin a press run (after dampening the plate):

1. Turn on press motor. Always start the press at a slow speed, increasing the speed only when sheets are feeding satisfactorily and the test sheets have been okayed.

2. Drop the dampener form rollers.[1]
3. Drop the ink form rollers.
4. Bring the plate into contact with the blanket.
5. Feed the sheets.

To stop the run, the procedure is reversed:

1. Shut off the feeder.
2. Break contact between the plate and the blanket.
3. Lift the ink form rollers.
4. Lift the dampener form rollers.
5. Stop the press.

If minor adjustments are needed during the press run, stop feeding ink to the plate. Break the contact between the plate and blanket to avoid piling up ink on the blanket.

Problems to Watch for During the Run: Carefully read Chapter 19, "Offset Presswork Troubleshooting," for common troubles which may develop during the press run, and note the remedies given for these. In addition, watch constantly for:

1. Sheet register.
2. Color and coverage of ink.
3. Level of fountain solution.
4. Amount of ink in fountain. Keep ink worked from side to side, using an ink knife.
5. Complete coverage of image on paper.
6. Clear areas picking up ink, or other evidence of clear area fouling up.
7. Level of paper pile in receiver.
8. Halftones plugging up or losing highlight areas.

Keep handy an okayed test sheet for comparison from time to time with a sheet pulled from the press run. Printed sheets should match with the test sheet throughout the job.

If registration gradually creeps vertically during the press run, stop the press. First check that the adjustment for vertical positioning of the image is secure. Then check to see whether

---

[1]When "rolling up" a newly installed plate an alternate method is to first sponge off the plate, start the press, then drop the ink form rollers before the dampener form rollers. After the press revolves several times, dampener form rollers may be dropped. This allows the image to pick up ink coverage to protect it against possible effects of the dampening solution.

the punched holes in the plate ends are being torn longer by the hooks on the plate cylinder. If may be that (1) excessive pressure has been used in securing the plate to the press; (2) excessive moisture is being or has been used on the plate; (3) rollers or cylinders are exerting undue pressure; or (4) the run is too long for the type plate being used. The latter especially may be true with plates of a soft base.

After Operation

At the end of the press run, lift the dampeners, lift the ink form rollers, run down the plate[2], break contact (blanket to plate), stop the feeder, and stop the press. Gum the plate and remove to the bench for preparation for storage or preservation. See page 241.

Remove the printed sheets, being careful not to smudge wet ink. Also remove any remaining sheets in the feeder and any sheets which may have been deflected.

At the end of the day, prepare the press for shut-down, and proceed with "Press Wash-Up" as described below.

Press WashUp

Assuming that the offset plate has been run down, gummed, and removed from the press, proceed to wash up the press as follows:

1. *Turn all operating controls OFF.*
2. *Remove paper stock* from the feeder and receiver tray or stacker. Take out any deflected sheets from beneath the feed board.
3. *Blanket.* Remove the image with a cloth dampened with solvent, being sure to clean the edges of the blanket. Wash the blanket with water to remove any dried gum, and again wash with solvent. Wipe dry with a clean cloth. See "Solvents," page 369.
4. *Water Fountain.* Remove the fountain bottle. Drain off the water fountain and discard the solution.

---

[2]To run down a plate means to remove much of the ink on the plate image (before gumming it) by feeding a dozen or so waste sheets through, with impression *on*, but ink and water *off*.

• **Note:** Fountain solution which is allowed to remain in the fountain overnight (or for long periods of disuse) tends to build up a fungus growth. Also the water evaporates faster than the etch, which causes the remaining fountain solution to have a stronger pH.

Remove the fountain roller. Wash it with a pad moistened with fountain solution on which has been sprinkled a little FF pumice. Wipe first with a pad moistened with fountain solution, then with a dry pad. Place in rack. Keep fingers off surface of the roller.

Wipe the inside of the fountain tray with a clean cloth. If any scum is present, wipe it out with a water-wet pad and a little FF pumice. Then flush with water.

5. *Other Dampener Rollers.* Remove molleton-covered ductor and form rollers and place in rack. If dirty, soak them for a few minutes in a detergent solution. Work out the ink by hand, squeezing in the direction of the nap, or roll on paper. Rinse thoroughly with clean water, and roll on clean paper to remove excess water. Place on rack for storage.

Rollers that are not covered should be washed with water and pad and dried. For extended shut-down, metal rollers should be gummed. This must be washed off with water and pad before re-use.

6. *Gum Bowl and Water Pail.* Discard any gum that is left in the gum bowl. Rinse out the bowl and the sponge with warm water, and set on the bench.

Empty plate-dampening water pail. Flush out the sponge with warm water, and set on the bench. This sponge is only for plate use. Do not use for washing the pail or sink! Use no soap on it! Wash out pail with hand soap and warm water, rinse well, and set on the bench.

7. *Ink Fountain and Ductor.* Remove ink from the fountain with the ink knife, sliding the knife down between blade and roller and lifting out against the roller. Discard ink.

Remove and discard the fountain liner, if one is used.

Lift off the fountain and remove as much ink as possible with the ink knife. Clean the fountain and the fountain roller with a cloth and solvent.

Clean the ductor roller with a cloth and solvent. Remove from press and set on rack.

8. *Ink Rollers.* The ink rollers may be cleaned by hand, with cleaner sheets, with a roller-cleaning device, or by a combination of these three methods.

a. *By Hand.* Place all removable rollers on papers on the bench. Clean rollers with cloth and solvent, and place them in the rack.

Now, turning the press when necessary *by hand — your own hand —,* clean all the remaining rollers, wiping side-to-side, and then holding the cloth against the roller ends as you turn the press. Be careful to get the ends clean.

Never clean rollers by hand when the press is in operation. The press *must be stopped.*

b. *With Cleaner Sheet.* Cleaner sheets are made of blotting paper, Fig. 17-13. They are the same size and have the same ends as offset plates, and they are mounted on the plate cylinder in the same manner.

Remove the dampener form rollers to avoid smudging them.

If the press has a protective cover beneath the inking unit, see that it is lined with blotting paper and set it in place.

With a cleaner sheet on the plate cylinder, start the press revolving at its slowest speed. Using a hand oiler (spouted oil can) filled with solvent, apply some solvent to the uppermost distribution roller (Fig. 17-14). Lower the spout of the oiler slowly to the roller, and feed the solvent slowly across the roller. Allow the press to revolve, thus working in the solvent.

After the ink has been softened by the solvent, drop the ink form rollers to the cleaner sheet as the press continues to operate.

Fig. 17-13. **Attaching a cleaner sheet (Multilith 1250).**

Fig. 17-14. **Applying solvent to uppermost distribution roller (Multilith 1250).**

Now feed some solvent to the left half of the rollers. When that is picked up by the cleaner sheet, feed some solvent to the right half of the rollers. Cleaning only half of the bank of rollers at a time prevents them from skidding.

When the cleaner sheet is dirty, lift the form rollers and stop the press. Replace with a clean sheet. Repeat the process and remove the second sheet. Since the sheets are dirty on only one side, they may be used for cleaning the press at another time (but in reverse order — start with the cleanest one).

With the press stopped, inspect all the rollers, especially the ends. Touch up by hand.

FRAME

SQUEEGEE PLATE

TROUGH (PAN)

ATTACHMENT AND PRESSURE ADJUSTMENT SCREWS

Fig. 17-15. Roller-cleaning device (Multilith 1250).

c. *With Roller-Cleaning Device.* The roller-cleaning device is essentially a fixture with a rubber-bladed squeegee and a metal pan which attaches below the ink unit on the press. See Fig. 17-15. It has adjusting screws which bring the rubber blade into forced scraping contact with one of the ink rollers. To use the device, proceed as follows:

With the press *stopped*, attach the roller-cleaning device to the press. Bring the rubber blade into contact with the adjacent ink roller (for testing); then bring it away.

Start the press. Slowly apply press solvent to the uppermost distribution roller and along the top. Allow solvent to work in.

While the press is still operating, adjust the cleaning device so its blade contacts the ink roller. Then bring it in somewhat tighter.

As the blade squeegees off the ink-and-solvent mixture from the rollers, the metal pan catches the drippings. Apply a little more solvent to the left-hand half of the rollers until they are clean. Then apply solvent to the right-hand half.

When the rollers appear clean (that is, dull and velvety), stop the press. Loosen the blade tension, and remove the metal pan. Drain and clean the pan as recommended by your instructor.

Remove the washing device from the press, clean it thoroughly, and put it away.

While the press is stopped, inspect the rollers and clean off any remaining ink or solvent, especially on the roller ends. Carefully inspect for and remove any ink from press parts.

• **Note:** For presses equipped with combination ink-and-water system, drain the water fountain. Remove and clean the ink fountain, the ink fountain roller, and the ink ductor roller. Then proceed to clean remaining rollers as above.

9. *Replacing Rollers.* Make certain that all rollers, especially the form rollers, are replaced in the same holders from which they were removed. Check that their position has not been reversed, left-to-right. Often they are marked or numbered on the end toward the operator. Lubricate roller shafts and bearings as specified by the manufacturer. If rollers are to be left in the press overnight, set them in night-latch position.

10. *Final Check.* Examine the press carefully, and clean off any ink which may have been thrown or dropped on any part. Clean off any spots caused by fountain solution. Wipe all bright work, especially around the printing unit, using a clean cloth moistened with light machine oil.

Wipe ejector rollers and collars with oil and cloth, sliding them to one side to oil the shaft beneath.

Wipe the plate cylinder with solvent and cloth. Chrome-plated cylinders may be cleaned with special chrome cleaner. Using a dry cloth, wipe away any dust and lint from the feeder, register table, and jogger assemblies.

At least once a week (perhaps more often, and especially before extended shut-down) remove the blanket (see page 308) and wipe down the blanket cylinder with a pad moistened with machine oil. Overly generous use of fountain solution may work beneath the blanket and etch the metal cylinder.

If available, place the protective fabric cover over the press. Replace all tools on the tool panel, straighten the items on the work bench, and be sure all bottles are capped. Put all used cloths into the safety can. Discard unwanted ink, old cleaner sheets, and other such items. Pick up clutter from the floor, and then wash your hands thoroughly with soap and warm water, especially between the fingers.

Roller Glaze. Ink and fountain solution may tend to form a shiny, glossy accumulation on the surface of ink rollers. This glaze prevents the rollers from picking up ink.

Approximately once a week, remove the rollers and scrub them with a solvent-wet cloth on which has been sprinkled a little FF pumice. Commercial glaze removers also are available.

Fig. 17-17. Test press sheet inspected prior to final approval of a press run.

Questions

1. When may a student operate (or assist in the operation of) an offset press in the shop?
2. What safety precautions regarding personal dress should be observed when operating an offset press?
3. What essential items should be provided at the press?

Fig. 17-16. Become acquainted with adjustments and operation of a press before you begin a production run.

4. Describe the procedure for making a visual inspection of the press.
5. Describe the procedure for making a power check of the press.
6. When should the press speed be adjusted?
7. Explain the proper procedure for lubricating the press.
8. What is meant by "checking the specifications" for the job to be printed?
9. What is an ink-fountain liner? Why is it used?
10. How should ink be placed in the fountain?
11. Explain how to ink up the ink rollers.
12. How should the dampening system be prepared for operation?
13. What pressure checks should be made prior to operating the press?
14. Tell how to prepare the feeder setup.
15. What sheet controls and conveyor-board settings must be made?
16. Tell how to feed test sheets.
17. What items should be checked on the printed test sheet?
18. How is an ink-and-water balance obtained?
19. Why must the blanket be washed (on most presses) when the image position is moved?
20. Name two methods of making a vertical adjustment of the image.

21. What are the usual steps to follow in commencing a press run?
22. What is the usual procedure for stopping the press?
23. What, especially, should be watched for during the run?
24. Outline the procedure for press wash-up.
25. What three methods may be employed for washing the ink rollers?
26. What is roller glaze? How is it removed?

Problems and Projects

1. Lubricate an offset press, including the vacuum-blower pump, according to the manufacturer's lubrication instructions.
2. Secure from the manufacturer or distributor one or more operator's manuals for each of the offset presses in the shop.
3. Design and construct a tool panel for each press, so that the wrenches and other small tools needed for operation of that press may be mounted.
4. Under direction and supervision of your instructor, set up an offset press for operation.
5. Install and remove an offset plate.
6. Perform the necessary and recommended pressure checks for the press assigned by your instructor.
7. Feed test sheets, and make necessary adjustments to the press so that the final test sheet is okayed by the instructor.
8. Prepare plates for storage after a run.
9. At the termination of a press run, wash up the press and prepare it for extended shutdown. On successive occasions, demonstrate all three methods of washing the ink rollers.
10. Make a storage rack for press rollers. Also, make one for storing spare rollers and one for use during press wash-up.

New Terms

bank	night latch
conveyor tapes	pile guide
detector roll	pullout rolls
feed board	riders
felt side	roll up
front stops	run down
gum bowl	separator
lateral	sheet caliper
magnifier	tail guide
micrometer lever	

Sheet-Fed and Web Offset Presses and Duplicators

This chapter contains additional information and illustrations on sheet-fed offset presses and duplicators as well as web presses. Topics common to most presses and duplicators have been discussed in previous chapters and therefore are omitted here. It is assumed that the reader will have access to manufacturers' instructions and manuals, and will be helped and guided by the instructor.

The sheet-fed presses, Fig. 18-1, include the familiar rotary presses and the more specialized flat-bed presses. A roll converter may be added to a rotary press to feed cut sheets from a roll; or, the roll converter may be used as an independent unit to provide cut sheets for either a rotary press or a flat-bed press.

Rotary Offset Presses

A number of specific rotary offset presses are described below.

Multilith 1250

The Multilith 1250 is vacuum fed, has separate inking and dampening systems, and is of the conventional three-main-cylinder design.[1] See Figs. 18-2 and 18-3.

Earlier production models were equipped with separate controls for operating the Repelex

[1]Multilith 1250 illustrations are reproduced by permission of the manufacturers, AM International, Inc.

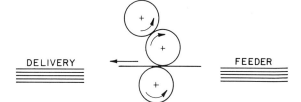

A. Rotary offset press.

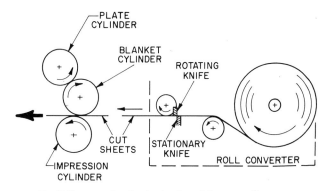

B. Roll converter feeds sheets cut from a roll.

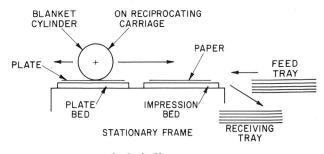

C. Flat-bed offset press.

Fig. 18-1.   Sheet fed offset presses.

Fig. 18-2. Multilith 1250 with single-lever operating control.

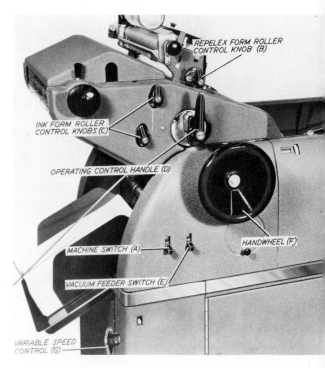

Fig. 18-4. Multilith 1250 equipped with separate (individual) operating controls.

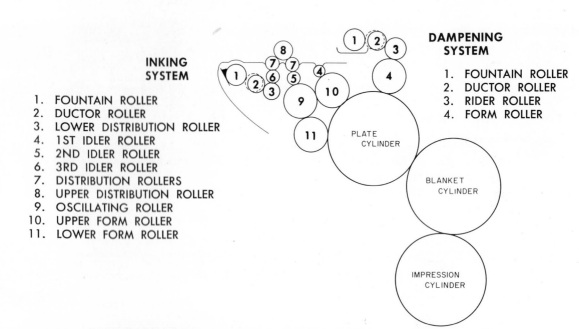

INKING SYSTEM

1. FOUNTAIN ROLLER
2. DUCTOR ROLLER
3. LOWER DISTRIBUTION ROLLER
4. 1ST IDLER ROLLER
5. 2ND IDLER ROLLER
6. 3RD IDLER ROLLER
7. DISTRIBUTION ROLLERS
8. UPPER DISTRIBUTION ROLLER
9. OSCILLATING ROLLER
10. UPPER FORM ROLLER
11. LOWER FORM ROLLER

DAMPENING SYSTEM

1. FOUNTAIN ROLLER
2. DUCTOR ROLLER
3. RIDER ROLLER
4. FORM ROLLER

Fig. 18-3. Schematic of inking and dampening systems and cylinder arrangement for Multiliths 1250, 1250W, 1275, and 1275W.

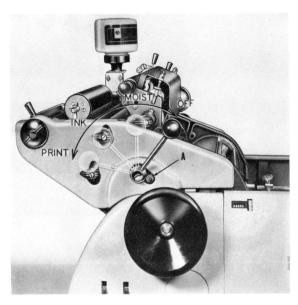

Fig. 18-5. **Single-lever operating control, Multilith 1250.**

(dampening) form roller, ink form rollers, and master-to-blanket contact, Fig. 18-4. However, recent models have a single-lever control to operate these three functions, Fig. 18-5.

Specifications

Minimum gripper margin is $5/16''$ at lead edge of paper. Recommended duplicating (image-printing) area is $9\frac{1}{2}'' \times 13''$. Recommended range for paper size is $3'' \times 5''$ to $11'' \times 14''$.

Operating Procedure

This procedure is followed for models equipped with the single-lever operating control.

First, turn the Repelex (dampener) form roller knob and ink form roller knobs to ON position (one-quarter turn left) and leave them in that position during period of operation.

1. Apply fountain solution to plate with sponge.
2. Turn machine power switch to ON.
3. Move single-lever control to MOIST position. Allow master to revolve one or two revolutions.
4. Move single-lever control to INK position, contacting ink form rollers to master. Allow cylinders to revolve until image picks up ink (one to three revolutions).
5. Move single-lever control to PRINT position. Allow cylinders to revolve until image offsets on blanket (two or three revolutions).
6. Turn vacuum feeder power switch to ON and allow one or two sheets to pass. Return feeder switch to OFF position.
7. Move single lever to INK position.
8. Examine one or two of the first few copies duplicated. If it is necessary to change the position of the image on the paper or to make any other adjustments, or if you wish to stop the duplicator, move the single-lever control to OFF position and turn machine switch OFF.

Pressure Adjustments

The following pressure checks should be performed in the order given.

Repelex (Dampener) Form Roller

Roller must be "run-in" and damp before testing. (Note that all letters that follow are keyed to Fig. 18-6.)

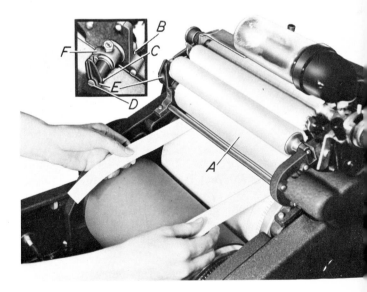

Fig. 18-6. **Adjusting Repelex (dampener) form roller, Multilith 1250. Guard is removed from rollers only for the purpose of illustration.**

1. *Parallel Adjustment.* First, turn single-lever control and Repelex (dampener) form roller knob to OFF position. Place two 1″ strips of 20-pound paper between the Repelex (dampener) form roller and the master, as shown in Fig. 18-6.

   Turn form roller control knob one-quarter turn left to ON position. Move single-lever control to MOIST position, contacting roller to master. Test for equal pull on the paper strips. To adjust (only the left end is adjustable), loosen the set screw (B) and turn the eccentric bearing (F) *clockwise* to *decrease* tension on the left end of the roller (*counterclockwise* to *increase* tension). Tighten set screw.

2. *Removing End Play.* Remove rider roller (above Repelex form roller) and turn Repelex form roller control knob to OFF position. Loosen set screw (B), press inward on eccentric bearing (F), and tighten set screw. Roller should revolve freely without end play.

3. *Overall Pressure.* Using test strips, turn Repelex form roller knob to ON position and single-lever control to MOIST to contact roller to master. Loosen set screw (C).

   With a screwdriver, turn eccentric shaft (D) *counterclockwise* until a fairly strong pull is felt on the test strips. Then tighten set screw. Knob must point to left when form roller is contacting master.

Ink Form Rollers

The upper and lower ink form rollers are both tested and adjusted in the same manner: first one roller, then the other.

Ink rollers must be inked-up, and then *the press is stopped.* A dry master is now mounted on the plate cylinder. The ink form roller disengaging knob (night latch) must be in OFF position (horizontal) so ink form rollers will be able to contact the master.

The Repelex (dampener) form roller control knob should be in OFF position. Both ink form roller control knobs and the single-lever control are placed in OFF position. Now, test and adjust one ink form roller at a time as follows:

Fig. 18-7. **Ink-band test for checking ink form roller-to-plate contact, Multilith 1250. Ink band should be a uniform $\frac{1}{8}$″ to $\frac{3}{16}$″ width all across the plate.**

Turn the ink form roller control knob (for the particular roller being checked) to ON. Turn single-lever control to INK position, allowing form roller to momentarily contact the master. Then turn control lever to OFF. The resulting ink line (or "bead") on master should be a uniform $\frac{1}{8}$″ to $\frac{3}{16}$″ width all the way across the master, Fig. 18-7.

1. *Overall Pressure.* (Keyed to Fig. 18-7). Loosen set screw (A) in form roller control knob. With a screwdriver, turn eccentric shaft (B) *counterclockwise* to *increase* width of bead, and *clockwise* to *decrease* the width. Lock adjustment with set screw.

2. *Parallel Adjustment.* (Keyed to Fig. 18-8). Remove right side plate from ink unit. Disengaging cam (B) must be out of contact with eccentric bearing brackets. Loosen lock screw (A), and turn bearing, (C) *clockwise* to *decrease* the width of right-hand end of contact line; *counterclockwise* to *increase* the right-hand end. (Only the right-hand end of the rollers is adjustable.) Then tighten the lock screw.

   If the overall width of the test line is too great or too small, repeat the overall adjustment, as described above.

3. *Removing End Play.* (Keyed to Fig. 18-8.) Turn disengaging cam (B) until it contacts eccentric bearing brackets. Loosen lock screw (A), and press inward on eccentric bearing (C) until side play is eliminated, but roller is free to rotate easily on its shaft. Adjust both rollers. Recheck parallel adjustment.

Fig. 18-8. Ink form roller adjustments, Multilith 1250. Right cover is removed.

Fig. 18-9. Plate cylinder-to-blanket cylinder (master-to-blanket) pressure test, Multilith 1250.

Master-to-Blanket Pressure

To check pressure, mount a dry master on the cylinder. Do not dampen the master. Turn Repelex form roller knob OFF. Turn ink form roller knobs ON. Start the duplicator (not vacuum feeder), and then turn single-lever operating control to INK position, allowing master to completely ink up. Turn single-lever control OFF and stop the press.

With duplicator stationary, turn single-lever control to PRINT position; then draw it away to OFF position. Inspect ink bead on blanket. See Fig. 18-9.

Adjust master-to-blanket pressure by moving single-lever control to PRINT position. Then loosen lock bolt (part A of Fig. 18-10) with T-wrench. Turn single-lever control *slightly to left* to *increase* pressure, or slightly to *right to decrease* pressure. Tighten lock bolt, and return lever to OFF position. Recheck width of bead.

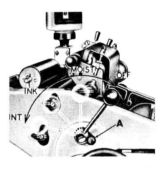

Fig. 18-10. Master-to-blanket pressure adjustment, Multilith 1250.

Fig. 18-11. Impression-cylinder adjusting sector, Multilith 1250.

Impression Adjustments

Two adjustments for impression may be performed: (1) an *overall* adjustment, when changing from one thickness of stock to another; and (2) a *leveling* adjustment, to give the same impression on the left and right side of the sheet.

Overall Adjustment. (Keyed to Fig. 18-11.) When changing to a heavier stock, first loosen clamp screw (C). Turn micrometer screw (A) several turns clockwise in order to draw the impression cylinder away from the blanket cylinder. Using the handwheel, run a sheet of the paper to be used between the blanket and impression cylinders. Turn micrometer screw counterclockwise (to increase pressure) by drawing the index finger over the top of the screw until it can no longer be turned in this manner. Then, with thumb and index finger, turn it another one-quarter turn. Tighten clamp screw.

When a change to a lighter stock is made, it is not necessary first to bring the impression cylinder away from the blanket cylinder. Otherwise, proceed as in the above paragraph.

If test sheets show need for further impression adjustment, loosen the clamp screw, and turn the micrometer screw *clockwise* to *decrease* pressure, or *counterclockwise* to *increase* pressure. Then tighten the clamp screw.

Leveling the Impression Cylinder. (Keyed to Fig. 18-12.) A leveling adjustment is indicated when the blanket image is complete, yet the printed image on the sheet is distinct only along one side or is heavier on one side than on the other.

To level the impression, remove register board side cover. Loosen lock screw (A), and move sector (B) *left* for *increasing* pressure, or *right* for *decreasing* pressure. Then tighten the lock screw. This adjustment affects only the *right* side of the sheet.

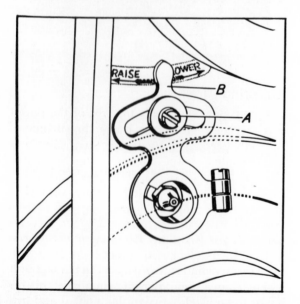

Fig. 18-12. Impression-cylinder leveling sector, Multilith 1250.

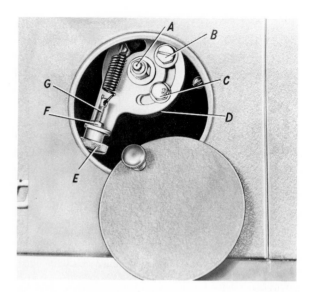

Fig. 18-13. Compensating impression device, Multilith 1250.

Compensating Impression Device

Instead of the impression-cylinder adjusting mechanism shown in Fig. 18-11, your Multilith may be equipped with a *compensating impression device* as in Fig. 18-13. This device permits the press to be operated either on *fixed impression* for any given weight of paper, or it may be set to operate on spring-controlled *compensating action*, which automatically adjusts the impression for varying thicknesses of paper (from job to job or from sheet to sheet). The following description of this device is keyed to Fig. 18-13.

1. *For Fixed (Constant) Pressure.* Revolve handwheel until compensating impression device is as shown in Fig. 18-13. Loosen A, B, and C. Turn knurled adjusting disc (D) *clockwise* to *increase* pressure, or *counterclockwise* to *decrease* pressure. Then tighten A, B, and C.
2. *For Compensating Action (Pressure).* Adjustments a and b, below, are necessary in this order:
    a. Entirely *remove* lock screw (C). Loosen Alemite fitting and screw (B). Then turn adjusting disc (D) *clockwise* to *increase* pressure, or *counterclockwise* to *decrease* pressure. Now tighten A and B.

b. To regulate the compensating pressure (after performing adjustment *a*, above), loosen locknut (F), and adjust knurled thumbscrew (E). Then tighten locknut (F). Normal setting is achieved when end of threaded screw (G) is even with surface of knurled nut (E).

In adjusting for printing sets composed of heavy and light sheets, make adjustments *a* and *b*, above, to obtain clearest impression on the *lightest* sheet. Correct impression automatically will be provided for the heavier sheets.

Feed Roller Adjustment

Lower feed roller pressure must be equal over all and parallel with the upper feed roller pressure.

Parallel Adjustment. Place two 1″ strips of 20-pound paper between the feed rollers as shown in Fig. 18-14. Then, turn handwheel until upper feed roller contacts lower feed roller. Pressure is right between rollers if moderate and equal resistance is offered when the paper strips are pulled. To adjust for parallel pressure, loosen lock screw (A) in Fig. 18-15, and lightly turn bearing (B) until equal tension is obtained. Turning the bearing *clockwise increases pressure* between left end of rollers; turning it *counterclockwise reduces left-end pressure.*

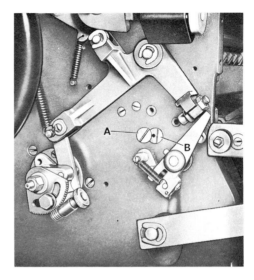

Fig. 18-15. **Leveling lower feed roller, Multilith 1250.**

Then tighten lock screw. The oil-hole in bearing should face left. It may be necessary to reduce the overall pressure in order to level the lower feed roller.

Overall Pressure Adjustment. Using test strips of paper, check overall pressure adjustment between feed rollers. To *increase* overall pressure between rollers, turn adjusting screw (A) in Fig. 18-14 *counterclockwise.* To *decrease overall pressure*, turn this screw *clockwise.* The screw is self-locking.

Adjusting Paper Fingers

For proper clearance, the tips of the paper fingers should be slightly below the surface of the plate (D in Fig. 18-14) when the feed rollers are in contact. If the fingers are too high, they will "nick" the lead edge of the sheet as it is fed through. If fingers are too low, they will fail to stop and hold the sheet until the feed rollers close. The ends of the paper fingers may be seen when feed rollers are apart.

To adjust the paper finger shaft, loosen locknut (B in Fig. 18-14). Turn screw (C) with a screwdriver — *clockwise* to *lower* the fingers or *counterclockwise* to *raise* them. Tighten locknut (B) after making adjustment.

Fig. 18-14. **Paper fingers — feed roller adjustments.**

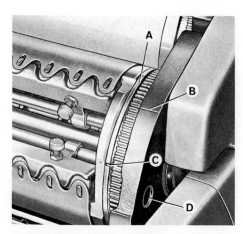

Fig. 18-16. Cam for grippers, Multilith 1250.

Gripper Cam

The cam (A in Fig. 18-16) actuates the elevating frame for the upper feed roller and controls the timing of sheets with the grippers on the impression cylinder to obtain register of sheets. The cam is factory-adjusted for paper of average weight.

Checking Adjustment of Cam

First, be sure that the feed roller pressure is correct for the stock being run. Place a sheet of the correct size paper on the conveyor tapes inserting it between the feed rollers and squarely in contact with the paper stop fingers of the du-

18-17. Grippers and paper stops, Multilith 1250.

plicating head. Turn the handwheel *counterclockwise* until the grippers (B in Fig. 18-17) begin to open. To determine the adjustment of the cam, refer to conditions outlined in the following instructions:

Condition "A", Normal. Cam is correctly adjusted when the lead edge of the sheet is under the grippers (B in Fig. 18-17) and firmly against the stop plates (A).

Condition "B", Retarded Cam. The cam is retarded too far if the lead edge of the sheet is under the grippers (B in Fig. 18-17) but not in contact with the stop plates (A). This condition will cause inaccurate register of sheets. In extreme cases, paper will fail to enter the grippers and will flutter out of the machine.

Remedy is to advance the cam (A in Fig. 18-16) slightly by moving it toward the open part of the cylinder (counterclockwise).

Condition "C", Advanced Cam. The cam is advanced too far if the lead edge of the sheet is under the grippers (B in Fig. 18-17) but extends over the top of stop plates (A), or if the sheet is actually jumping over the grippers. The former condition will generally cause nicking of lead edge of sheets; the latter condition will result in sheets fluttering out of the machine.

Remedy is to retard the cam (A in Fig. 18-16) slightly by moving it away from the open part of the cylinder (clockwise).

Adjusting the Cam

The cam band is locked in position on the blanket cylinder by three lock screws equally spaced around the end of the cylinder. In adjusting the cam, do not move the cylinder after the screws have been loosened, or the cam may be thrown completely out of adjustment.

To adjust the cam, proceed as follows:

1. Turn handwheel until trailing clamps of blanket and master cylinder are approximately 1″ apart.
2. Loosen the two lock screws which are accessible through the two holes in the side plates (D in Fig. 18-16).
3. Turn handwheel counterclockwise until open part of blanket cylinder is approximately in line with the reference mark (B in Fig. 18-16) on the side plate.

4. At this point, loosen the third lock screw near the lead clamp of the blanket cylinder.

5. Move the cam band in the desired direction by inserting a screwdriver into the slot (C in Fig. 18-16) in the band.

Caution: Only a slight, almost imperceptible movement of the cam is required to change the point at which the paper enters the grippers.

If the cam is inadvertently advanced or retarded too far, the original factory setting may be approximated by turning the cam band until the center of the slot (C in Fig. 18-16) is in line with the punch mark on the rim of the gear.

Whenever adjusting the cam, tighten *all three cam band lock screws* before attempting to check adjustment or operate the duplicator. In tightening the lock screws, tighten the screw nearest the lead clamp, then turn the cylinder to line up the other two screws with the holes in the side plates. Now, tighten these screws.

Cleaner Sheets

When cleaner sheets are to be used for cleaning ink rollers on Multilith presses equipped with single-lever control, first remove the Repelex (dampener) form roller to prevent it from picking up ink.

Heidelberg Model KOR

The Model KOR Heidelberg is a single-color, sheet-fed rotary press equipped for both letterset and offset (Fig. 18-18).[2] Removable segments on the plate cylinder can be interchanged for either process. For letterset, only the inking-roller system is used — the dampening system is not used. For offset, naturally, both the inking and dampening systems are used.

[2]Model KOR illustrations are by permission of Heidelberg Eastern, Inc.

Fig. 18-18. Heidelberg offset or letterset press, Model KOR.

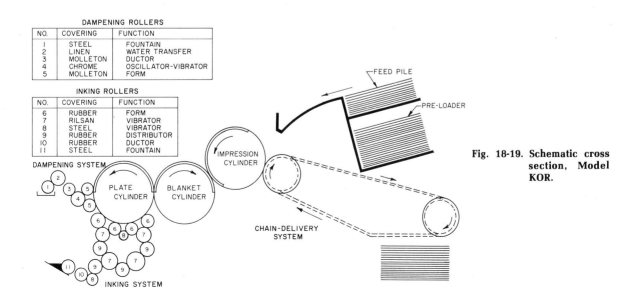

DAMPENING ROLLERS		
NO.	COVERING	FUNCTION
1	STEEL	FOUNTAIN
2	LINEN	WATER TRANSFER
3	MOLLETON	DUCTOR
4	CHROME	OSCILLATOR-VIBRATOR
5	MOLLETON	FORM

INKING ROLLERS		
NO.	COVERING	FUNCTION
6	RUBBER	FORM
7	RILSAN	VIBRATOR
8	STEEL	VIBRATOR
9	RUBBER	DISTRIBUTOR
10	RUBBER	DUCTOR
11	STEEL	FOUNTAIN

Fig. 18-19. Schematic cross section, Model KOR.

Fig. 18-20. Interchanging the plate shell for dry offset, Model KOR.

Fig. 18-21. Single-lever operating control for RUN, PAPER, or IMPRESSION, Model KOR.

Fig. 18-22. Micrometer control of rollers from operator's side of press, Model KOR.

Nomenclature. Figure 18-19 shows the partial nomenclature and arrangement of some of the components of the Model KOR. Notice the almost horizontal arrangement of cylinders, the feeding and delivery of sheets from the same end, and the fact that no tapes or friction devices are used in the paper-feeding mechanism.

Specifications

Sheet size $15^{3}/_{4}'' \times 22^{1}/_{2}''$ to $4^{15}/_{16}'' \times 5^{7}/_{8}''$
Image area $15^{3}/_{8}'' \times 22^{1}/_{8}''$
Minimum gripper margin $^{25}/_{64}''$

Settings for Letterset

For printing by letterset, the offset plate shell is removed from the plate cylinder and is replaced with the letterset plate shell, Fig. 18-20. Only the inking system is used. It is also recommended that a *wrap-around* letterpress plate be used.

ATF Chief 20A

The American Type Founders Chief 20A offset press is a single-color, sheet-fed, four-main

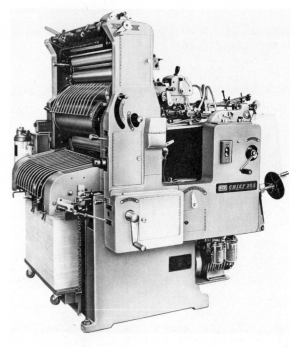

Fig. 18-23. ATF Chief 20A.

cylinder offset press with conventional inking and dampening systems.[3] It is equipped with vacuum feeder, chain delivery, and receding stacker. See Figs. 18-23 through 18-25.

Specifications

The range for the printing sheet size is from 8″ × 10″ minimum to 14″ × 20″ maximum. Maximum printing area is 13½″ × 19½″, with a gripper bite of ³/₁₆″ to ⁵/₁₆″.

The blanket cylinder is undercut .071″. The undercut of the plate cylinder is .012″.

Whitin-Manufactured Offset Duplicators — Ditto 2I5; ATF Chief I5; Itek II.I5

Instructions and illustrations in this section apply equally to the Whitin-manufactured off-

[3]ATF Chief 20A illustrations are by permission of American Type Founders Co., Inc.

set duplicators marketed as ATF Chief 15, Ditto 215, and Itek 11.15.[4]

[4]Distributors of these duplicators are, respectively, American Type Founders Co., Inc.; Ditto, Inc.; and Itek Business Products. Illustrations are by courtesy of Ditto, Inc.

Fig. 18-25. View of feeder components, ATF Chief 20A.

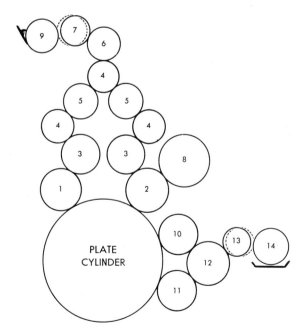

Fig. 18-24. Inking and dampening rollers, ATF Chief 20A.
Inking Rollers: 1 and 2 are form rollers; 3 and 5 vibrator rollers; 4 distributor rollers; 6 rider roller; 7 ductor roller; 8 auxiliary vibrator roller; 9 fountain roller.
Dampening Rollers: 10 and 11 are form rollers; 12 vibrator roller; 13 ductor roller; 14 fountain roller.

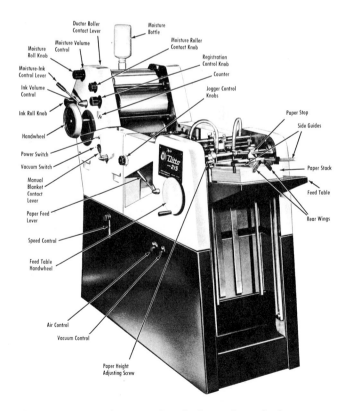

Fig. 18-26. Nomenclature and controls — from feeder end.

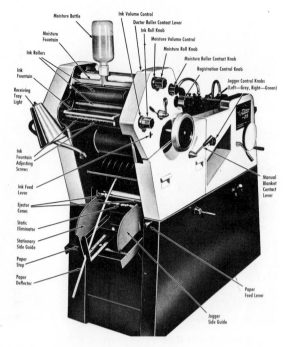

Fig. 18-27. **Nomenclature and controls — from receiver end.**

Description

Figures 18-26 through 18-28 show the nomenclature and location of the operating controls. The duplicators have a gripper margin adjustable from $3/16''$ to $5/16''$, an image area of $9\ 3/4'' \times 13\ 1/4''$, and will accommodate paper stock from $3'' \times 5''$ to $11'' \times 15''$.

The duplicators employ conventional (separate) inking and dampening systems, Fig. 18-29. Also, they have a single-lever moisture-ink control, Fig. 18-30.

Feeder Table Components

Figures 18-31 through 18-36 show the feeder table components set up for a run.

To adjust the double-sheet detector, start up both motors. While feeding the sheets, loosen the locknut, and turn the sheet detector thumbscrew *counterclockwise*, until single sheets are ejected. Then turn clockwise slightly, until the ejector does not trip on a single sheet. Tighten the lock nut.

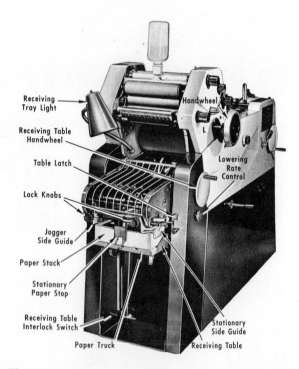

Fig. 18-28. **Duplicator equipped with chain delivery and receding stacker.**

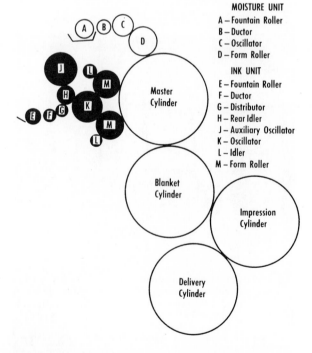

MOISTURE UNIT
A – Fountain Roller
B – Ductor
C – Oscillator
D – Form Roller

INK UNIT
E – Fountain Roller
F – Ductor
G – Distributor
H – Rear Idler
J – Auxiliary Oscillator
K – Oscillator
L – Idler
M – Form Roller

Master Cylinder

Blanket Cylinder

Impression Cylinder

Delivery Cylinder

Fig. 18-29. **Schematic of roller and cylinder arrangement.**

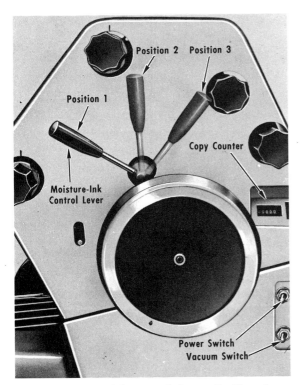

Fig. 18-30. Moisture-ink control lever. Position 1 — dampener form roller and ink form rollers OFF; Position 2 — dampener form roller ON, and ink form rollers OFF. Position 3 — dampener form roller and ink form rollers ON.

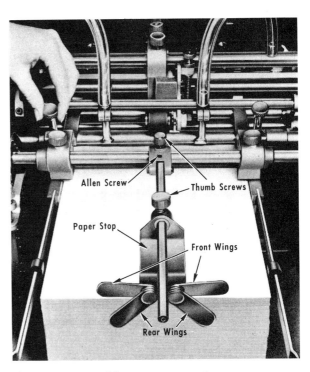

Fig. 18-32. Paper table setup components.

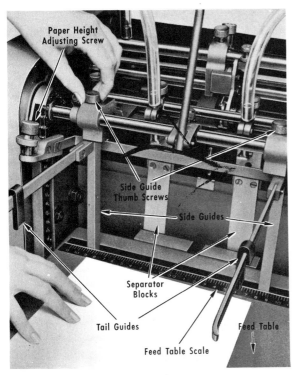

Fig. 18-31. Feed table components.

Fig. 18-33. Sheet suction and blast components.

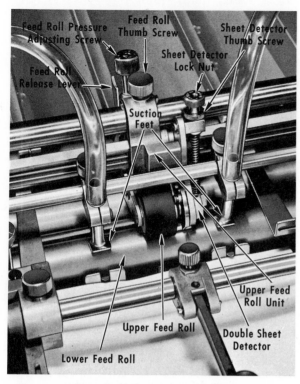

Fig. 18-34. Sheet detector and feed roll components.

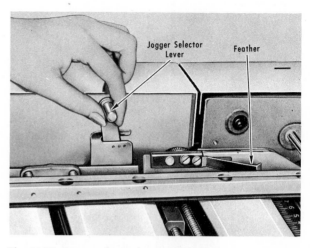

Fig. 18-36. Jogger-selector lever and feather.

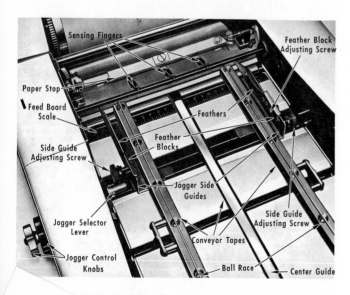

Fig. 18-35. Feed board setup.

Feed Board

The feed board may be set to jog left, right, or both left and right, since the duplicator is equipped with two joggers. See Fig. 18-35. Both joggers are set into motion while the press is running.

To set the left-hand jogger into motion, hold the right jogger with your left hand, and pull it toward you. At the same time, with your right hand, move the jogger-selector lever back toward the feeder, Fig. 18-36.

To set the right-hand jogger into motion, hold the left jogger with your left hand and push it away from you as you move the jogger-selector lever into its forward position, toward the delivery end of the press.

To set both joggers into action (for running small sheets), move the jogger-selector lever into its center position. For accurate side register, the feather on the idle jogger should be lowered (by pressing on its front part), and the feather on the jogger being used should be raised (by pressing on its back part). Refer again to Fig. 18-36.

The jogger control knobs, (Fig. 18-35), move the paper joggers, ball races, and tapes, all at the same time, towards or away from the center of the feed board. These knobs should be turned only when the duplicator is operating, except for initial jogger positioning.

A.B. Dick Company

Fig. 18-37. A.B. Dick Model 310 offset duplicator.

A. B. Dick and Related Presses

The A. B. Dick Model 310 is a table-model off-set duplicator with friction feeder. Like all A. B. Dick offset duplicators, it has combined ink and dampener units. See Figs. 18-37 and 18-38.

The Models 350 and 360 are floor models with suction feeders and more rollers. See Figs.

A.B. Dick Company

Fig. 18-39. A.B. Dick Model 350 offset duplicator with chain delivery and receding stacker.

A.B. Dick Company

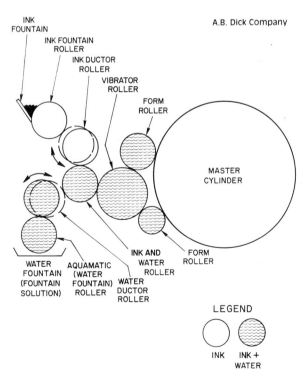

Fig. 18-38. A.B. Dick Model 310 arrangement of ink-water (Aquamatic) system and cylinders.

A.B. Dick Company

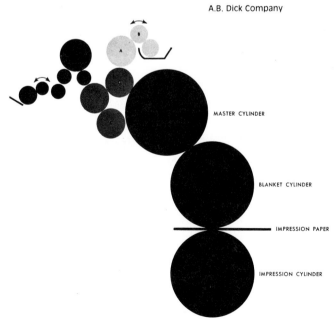

Fig. 18-40. A.B. Dick Model 350 arrangement of ink-water (Aquamatic) system and cylinders.

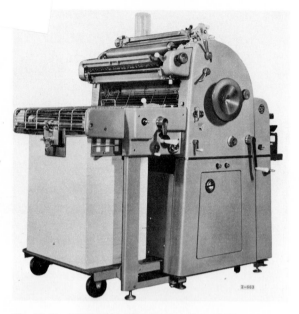

Fig. 18-41. MGD Offset Duplicators 20 and 22.

Fig. 18-43. Davidson Dualith 400.

18-39 and 18-40. These duplicators are more compact than many competing models because of the elimination of the long conveyor board.

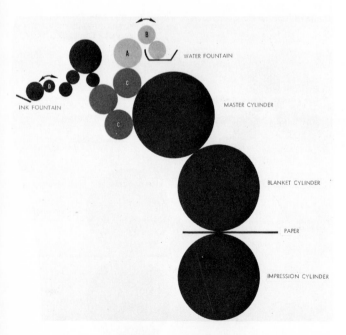

Fig. 18-42. MGD Offset Duplicators 20 and 22 diagram of cylinders and rollers. (A) water oscillating roller; (B) water fountain ductor roller; (C) form rollers; and (D) ink ductor roller.

Sheets are transferred directly from the feeder pile to the feed rolls.

The MGD Models 20 and 22 are quite similar in construction and operation to the larger A. B. Dick duplicators, except that they are much wider. In addition, the sheet size is enlarged to 14″ × 20″ or 17½″ × 22½″. See Figs. 18-41 and 18-42.

Davidson Dualiths

The Davidson press, Fig. 18-43, features the two-cylinder principle explained earlier. If the impression segment of the main cylinder is replaced with a lithographic plate (wrong reading for printing directly against the paper), both sides of the sheet can be printed in one pass. The press can also be equipped for printing from rubber relief plates and for embossing.

Selected Other Models

Various other models of duplicators and presses are shown in Figs. 18-44 through 18-51.

Flat-Bed Offset Presses

The flat-bed offset press, Fig. 18-50, is used as both plate-proofing press and printing press.

AM International, Inc.

Fig. 18-44. Multlith 2575. In one pass through the machine, a sheet is printed on both sides in the same color or different colors, or one side may be printed in two colors.

Roberts & Porter, Inc.

Fig. 18-45. Harris 25$\frac{1}{4}$" × 37$\frac{1}{2}$" single-color offset press.

MGD Graphic Systems, Rockwell International

Fig. 18-46. Miehle 38 two-color common-impression-cylinder offset press.

MGD Graphic Systems, Rockwell International

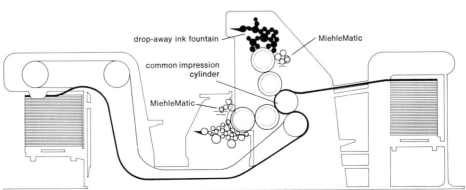

Fig. 18-47. Schematic of rollers, cylinders, and sheet flow for Miehle 38 two-color common-impression-cylinder offset press.

Roberts & Porter, Inc.

Fig. 18-48. Heidelberg GTO $12^{5}/_{8}" \times 18"$, single-color offset press.

Fig. 18-49. Harris $28^{3}/_{8}" \times 41"$ four-color sheet-fed offset press.

Vandercook, Division of Illinois Tool Works, Inc.

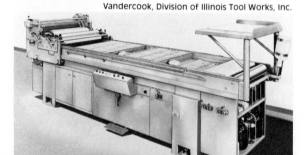

An adjustable-height impression-stock bed makes this type of press suitable for printing on paper, paper board, calendar backs, covers of bound booklets, metal, glass, wood, etc. This press is available in either hand-powered or motor-driven models. Both types are hand fed.

The stationary bed of the press contains on one end the stationary dampening system and at the other end the stationary inking system. In between are the flat plate bed and the flat impression table, or stock bed, Fig. 18-51.

The traveling carriage carries the blanket cylinder and the plate dampening and inking

Fig. 18-50. Vandercook 20-26 flat-bed offset press, used for pulling reproduction proofs and for printing on materials up to $1/_4"$ thick.

Vandercook, Division of Illinois Tool Works, Inc.

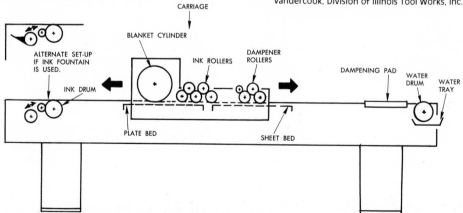

Fig. 18-51. Schematic of Vandercook 20-26 flat-bed offset press.

Goss Division, MGD Graphic Systems, Rockwell International

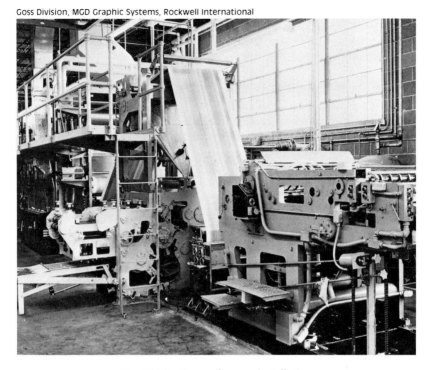

Fig. 18-52. Goss web press installation.

form rollers. In its reciprocating flat stroke, the carriage replenishes its dampening and inking form rollers, dampens and inks the flat plate, picks up the plate image on its blanket cylinder, and offsets the blanket image onto the flat sheet of stock.

Web Offset Press

A web offset press feeds paper from a roll (or rolls) in a continuous sheet, called a *web,* through each of its printing and auxiliary units. It delivers its printed product as cut sheets, folded signatures, or rewound on a roll, depending on the design of the individual press. See Fig. 18-52.

Web Press Schematic

Figure 18-53 illustrates, in schematic form, a web press with four blanket-to-blanket printing units. This press will print four colors on each

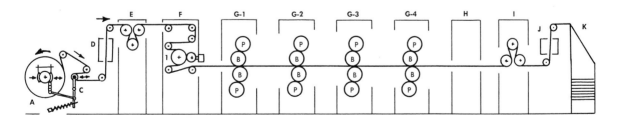

Fig. 18-53. Schematic of a four-unit blanket-to-blanket web press, one of many web press designs. (A) Paper roll on a roll stand (feeding from end or "in-line"); (C) core brake tension system; (D) web cleaning and preheating device; (E) chill rolls; (F) infeed drive: (G-1, G-2, G-3, G-4) blanket-to-blanket printing units; (H) dryer; (I) chill rolls; (J) remoisturizer; (K) delivery; (P) plate cylinder; (B) blanket cylinder.

side of the web. A press which prints both sides of a sheet or web — either in the same or separate units in one pass through the press — is called a *perfector press.*

The infeed roll stand, A in Fig. 18-53, is carrying one roll of paper which is maintained at infeed web tension by a floating roller tension system (C) acting on the paper roll core brake. Another roll stand, feeding at 90°, is shown in Fig. 18-54.

At D in Fig. 18-53, dirt, dust, and lint are removed by gas flame or vacuum. Controlled heat stabilizes the moisture content of the paper for precise registration.

Chill rolls, at E, restore the web to proper printing temperature.

At the infeed drive, F, the driven steel roller F-1, acting against its rubber-covered idler roller, maintains the desired tension in the web and meters the paper into the printing units.

Printing units G-1 through G-4 illustrate blanket-to-blanket printing of four successive colors on each side of the web.

After passing through dryer H in Fig. 18-53, the heated web (with its still semi-fluid ink) passes through chill rolls, I, to cool the web and set the ink.

At J, the remoisturizing unit replaces the moisture which was removed in the prior heating step. Proper moisture content, at this step, helps eliminate static, maintains cut-off length, and prevents cracking in folding.

Fig. 18-55. Operating controls for Baker Perkins web offset press.

The delivery end of the web press, at K, may contain a perforator, former, folder, cut-off, delivery system, and so on, depending on its equipment.

Because the paper is pulled through the press in a continuous web, the web press uses no transfer or cylinder grippers as do the sheet presses. This absence of sheet grippers permits narrower cylinder gaps (as small as $^3/_8$″) and faster speeds.

The circumference of the plate cylinder determines the *length* of the printed page, and is referred to as the *cut-off.* On most web presses, this is a fixed dimension.

The high operating speeds of web presses have made popular the use of automated press controls. Most operating controls for on, off, speed, temperatures, register, water, ink, and so on are commonly controlled from a remote master console panel. See Fig. 18-55.

Unitized Construction

Almost exclusively, web presses are of unitized construction. That is, the presses are com-

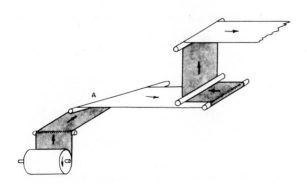

Fig. 18-54. Use of 90° angle bar (at A) allows roll stand to be positioned on side of press.

posed of units selected to achieve the type work to be done on that press. Thus, a given press may be ordered, designed, and built to feed from one or more rolls simultaneously; to have up to eight, or more, printing units; to print on one or both sides of each web in one to six, or more, colors; to include units which perforate, punch, slit, imprint, fold, cut, glue, and varnish; and to deliver as sheets, signatures, or rewound on rolls. The possible variations in design are innumerable.

Current listings show web presses in a wide range of sizes — from the smaller webs which accept a minimum web width of 5″ and have a sheet cut-off of 8½″, all the way up to the huge presses of 76″ roll width and 55″ cut-off.

Printing Unit Designs

Several common arrangements of plate, blanket, and impression cylinders in the printing units of web presses are the open-unit design, the blanket-to-blanket perfecting design, and the common-impression-drum design.

Open-Unit Design, or Unit Design

Each printing unit of the open-unit design has its own plate, blanket, and impression cylinder. Thus, each unit will print one color on one side of the web.

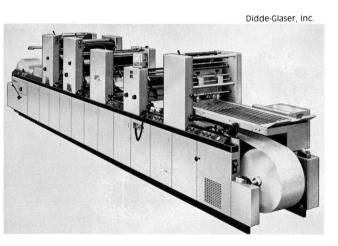

Didde-Glaser, Inc.

Fig. 18-56. Didde-Glaser Model D-G 175 (17½″) web offset press equipped with two printing units, numbering and perforating units, and delivery as either folded sheets or rewound on reel.

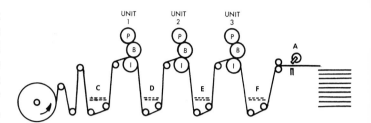

Fig. 18-57. Schematic of a three-color open-unit design web offset press. The platforms at C, D, E, and F allow the press operators walk-through access to units. Note sheet cut-off cylinder at A.

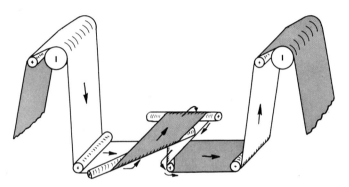

Fig. 18-58. Diagram showing how the turning bars turn the web over between printing units of a web press.

Figure 18-57 illustrates an open-unit web press with three units, each unit capable of printing one color on one side of the web. Between units, the web is brought down and under the platforms C, D, E, and F, which are provided to allow press operators to walk between the units and service them.

In this design of press, it is common to provide angled turning bars between units to turn the web over 180° so that succeeding units of the press may print on the other side of the web, Figs. 18-58 and 18-59. For instance, if angled turning bars are used on this press between units 2 and 3 (Fig. 18-57), units 1 and 2 will print two colors on the top side of the web. The web will then be turned over 180° by the turning bars, and unit 3 will print one color on the other side of the web.

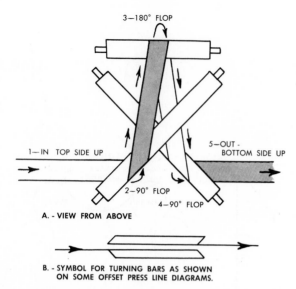

A. - VIEW FROM ABOVE

B. - SYMBOL FOR TURNING BARS AS SHOWN ON SOME OFFSET PRESS LINE DIAGRAMS.

Fig. 18-59. Schematic of 180° angled turning bars showing how the web is flopped 180° between the press printing units.

Blanket-to-Blanket Design

The blanket-to-blanket perfecting web press prints an impression on each side of the web. Each blanket cylinder acts as the impression cylinder for its opposing blanket cylinder, Figs. 18-60 and 18-61.

In Fig. 18-53, the four-unit blanket-to-blanket web press will print four colors on each side of the web.

Common-Impression Drum Design

The common-impression drum web-press printing unit uses one large impression cylinder to furnish impression for all the blanket cylinders surrounding it. In Fig. 18-62, the web, in passing around the impression cylinder, re-

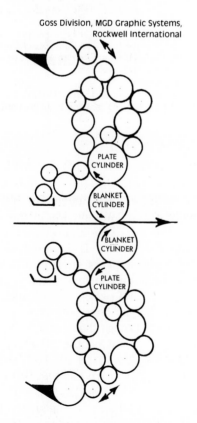

Goss Division, MGD Graphic Systems, Rockwell International

Fig. 18-60. Schematic cross section of one unit of the Goss commercial 38 blanket-to-blanket perfection web offset press.

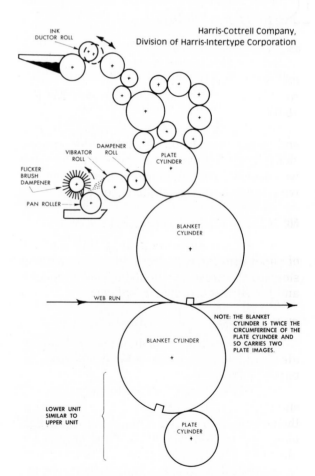

Harris-Cottrell Company, Division of Harris-Intertype Corporation

NOTE: THE BLANKET CYLINDER IS TWICE THE CIRCUMFERENCE OF THE PLATE CYLINDER AND SO CARRIES TWO PLATE IMAGES.

LOWER UNIT SIMILAR TO UPPER UNIT

Fig. 18-61. Schematic roller and cylinder diagram of one unit of a Harris-Cottrell Model 1000 web-offset blanket-to-blanket perfector press with flicker brush dampening system.

Fig. 18-62. Schematic of Baker Perkins common-impression drum web offset press. This press has twin satellites, each with four plate-and-blanket printing couples, thus printing four colors on each side of the web in one pass.

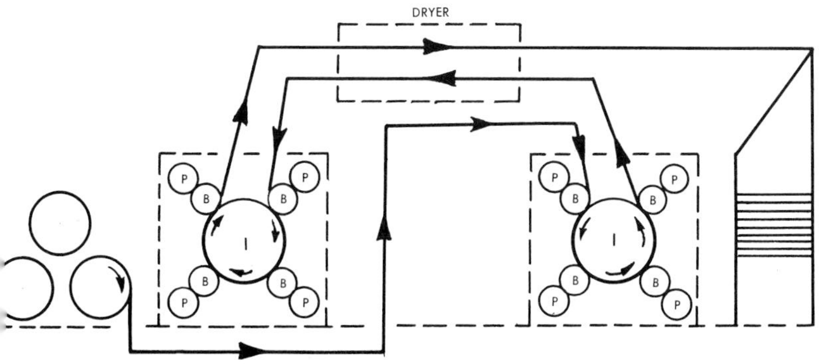

ceives four separate images (usually four separate colors) on the one side of the web. See Fig. 18-63.

After drying, the web passes around the second impression drum, receiving four impressions on the other side of the web. Thus, the web is printed in four colors on each side of the web in one pass through the press.

Nonstop Web Roll Replenishment

Two devices for introducing a full, new roll of paper into the web press feed cycle without stopping the press are the flying paster (splicer) and the zero-speed paster (splicer).

Flying Splicer

The flying splicer, or paster, Fig. 18-64, operates at full press speed without stopping the paper rolls.

As the feeding roll 1 nears depletion, the roll stand is rotated to bring spare roll 2 close to the running web and up to the speed of the running web, as shown. Double-sided tape is applied to the leading end of roll 2. Then, instantly, spare roll 2 is moved into contact with the running web, the taped leading edge of spare roll 2 is pressed against and adheres to the running web, the web from roll 1 is cut off, and roll

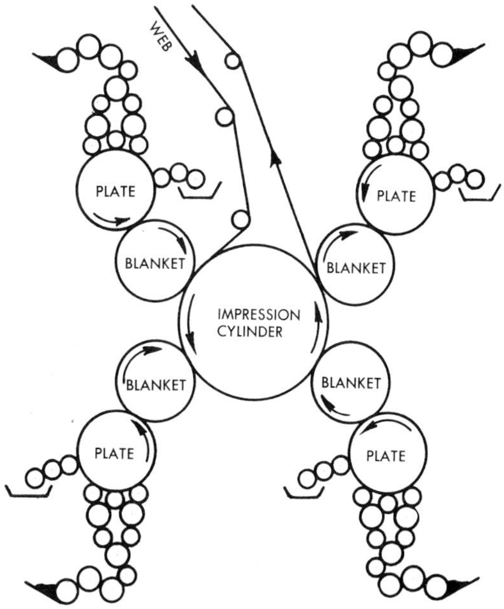

Fig. 18-63. Schematic of one satellite of the Baker Perkins twin satellite common-impression drum offset web press. Note the one large impression cylinder for the blanket cylinder of each of the four separate printing couples. This satellite can print four colors on one side of a web.

1 is brought to a stop. Roll 2 is now feeding the press.

Zero-Speed Splicer

With the zero-speed splicer (paster), a fresh, new roll is brought to feed as follows: As the roll in use approaches depletion, the paster-mechanism rolls draw out considerable slack

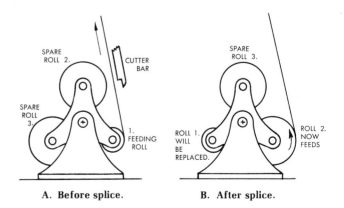

A. Before splice.   B. After splice.

Fig. 18-64. How the flying splicer works.

Fig. 18-65. Double-roll stand infeed.

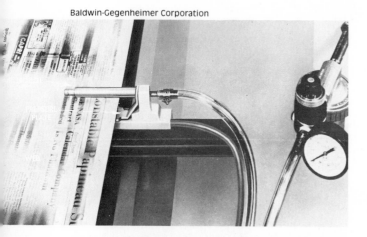

Fig. 18-66. Air-stream type web-break indicator. Action: air nozzle directs air stream at moving web; when web breaks, air stream strikes pressure plate, activating micro switch to automatically stop the press.

in the running web. The end of the fresh roll is taped, and then the splice is made to the spare roll while both rolls are stopped. The paper is severed from the old roll, and the new roll is brought up to press speed. All this occurs before the slack in the splicer-mechanism rolls is absorbed, and without stopping the press.

Web-Break Detector

Web presses are fitted with web-break detectors which activate controls to automatical-

ly stop the press in case the paper web should break during operation. See Fig. 18-66. Web-break detectors may be of the riding shoe, riding roller, or air-stream type. Each is activated by the absence or break in the continuity of the web.

Should the paper web break during operation, the web-break detector activates (energizes) the stop circuit of the press controls, bringing the press to a normal "red button" stop. At the same instant, the detector energizes a device that severs the web just ahead of the printing unit, propelling the oncoming paper out of the printing unit, and thereby preventing any free paper from lashing back and wrapping around the cylinders. All of this action takes place in a fraction of a second.

Printing Unit Adjustments to Image

Figure 18-67 illustrates a number of adjustments which may be made to a typical web-press printing unit in order to place images correctly on the face of the web and achieve register in back-up and with images printed by other units on the press. The adjustments can be made while the press is stopped or from a remote control master console while the press is running.

By use of fixed or portable strobe lights, the press operator can check the print quality and the register on one or both sides of the web

Goss Division, MGD Graphic Systems, Rockwell International

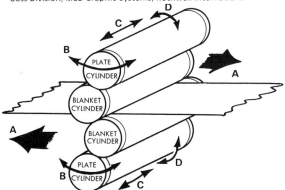

Fig. 18-67. Individual printing unit adjustments for register as used on Goss Commercial 38 web offset press.
  A. Forward or backward movement of entire printing unit to achieve register with other printing units.
  B. Angular (plate-cocking) adjustment of plate cylinder.
  C. Lateral (side-lay) adjustment of plate cylinder.
  D. Circumferential adjustment of plate cylinder.

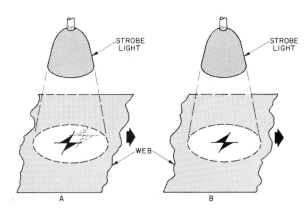

Fig. 18-68. Strobe light checks the image for register on the moving web.
  A. Second printing image is out of register.
  B. Both images are in register; they appear as one.

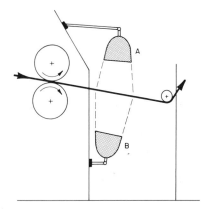

Fig. 18-69. Positions of strobe lights on web press. "A" indicates primary lamp for checking register on face of web; "B" indicates secondary lamp for show-through of back of printing (back-to-back register).

while the press is running. See Figs. 18-68 and 18-69.

The strobe light, actuated by the printing cylinder, flashes an intense beam of light once for every revolution of the printing cylinder, making the illuminated object area appear to be standing still. This synchronized flashing stops or freezes the motion of the web and allows the press operator to examine and adjust the register (or make other needed adjustments) as though the press were stopped.

Possible adjustments are:

1. *Unit-to-unit register.* The entire printing unit is moved forward or backward to achieve register on the web with images printed by other units (color-to-color register).

2. *Angular (plate-cocking or skewing) adjustment.* This adjustment of plate cylinder (on one end, only; other end is pivoted) is to cock its plate image.

3. *Lateral (side-lay) adjustment of plate cylinder.* The plate cylinders may each be moved longitudinally across the press.

4. *Circumferential register.* Each plate cylinder may be adjusted circumferentially to achieve back-to-back register with the opposite plate image. Refer again to Fig. 18-67.

Double-Ender Web Press

The double-ender web press feeds from a half-width roll of paper. The web is fed through one side of the press, then turned back, flopped, and run through the other side of the press units.

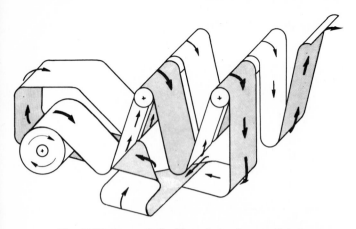

Fig. 18-70. Two-unit double-ender web press. Printing two colors on each side of the half-width web.

Goss Division, MGD Graphic Systems, Rockwell International

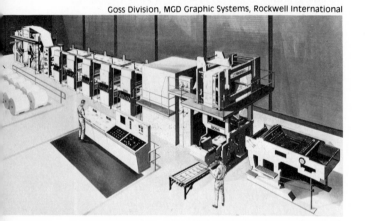

Fig. 18-71. Goss Commercial 38 web offset press.

Figure 18-70 shows a schematic drawing of a two-unit, double-ender press printing two colors on each side of the web in one complete pass through the press.

Conversion from Rotary Letterpress to Direct Lithography (Di-Litho[5])

Present rotary letterpress printing presses can be converted to print by direct lithography. In this direct-lithographic process, the printing is done from a lithographic printing plate which prints *directly onto* the paper. Figure 18-72 shows a typical rotary letterpress unit converted to direct lithography. Note that, in the conversion in View B, the plate cylinder now carries saddles, with the litho plates attached to the saddles; and the right-hand ink form roller has been replaced with a lithographic dampening system.

Note, also, that no offset blanket cylinder is used between the plate and impression cylinders. And, since the litho plate prints directly onto the paper, the litho plate image must be a wrong-reading image, Fig. 8-73.

[5]Di-Litho — a registered term of the American Newspaper Publishers Association.

Fig. 18-72. Converting from rotary letterpress to direct lithography.

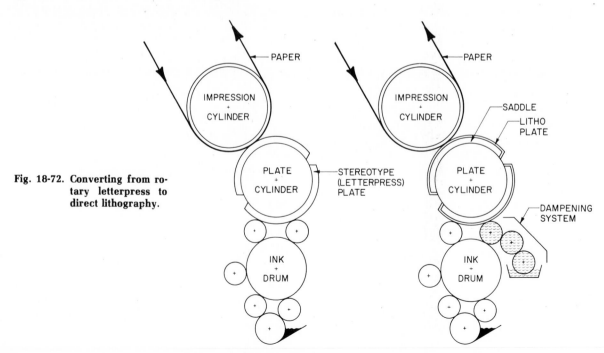

A. ROTARY LETTERPRESS PRINTING UNIT   B. CONVERSION TO DIRECT LITHOGRAPHY

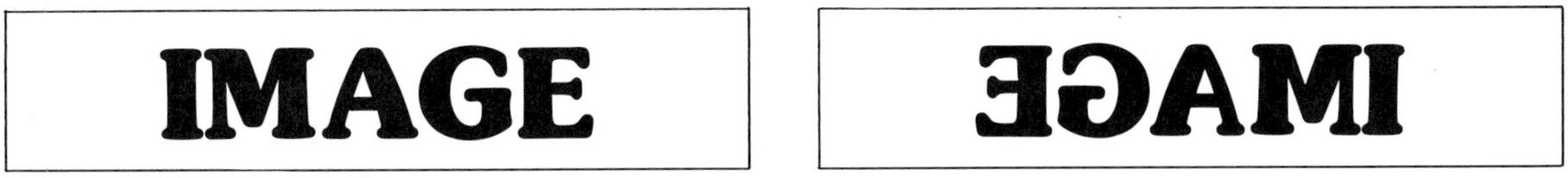

IMAGE

A. Right-reading image as on conventional offset plate.

IMAGE *(wrong-reading)*

B. Wrong-reading image as on Di-Litho plate.

Fig. 18-73. The Di-Litho plate has a wrong-reading image.

Questions

1. Describe the inking and dampening systems of both the 1250 Multilith and the ATF Chief 20A.
2. What advantage is there in having a press (such as with the Whitin-manufactured duplicator) capable of jogging left and jogging right, as desired?
3. Compare the ink-water feed systems on the A. B. Dick 350 and the MGD 20.
4. Tell why the flat-bed offset press can print on the following materials, but the rotary offset press cannot: glass, bound booklets, wood, heavy paper board.
5. In what other forms besides flat cut sheets does the web offset press deliver its printed product?
6. Name two methods of removing dust and lint from the traveling paper web.
7. Why is it desirable that the remoisturizing unit of the web press restore the proper moisture content to the web?
8. What are some types of equipment that a web press may contain at its delivery end?
9. Why is it that the web press uses no transfer grippers or cylinder sheet grippers?
10. On a web press, what determines the length (the cut-off) of the printed page?
11. Name three common arrangements of plate, blanket, and impression cylinders in the printing units of web presses.
12. Describe the operation (action) of a web-break detector.
13. Tell how the strobe light aids the press operator in achieving register on one or both sides of the web.
14. Why does the Di-Litho plate have a wrong-reading image?

Problems and Projects

1. With the cooperation of your instructor, plan one or more field trips to printing plants which are equipped with single- and multi-color offset presses not present in your shop.
2. Make a large wall diagram of the roller and cylinder arrangement of each of the sheet-fed presses in your shop. Identify each roller and cylinder by name.
3. Prepare a schedule of rotating assignments so that each student, for a proportionate share of class days, is chiefly responsible for performing the preparation, adjustments, and maintenance for each of the presses in the shop. (This student works along with and under supervision of the instructor.)
4. Arrange a bulletin board display of illustrations of sheet-fed rotary and flat-bed offset presses. Use pictures obtained from trade magazines and advertising literature.
5. Arrange a bulletin board display of printed samples of work done on single- and multi-color sheet-fed offset presses.
6. With the cooperation of your instructor, plan a field trip to a plant equipped with one or more web presses. If possible, obtain and study beforehand descriptive literature regarding the presses to be observed.
7. Using advertising literature and magazine and textbooks sources, prepare a bulletin board display of schematic diagrams of web presses showing arrangements of rollers and cylinders and the sheet-flow of each.

New Terms

chill rolls
compensating action
console
eccentric shaft
feather
form roller
handwheel

idler rollers
infeed drive
knurled nut
perfector press
propelling
remoisturizing
roll converter

set screw
skewing adjustment
splicer
synchronized
underlay
unitized
vacuum feeder

Chapter 19

Offset Presswork Troubleshooting

Preventing problems is a far better approach to presswork than trying to correct them. To prevent trouble, the press operator should study the manufacturer's instruction manual as well as the press until thoroughly familiar with the press parts, their functions, and their lubrication.

Initially, the press should be properly installed and then maintained in good operating condition. If proper attention is given to preparing the offset plates, preparing and balancing the ink and water fountains, and preparing and maintaining the press, the troubles described may never appear.

Use the following series of illustrations[1] as a handy guide to the quick identification and elimination of many common troubles which may occur during the press run. Additional information on these and other common troubles and their probable causes and remedies are listed in tabular form on the following pages.

[1] 3M Company photos by courtesy of Minnesota Mining and Manufacturing Company.

Fig. 19-1. Image okay! Good copy has crisp, dark lines and solids; a clean background; clear halftones, screens, and reverses; good registration; and each sheet dries completely.

Fig. 19-2. Gray, washed out? Causes: too much moisture; not enough ink; incorrect ink- or dampener-form-roller pressure, or both; incorrect plate-to-blanket pressure; or incorrect impression-to-blanket pressure.

Fig. 19-3. Scumming (dirty background)? Causes: too much ink, not enough moisture, dirty dampener roll covers, or dampener covers tied too tightly on ends.

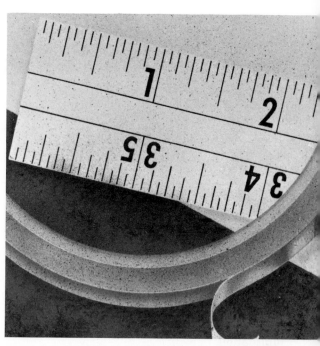

Fig. 19-5. Too dark (halftones and fine reverses fill in and sheet dries slowly)? Causes: too much ink or too much impression-to-blanket pressure.

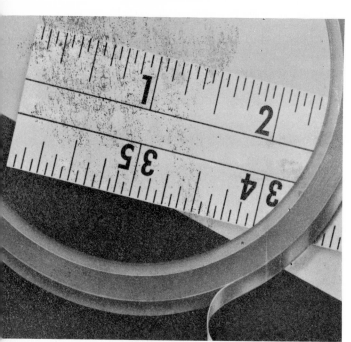

Fig. 19-4. Both scumming (dirty background) and gray, washed-out copy? Causes: glazed ink rollers, glazed blanket, too much ink-form-roller pressure, or too much dampener-form-roller pressure.

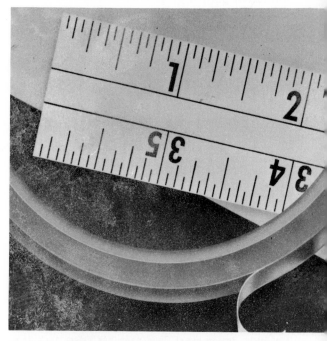

Fig. 19-6. Weak spots? Causes: incorrect plate-to-blanket pressure; incorrect impression-to-blanket pressure; low spot in blanket; "blind" image caused by dried gum, strong fountain solution, or glazed blanket.

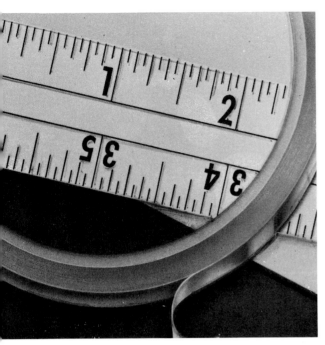

Fig. 19-7.   Blurred copy (double image)? Causes: too much ink, loose blanket, torn plate anchor, not enough plate-to-blanket pressure, incorrect impression-to-blanket pressure.

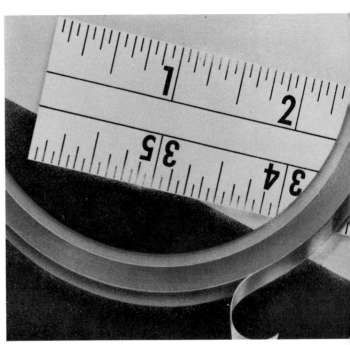

Fig. 19-9.   Image breaks down while plate is running? Causes: too much form-roller pressure (ink or dampener), too much plate-to-blanket pressure, fountain solution too strong, or end play.

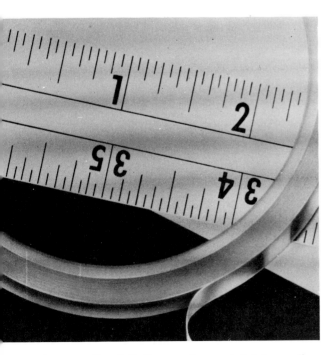

Fig. 19-8.   Streaks? Causes: incorrect ink-form-roller pressure, incorrect dampener-form-roller pressure, incorrect plate-to-blanket pressure, incorrect impression-to-blanket pressure, improper ink, or loose blanket.

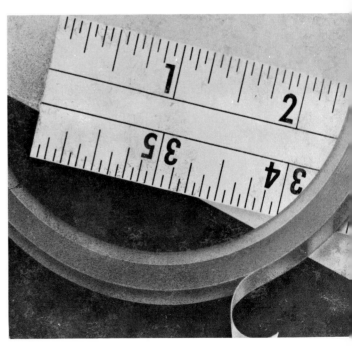

Fig. 19-10.   Uneven printing? Causes: incorrect ink distribution; or incorrect parallel pressure (heavy on one end and light on the other) on dampener form rollers, ink form rollers, plate-to-blanket, or impression-to-blanket.

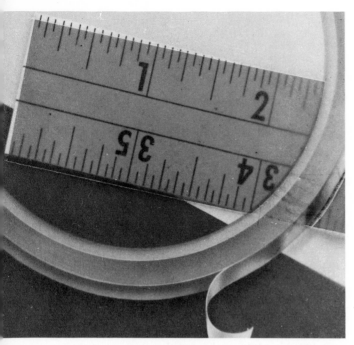

Fig. 19-11. Out of register? Causes: loose feeder side guide, loose plate, incorrect feed-roll pressure.

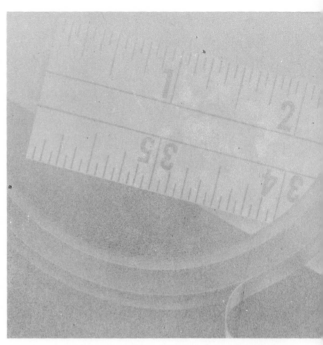

Fig. 19-12. What, no image at all? Causes: not enough ink-form-roller pressure, not enough plate-to-blanket pressure, not enough impression-to-blanket pressure, too much moisture, glazed blanket, or glazed ink rollers.

Scumming

Scumming is evidenced by the plate picking up ink in the clear areas and transferring this ink to the clear areas of the sheet.

Probable Cause	Remedy
1. Clear areas of plate not etched properly and therefore cannot repel the ink.	1. Re-etch the plate, or make a new plate.
2. Too little fountain solution.	2. Increase flow of fountain solution.
3. Dampener form rollers not parallel, or set too far from plate cylinder.	3. Set according to instruction manual. Make new plate if damaged, or re-etch the plate.
4. Dirty dampener rollers.	4. Clean or replace the dampener rollers. Check the pH of fountain solution. Feed less ink. Replace ink, if emulsified.
5. Unevenly applied molleton cover on dampener roller.	5. Even out; re-cover if necessary.
6. Dampener roller not parallel with the plate.	6. Re-set according to instruction book. Make new plate, if damaged.
7. Dampener roller dragging or bouncing on plate.	7. Re-set according to instruction book. Make new plate, if damaged.
8. Fountain solution too strong or too weak.	8. Maintain at recommended pH.

9. Plate and blanket cylinders not properly packed.
10. Flattened form rollers.
11. Plate not perfectly concentric with cylinder.

12. Skidding form roller.

13. Too much ink during makeready.
14. Loose blanket.
15. Oxidation on plate.
16. Overdeveloped plate.
17. Residual coating solution on plate.

9. Set according to instruction manual.

10. Replace rollers.
11. Take up slack. Make new plate if the image is damaged.
12. Maintain proper contact between the rollers and their riders.
13. Cut down on ink, and re-etch the plate.
14. Take up the slack.
15. Re-etch, or make a new plate.
16. Make new plate.
17. Make new plate.

Tinting

Tinting appears as a uniform, light-colored tint over the entire sheet of paper.

Probable Cause	Remedy
1. Poor (weak) varnish in ink.	1. Replace with better ink.
2. Breakdown of pigment particles in the ink.	2. Ink may be at fault. Notify the ink manufacturer. May need reformulated ink.
3. Fountain solution.	3. Check pH. Check mixing procedure used. Replace with a different fountain solution.
4. Paper coating particles getting into fountain solution.	4. Replace the fountain solution.
5. Acid getting into ink from an improperly washed-out plate.	5. Wash up press. Replace ink. Re-process the plate.

Filling Up

Filling up is evidenced on the printed sheet and plate by the type matter and halftones filling in with ink.

Probable Cause	Remedy
1. Dust from dull-finished or soft papers.	1. Dust off each sheet of paper before using. Use a better paper stock.
2. Ink is too tacky.	2. Add thin varnish or a non-pick compound.
3. Too much ink.	3. Adjust the ink fountain.
4. Lack of coloring matter in ink.	4. Add transparent white ink to the ink in the fountain.

Piling

Piling occurs when the ink builds up, or piles, on the plate or blanket, or on both.

Probable Cause	Remedy
1. Pigment is not carried by the vehicle.	1. Add a #3 or #4 varnish to the ink.
2. Ink has not been sufficiently ground.	2. Same as above.
3. Ink is over-pigmented.	3. Same as above.

Set-Off

Set-off is a term which indicates that the obverse (other side) of the paper is picking up an image from the sheet below it in the stacker.

Probable Cause	Remedy
1. Excessive ink.	1. Reduce the fountain setting, or use an anti-offset device.
2. Ink lacks a drier.	2. Add a drier. Use an anti-offset device.

Vanishing

Vanishing is the gradual disappearance of some lines and some halftone dots from the plate image.

Probable Cause	Remedy
1. Friction of the form rollers.	1. Readjust the form rollers.
2. Chemical action of certain inks.	2. Add a little stearic acid to the ink.

Sticking

The sheets may stick together in the stacker, or delivery pile. The sheets tear when pulled apart.

Probable Cause	Remedy
1. Ink is being run too heavily.	1. Feed less ink. Use an anti-offset device.
2. Too much drier in the ink.	2. Use less drier. Use an anti-offset device.
3. Paper stock will not absorb the ink.	3. Try a different ink. Run less ink. Use an anti-offset device. Remove the sheets from delivery end in small lifts. Use another kind of paper.
4. Relative humidity is too high.	4. Maintain relative humidity. Add drier to the ink.
5. Moisture content of the paper is too high.	5. Condition paper before using. Adding drier may help.
6. Paper surface too acid.	6. Add drier to the ink.

Picking

Picking is evidenced when hickies (black spots) appear in the blank areas of the printed image and white spots appear in the solid areas.

Probable Cause	Remedy
1. Ink is too tacky. It pulls off particles of paper coating. These stick to plate, blanket, and ink rollers.	1. Reduce tack. Add a thin-bodied varnish or a non-pick compound.
2. Paper stock has too much lint.	2. Clean up press. Use a different paper stock.
3. Stock is poorly coated.	3. Same as above.

Roller Stripping

An uneven printing of the image may be caused by bare sections on the rollers.

Probable Cause	Remedy
1. Fountain solution is too strong. It is getting into the ink.	1. Check pH of fountain solution. Replace if too strong.
2. Ink rollers are glazed.	2. Remove the glaze with pumice and water. Wipe clean; then wash with solvent.

Spraying

The ink may spray over the press, especially at high temperatures.

Probable Cause	Remedy
1. If dots appear on press parts, ink is too thin.	1. Add mixing white and heavy varnish. Use a heavier ink.
2. If little ink lines appear on press parts, ink is too thick.	2. Add thin varnish.
3. Too much ink being fed.	3. Adjust fountain for less ink.
4. Ink rollers set too lightly.	4. Re-set ink rollers.
5. Ink rollers too hard.	5. Replace rollers.
6. Ink rollers swollen.	6. Use a more volatile press wash. Re-set the rollers.
7. Ink rollers too soft.	7. Replace the rollers.

Mottling

Mottling occcurs as a muddy image on the paper. The ink does not cover evenly.

Probable Cause	Remedy
1. Too much reducer in the ink.	1. Add heavy varnish, liquid glass, or magnesia to the ink.

Gray Type

Probable Cause	Remedy
1. Too little pressure.	1. Increase pressure.
2. Too much water.	2. Decrease water.
3. Starved for ink.	3. Increase ink.

Chalking

Chalking is evidenced by the ink on the paper turning dry and powdery. It falls off the sheet as dust.

Probable Cause	Remedy
1. Lack of sufficient binder in the ink.	1. Add heavy varnish or drier to the ink.

Running

The ink is said to run if it penetrates through the paper stock.

Probable Cause	Remedy
1. Varnish in ink is too thin.	1. Add mixing white, or replace the ink.

Hicky Spots

A hicky[2] is a particle of foreign matter which usually attaches to the offset plate or blanket and causes an undesirable black or white spot on the printed image. Such foreign matter may include particles of crumbled ink roller, dried ink skin, fragments of paper coatings, paper cutter dust, or molleton cover fibers.

At first, the foreign particle (hicky) may be ink receptive and thus print an image on the paper. Then as the hicky becomes loaded with fountain solution, the hicky may repel the ink and appear as a white spot on the printed image, Fig. 19-13. In the case of the doughnut hicky (usually caused by a particle of dried ink), the hicky will print black; but the thickness of the hicky prevents the transfer of ink directly around the hicky.

• **Note:** Sometimes the spot on the printed sheet caused by the hicky may itself be referred to as a hicky.

[2] Also spelled hickey; hickie; hickeys; hickies.

Prevention of Hickies

Some measures to prevent hickies are:

1. Avoid ink skinning in cans and in press ink fountain. On the press, use an ink fountain agitator.
2. Use a vacuum sheet cleaner on the press feeder system.
3. Avoid excessive ink tackiness.
4. Be alert to new or to disintegrating molleton rollers which may give off lint and fibers.
5. Replace ink rollers which are cracked and crumbly, especially at ends.
6. Avoid use of excessive anti-offset spray.
7. Arrange to keep ceiling area above press free of dirt, dust, and paint chips.

Removing Hickies

A number of patented devices are employed to remove hickies as they occur while the press is in motion. These include the use of special leather- or plastic-covered rollers at recommended positions in the inking and dampening

Printing Management Magazine

A. HALF MOON

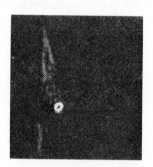

B. DOUGHNUT

C. FEATHER

D. CHIPS

E. TRACKS

F. EGGS

G. LINT

H. BUCKSHOT

Fig. 19-13. Typical hicky spots.

Anchor Chemical Company, Inc.

Fig. 19-14. Anchor "Hicky Picker."

system, a patented hand-held "hicky picker" (Fig. 19-14), and others.

> • **Safety Note:** To prevent injury to hands and the press, the student is cautioned to always *stop the press* before attempting to manually remove any hicky or other foreign particle from the press.

Questions

1. Describe the appearance of good, acceptable printed copies.
2. What are some of the causes of gray, washed-out copies?
3. What is scumming? What conditions might cause it?
4. What is the effect on halftones and fine reverses in the printed copies when running too much ink or when there is too much impression-to-blanket pressure?
5. By inspection of the printed sheets, how can it be determined that there are possible low spots in the blanket?
6. What might cause blurred copies?
7. What causes streaks in printed sheets?
8. What might cause an image to break down while the plate is running?
9. Name some causes of uneven printing.
10. Why might the press be printing out-of-register?
11. Why might the image be extremely light, or not printing at all?
12. Describe tinting. What might cause this?
13. How can piling be detected? What is the remedy?
14. Describe set-off. Give a remedy for it.
15. What is picking? Describe the remedies.
16. Tell how to overcome spraying.
17. What compensations can be made for ink running?
18. What trouble might develop if the ink rollers become glazed?
19. Tell how to prevent hickies and how to remove them.

Problems and Projects

1. Obtain a copy of the press instruction manual. Read it thoroughly.
2. Check the manufacturer's recommendations for the installation of the press.
3. Check the manufacturer's recommendations for the adjustments of the press parts. With the instructor's approval, make any adjustments which are needed.
4. During your actual operation of the press, consult with the instructor about any problems which arise in the actual printing of the sheets. Try to offer solutions for the difficulties.

New Terms

anti-offset	pumice
blind image	residual
chalking	scumming
concentric	stearic
filling up	volatile
mottling	

Chapter 20

Shop Safety

Because of the chemicals and equipment used in photo-offset lithography, certain situations could result in serious injury. To avoid injury and to minimize the effects of accidents, a continuous program of shop safety should be followed.

In all work in the shop, remember that the safety of yourself and of your fellow workers comes first. Naturally, the valuable shop equipment should be protected against damage, but that is secondary to personal safety.

OSHA

Those individuals responsible for the design, construction, direction, maintenance, and operation of graphic arts installations should insure that the physical plant, the working conditions and equipment, and the system for accident-recordkeeping are in full accord with the detailed requirements of the U.S. Department of Labor's Occupational Safety and Health Act (OSHA). Full information on OSHA requirements and recordkeeping can be obtained from the local OSHA office. It is listed in the phone book under *United States Government, Labor Department, Occupational Safety, and Health Administration.*

General Safety Precautions

A standard operating plan should be worked out for the shop so that, in case of injury, the students, instructor, and other school personnel know exactly what should be done and what assistance is available. This plan should be posted in the shop, and all should become familiar with it.

A complete first-aid kit (unlocked) should be available in the shop. This kit should contain instructions for the use of the first-aid materials for the most common accidents. It should be assembled by the school or plant physician, who should instruct the personnel in its use.

Should an accident occur, one person should be sent to phone for assistance, while another is sent immediately on foot. The results of their calls should be reported as soon as they return. The injured person never should be left alone or sent alone anywhere, no matter how slight the injury.

Every injury, no matter how slight, must be referred to the school or plant medical office.

A person never should work alone in the shop or in the darkroom. Neither should persons engage in shopwork when the medical personnel are not on duty in the building, nor when the telephone line to the outside is not functioning. This may be overly cautious, but such rules provide for the safest working conditions.

Shop Layout

The thought for safety should be uppermost when planning and equipping a shop. Otherwise, hazards may be built in.

The room itself should be of ample size with adequate lighting and ventilation. It should be free of posts or columns which prevent supervision of the entire room and all personnel.

Floors should be smooth and unwaxed. A nonskid abrasive paint may be applied to the floor areas around presses and other machinery. The floor in the darkroom should be of a non-electrical-conductive type, and a built-in floor drain should be provided. Absolutely necessary for the darkroom, also, is a strong intake air fan. If doors are used, light-tight louvers are needed to insure good exhaust of fumes.

Entrance doors to the shop should be extra-wide double doors to admit machinery and cartons without dismantling or carrying by hand.

No electrical conduits or other wire raceways should be permitted on the floor. Under-floor raceways should be installed. If this is not possible, raceways should be installed overhead.

Electrical outlets to machines, tables, and to other areas should be located under the items. Sufficient floor and wall outlets should be provided so that extension cords need not be used.

Wash-up and other working sinks should be provided in such locations and number as convenient for the workers. Hot and cold water, paper towels, and suitable hand cleaners should be in constant supply.

Arrangement of equipment should follow straight-line patterns, with ample aisle space between rows to allow the passage of stock carts and drying racks while workers are at their stations. Machinery should be arranged or protected so that no projecting parts, such as arms or gauges, will injure workers or passersby.

Coats, lunches, and books should be stored so as not to litter the work areas.

Where possible, equipment should be anchored to the floor or to the workbench tops.

Storage rooms should be provided for supplies, including paper stock. Storeroom shelving should not exceed six feet in height. Large or heavy items should not be stored above the shelving tops, since these might fall off and cause injury. Heavy or breakable items should be stored on the floor beneath the shelves or on the lowest shelves. A stepladder should be provided for reaching the high items. A chair or a box is *never* used as a substitute.

A telephone must be located in the shop for summoning assistance in case of accident or for reporting a fire.

Tote carts and drying racks should be provided to transport paper stock and heavy items around the shop.

Push brooms, counter dusters (brushes), dust pans, and a mop should be provided to encourage shop cleanliness. A sufficient number of covered, metal trash barrels should be conveniently located near such areas as paper cutter, presses, folder, and sinks.

Safety Tour

New classes or personnel should be conducted on a safety tour as one of the first items of business. The tour should include a visit to each location which might present a possibility of injury. Items that provide for cleanliness, first aid, and safety should be pointed out.

On this trip, the instructor should indicate the inherent dangers of such equipment as the paper cutter, presses, arc lights, and folder. Those persons new to the shop should become familiar with locations of master switch, panic buttons, fire alarm, and fire extinguishers. Students should understand the necessity of turning on the lights when working on machinery, working at stations, or entering storerooms (except where the process prohibits this).

Personal Conduct

No horseplay of any kind can be permitted. There must be no joking around a machine, no tossing of an item to another person, and no splashing of water. Such conduct encourages unsafe habits and is likely to cause serious injury. Unsafe conduct and practices by a student always should be promptly corrected. If these practices persist, the worker should be barred permanently from the shop for the protection of others as well as of the offender.

Permissions

It should be clearly understood that no one is to mix any solutions, handle any chemical, or operate or adjust any equipment unless that person has first been thoroughly instructed in its use and dangers and then is judged competent in its use by the instructor. Even then, permission of the instructor must be obtained in each instance.

Personal Cleanliness

Wash thoroughly with hot water and soap after handling chemicals and solvents, especially before eating lunch. Wash well between the fingers, and wash your face, ears, and neck.

Keep fingers away from the mouth and eyes, and never form the habit of eating while working. You may be eating a little solvent or chemicals each time. The effects of many chemicals, such as lead or carbon tetrachloride, are cumulative over a lifetime.

Change clothing which becomes soiled with press materials — chemicals, solvents, or ink.

Protecting Eyes and Face

Never mix solutions near your eyes and face. Keep them at arm's length. Especially when removing the snap top of a metal container, hold the container on the bench at arm's length, with the face and eyes turned away. This will protect the face and eyes from accidental gushing of the contents.

At all times when mixing or pouring chemicals, wear approved safety glasses. These glasses should be provided individually or by the school or shop and should remain there. There should be one pair for each student or worker, plus a cabinet to facilitate storage and sterilization.

Persons with prescription glasses may wear mask-type goggles over their glasses. Also, organizations selling safety glasses will make up attractive prescription safety glasses at a reasonable price for those students who wish to purchase them. These are intended for everyday general use, and they eliminate the need for the mask-type goggles.

Deliveries

Newly delivered crates and cases should be placed out of the travel lanes, and they should be unpacked with care. Attention should be paid to withdrawing all nails from boards and to properly and promptly disposing of all packing materials. The floor area should be kept clean.

Machinery and heavy items should be moved and installed by the supplier's agents or by the building superintendent's staff.

Crates of supplies, or bundles or skids of paper should be opened on the floor, as delivered. Individual reams or small "lifts" of paper or individual items should be picked out and

stored on shelves. Never demonstrate your strength by attempting to lift heavy items. This is inviting serious injury.

The instructor should demonstrate how to lift heavy items by *leg lifting*, that is, by lifting with the use of the leg muscles rather than the back muscles. The *risks in lifting heavy items* should be emphasized.

Fire Safety

Never smoke in the shop proper or in the darkroom.

Fire extinguishers for extinguishing gasoline, oil, and electrical fires should be furnished as specified by the fire marshal as to type, quantity, and location in the shop. These extinguishers should be inspected and serviced at the required intervals.

At the start of a term of school year, it is a good plan to arrange for an actual demonstration (outdoors) of the use of the fire extinguishers.

All personnel should know the location of the building fire alarm and how it is used. They also should know how to call in a fire alarm.

Periodic fire drills should be scheduled and practiced so that all become used to the procedure of quickly shutting down equipment, closing windows, and, after filing out of a room, closing the doors behind them.

Only those cleaning liquids permitted and approved by the fire marshal should be permitted in the shop — and, then, only in such quantity and in such containers as have been approved.

All-metal containers, with both self-closing top and leg supports, should be provided as the *only receptacles* in which to place cloths which have been used with oils or type- or press-cleaning solvents. The building custodian and the fire marshal should be consulted for the proper disposal of used cloths and dirty press solvents.

Oil and papers should not be allowed to accumulate on the floor around and beneath any equipment. Spilled liquids of all kinds should be wiped up immediately.

When pouring liquids such as solvents and oil from a large container into a smaller container, first place the smaller container in the sink, then pour. This avoids spilling the liquid on the bench, counter, or floor.

Chemicals

Store chemicals on the lowest shelves in their cabinets or racks so that if they fall, spill, or drip, they will then do the least damage.

When preparing solutions, wear safety glasses. Also, pour the *chemical into the water, never pour the water into the chemical.* In this latter situation, a violent reaction may occur! Note, that in published formulas, the ingredients are added in the order in which they appear in the formula.

Label every container into which any chemical preparation is to be placed. If it is a poisonous substance, be certain to plainly mark it POISON. If a container has no label, be suspicious of its contents. Take it to the instructor.

Whenever chemicals and solutions are not being used, return them to the chemical cabinet and *lock* the cabinet.

In handling graduates and jars, extend the little finger underneath the glassware so it will not slip out of your hand. Place containers toward the back of the countertop — not near the front where they might be knocked over or off.

Wear rubber gloves when the hands must come into contact with irritants which might cause dermatitis (skin infection). Some of these irritants are: bichromates (used in coating solutions), etching solutions, cyanides, developers, solvents, and strong cleansers such as lye and gasoline. If any skin blisters or other skin conditions develop, seek a physician's advice.

Never use a food or drink container for mixing, weighing, or storing chemicals. Accidental poisoning might result.

Wear a rubber apron in order to keep chemicals from staining your clothing and possibly reaching your skin.

When mixing or weighing chemicals, keep the fumes and rising dust from entering your nostrils, mouth, and eyes. Do not mix or weigh chemicals in the darkroom unless there is a strong exhaust fan in operation.

Occasionally, it is necessary to smell a chemical solution in order to identify it. When this is necessary, be careful to take only a little sniff — avoid inhaling deeply.

With chemicals, *never guess. Ask questions.* Ignorance can be excused, but not injury!

Solvents

There are many safe commercial solvents for removing ink from type and from offset press rollers, ink fountain, plates, and blankets. Use only those which are approved from samples submitted to the fire marshal's office.

No combustible liquids are to be used in photo, plate, or presswork operations. Avoid using gasoline (flammable and explosive), benzene and toluene (toxic and flammable), and turpentine (toxic).

Kerosene is relatively safe, with a flash point* of about 140°, but is slow-drying and has low solvent power. Still, avoid its use.

Carbon tetrachloride is nonflammable, but its vapors are toxic. It can irritate the skin and eyes. If heated, it can form *phosgene,* a deadly gas! *Never use this!*

Solvents are available which are nonflammable (or have a high flash point — at least 100° or more), are non-toxic, nonirritating to the skin, have a high solvent power, and are noninjurious to rollers and blankets.

Good, safe solvents tend to be expensive, but cost should be secondary to prevention of fire and health hazards. If ratings of a solvent are not available, check its fire safety, toxicity, and flash-point rating with your fire marshal.

A crude, but useful, test for fire-safety (but not toxicity) of a solvent is performed as follows: wipe a steel-top table clean; dip a ½″ × 4″ strip of paper into the solvent (half way); cover and place the can of solvent at a safe distance, then place the solvent-wet paper on the table; touch a lighted match to the wet paper. If the wet paper lights readily, this writer considers the solvent unsafe — not for use in the shop. If the wet paper first must be dried by the match before it will burn, then the solvent is considered safe. (Follow up with a test and ratings by the fire marshal.)

*Flash-point refers to the lowest temperature at which a substance will give off vapors that will support combustion. For example: white gasoline has a flash-point rating of 0°F. This means that at a temperature as low as 0°F., gasoline vapors are so highly dangerous that they will ignite or support combustion.

Adequate room ventilation is absolutely required when using solvents. For example, if a pint of solvent is used in washing a press, a good part of that pint is evaporated into the air for you to breathe (or cause a fire). This is a serious matter, since evaporation may be, at the least, a daily occurrence.

Electrical Equipment

A main disconnect switch (master switch) should be provided so that, when pulled, all power to machinery, appliances, and outlets will be disconnected. This will insure that when the shop is closed down, all power is OFF.

A sufficient number of "panic buttons" (emergency disconnect switches) should be installed at strategic locations throughout the shop. Thus, in event of an emergency, any person may hit the panic button, shutting off all power.

It is both convenient and safe to have a disconnect switch at each piece of machinery or equipment. Such a switch may be locked in the OFF position when desired to prevent use of the equipment or to prevent anyone from turning on the equipment when another is working on it. It is safest to open the disconnect switch before attempting such operations as machine repairs and installing carbons.

Wherever possible, a red pilot light can be installed on equipment, in a prominent location, to show that the item is under power. This is especially desirable for film or print dryers or for any item with heaters.

Damaged or frayed electric cords, plugs, and switches should be promptly replaced, or kept from use until replaced.

All electrical wiring — lighting, power, and appliance cords — should be inspected by the local electrical inspecting authority. All wiring should be checked to make sure that it conforms to existing regulations and that all equipment is adequately grounded.

All convenience outlet wiring and plugs should be converted (if not so already) to the three-prong, "U-ground" type so as to accomodate the three-pronged plugs and cords now in use. This is better than using the three-wire adapters in the plugs.

All appliances with a two-pronged plug and two-wire cord should be rewired with a three-wire cord and three-pronged plug. The extra prong and wire insures that a ground connection is automatically provided when the appliance is plugged in. This eliminates accidental electrical shock from defective equipment.

If possible, equipment should never be located so close to sinks or water pipes that it is possible to touch both at the same time.

Disconnect plugged-in electrical equipment by grasping the plug. Never yank at cords when removing plugs from outlets.

Operating Equipment

Before working on or using any machinery, the worker should tie back long hair, remove obstructive clothing (including gloves), and roll all sleeves above the elbow. Tuck in shirttails. Remove (or tuck in) necktie. All jewelry should be removed from fingers, wrist, and neck. Never carry wiping rags in pockets.

No one should use any equipment unless that person has already proven competency in the safe operation of that particular machine. Always secure the instructor's permission before using any shop machinery.

No person who has been authorized to operate a machine should allow anyone else to take a turn at operating that machine or to make an adjustment to that machine.

Persons observing the operation of a machine must keep back, out of the way, so as not to impede the operator's control of that machine. In addition, the observer must keep *hands off the machine* and *out of the machine.*

Machinery must be operated in the manner and at the speed demonstrated by the instructor. Only authorized adjustments should be performed by the student — and then only in the demonstrated manner. If faster speeds are considered safe for that operator, the instructor will so authorize.

The floor and aisle near a machine must be kept free of oil, paper, or other debris to prevent workers from slipping or falling.

A complete and accessible file should be kept of all service manuals, instruction manuals, parts lists, and lubrication manuals or charts for each piece of equipment in the shop. Personnel should be made to feel free to consult and study these items so as to better understand each piece of equipment and the manufacturer's recommended methods of operation, adjustment, repair, and lubrication.

Offset Presses

One person should be designated by the instructor as the operator of the press. If an assistant is appointed by the instructor, that person must keep hands *off* the switches, handwheel, and controls, and only perform those functions directed by the operator of the press. When changing a blanket, installing a plate, adjusting for register, setting up feeder or delivery, *only the operator* should touch the machine. Otherwise, someone might cause a movement of the machine and catch the operator's hands! Unauthorized persons should keep at a distance from the machine — hands off!

The press should not be operated at any time without the *cylinder guard in place.*

The student should operate the press at the speed designated by the instructor. There is a dangerous tendency for immature people to see how fast a machine will go.

The press should be lubricated, and the rollers and fountain, plate, and blanket washed *only when the press is stopped.* The instructor may demonstrate the use of the roller-cleaning device which is used on a press in motion, but this must be used only under supervision.

With a press in motion, it is easy and *disastrous* to get your fingers, a cloth, or a tool caught in the cylinder gaps, between rollers, or in other moving parts.

There are certain tests and adjustments which are made while the press is in motion. These will be demonstrated by the instructor, who then will check the operator's performance. Only after the instructor's approval of the operator's ability should tests and adjustments be performed on a moving press.

Even though the press is stopped, tools, cloths, or oil cans should not be placed on any part of the machine. They may be forgotten when the press is started and will fall into the machine. A press cabinet or bench should be provided near the press for these items.

For extensive repairs, or when the press is not in shape to be run, the disconnect switch should be pulled and locked *open.*

Stripping Tables

Do not use the stripping table as a depository for school books, lunches, or other items, or as a workbench. Above all, do not lean on it heavily, since the glass top might crash in, inflicting serious injury.

Cut films slowly and carefully, keeping thumb and fingers back from the guiding edge of the straightedge or triangle. This will prevent personal injury.

To prevent scratching the glass top, place a sheet of acetate beneath the film you are cutting.

When through with the knife, blade, or other sharp tool, place it in storage to keep it from playful and irresponsible persons.

Only the instructor should remove the glass table top. A large sheet of glass can cause serious injury if it breaks.

Folding Machine

Keep your hands away from swiftly moving paper edges. Never put your fingers into the rollers of the folding machine. Keep others away from the machine. Make all adjustments and setups only in the manner demonstrated by the instructor.

Card or Film Cutter

The card cutter, or film cutter, is strictly a one-person device. It is most dangerous since it is easy to slice off a thumb! Keep fingers and thumb back from cutting edge, and lock blade in *down* position when through using it.

An L-shaped guard (1″ wide × 5″ high) can be made of metal and installed along the bed, next to the knife edge and raised from the bed with a washer or two at each end. This will prove most effective in keeping fingers away from the knife, yet will allow paper and film to be slid under the guard for cutting.

Paper Cutter

Only one person, designated by the instructor, should operate the cutter at one time. No one else should be allowed to be within reach of the machine. This rule must be observed since the cutting action is swift, and amputation can easily result. Particularly, do not allow another person to assist in holding the paper stock. If you are having difficulties, call the instructor.

The cutter blade (knife) should be removed and installed *only* by the instructor or an approved maintenance mechanic. Watch how the work is done, and observe that the extra knife (or the removed knife) is always bolted into its cover guard to prevent accident when it is being transported to or from the machine. Before transporting the knife, thread two of the cap screws into the threaded holes at opposite ends of the knife. This serves to grip the knife securely to the guard.

Form the habit of using only a wooden ruler or yardstick at the cutter, and keep these and all other items *off* the cutter table. After each cut, dispose of trimmings in the trash barrel. Never leave scraps on the floor.

If you must talk to a person or look elsewhere while operating the cutter, first step away from the machine.

During the entire cutting operation, keep your eyes on the knife and keep *both* hands on the controls! Your instructor will show you how much of a "lift" of paper can be comfortably cut at one time.

Absolutely never attempt to beat or circumvent the safety devices by adapting the controls to be operated with one hand. Doing so is to invite the amputation of one of your hands!

When using a lever cutter, keep both hands on the lever during the entire stroke down and during the entire return of the lever to its extreme UP resting position. A lever cutter should be fitted with a two-hand safety control lever. When through using the cutter, run the clamp all the way down.

When through using both the power- and lever-operated cutters, take a large (2″ × 4″) block of wood — cut to the length of the bed — and place it in front of the knife on the bed of the machine. This will keep prying fingers out.

In handling the paper, never slide your hands along the edges since they can cut like a razor! Likewise, never experiment with testing the sharpness of the knife by running your finger along the edge. You certainly will be cut!

• **Remember:** With the paper cutter, an accident usually means *complete amputation of fingers or hands*. Be sure to observe all safety rules.

Exposure Devices

The lights (lamps) in cameras and platemakers run at high temperatures. Let them cool off before trying to change them. Because of the high voltage and exposed electrical parts in some platemakers, *always disconnect the platemaker* by pulling out the plug before attempting to change carbons or lamps or to make repairs to the underneath mechanism.

Avoid a blast of light into the eyes from any exposure device, since this may temporarily impair your vision. *Never, never* look directly at the light of the arc lights! This could cause serious and *permanent* damage to the eyes. It is a good idea to look away when turning on arc lights or other exposure light sources.

Stapler and Stitcher

Operate the stapling and stitching machine slowly enough so that you keep your fingers out of the open throat of the machine. In this way, you will avoid puncturing your fingers.

Do not allow another person to touch the machine or its controls when you are loading, setting up, or operating the stapler.

Paper Drill

Expect the drill to be hot when you remove it. Therefore, use suitable precautions to keep from burning your fingers.

Do not allow another person near the controls when you are setting up or operating the drill. Someone could drill through your fingers.

Keep fingers away from the drill head when drilling. Pull the plug when setting in a new drill or attachments. When finished, remove the drill or attachments to keep the curious from injury.

Using Small Tools Safely

More serious cuts, punctures, and skinned knuckles are caused by improper use of small tools than by that of power tools and machines.

To avoid dangerous consequences of improvising, the proper common tools should be provided for repairs, adjustments, unpacking, uncrating, and so on. The list should include a claw hammer, ball peen hammer, machinist's vise secured to the bench, drift punches, center punch, several types and sizes of screwdrivers, Allen wrenches, open-end wrenches, box wrenches, socket wrenches, tin snips, and knives. Other tools should be purchased as the need arises, so that the proper tool, in the proper size, is always available.

Instruction in the proper use of hand tools should be given. Here are some points to remember:

1. Wrenches should preferably be pulled. If pushed, keep the hand open, palm forward, to avoid skinning knuckles.
2. Two hands should be used on a screwdriver — one on the handle and one at the blade end — to keep the tool from jumping out and stabbing oneself or others.
3. In passing a sharp, or pointed, tool to another person, offer it in a vertical position, point down, so the person may grasp it by the handle.
4. If an edged or sharp tool is dropped, do not try to catch it. Let it fall.
5. Never rest an oil can (hand oiler) on the floor, a chair, or bench top. This is an invitation to injury. Store it on a shelf beneath the bench top.
6. In lubricating a machine, hold a cloth next to the oil hole to wipe any excess oil which might otherwise drip onto the floor or other parts of the machine.
7. Wear goggles (safety glasses) when hammering or chipping on metal.

Safeguard

As a member of an organized personnel system an instructor is bound morally and legally to be reasonably prudent in maintaining safe working conditions. If any unsafe conditions exist, or if any are brought to the instructor's attention, immediate steps should be taken to eliminate or correct them. Where necessary, requisition safe repair, replacement, or installation and keep a carbon copy of that requisition as a safeguard against possible charges of negligence. Also, keep a copy of any accident report, together with names of witnesses, dates, and circumstances.

Questions

1. What is the prime object of a program of shop safety?
2. In case of serious accident, why are two persons designated to summon assistance? Why would only one be insufficient?
3. Why should an injured person not be left alone or not be allowed to go alone to the medical center?
4. Why is it dangerous for a person to work in the shop when alone? When the medical center personnel are not on duty?
5. What danger is there in having an electrical conduit (pipe) on the floor from the wall to a machine?
6. What danger is there in storing heavy items on top of the shelving in the storerooms? In using a chair or a box for a ladder?
7. Why is it necessary to obtain permission before mixing chemicals or operating any machine?
8. What happens to a person in the shop who indulges in horseplay?
9. Why is smoking prohibited in the shop and darkroom?
10. What eye-protection measures should be observed when mixing chemicals?
11. What kind of a container is considered the only safe one for oily or dirty type-cleaning and press-cleaning cloths?
12. What danger is there in allowing oil or papers on the floor?
13. What is meant by "leg lifting"?
14. Why should chemicals be stored on the lowest shelves?
15. How would you turn in a fire alarm in your building?
16. What substances in your shop might cause dermatitis?
17. How do you minimize chances of contracting dermatitis?
18. Name four liquids which are unsafe to use as press solvents.
19. What is the "flash point" of a substance?

20. What is a "panic button"? When should it be used? By whom?
21. What precautions as to personal dress should be observed before operating any machinery? Why?
22. What are the conditions of instruction, demonstration, and permission which must be observed before a person may operate a machine?
23. What dangers are present for the operator when an unauthorized person touches or leans on the machine or on its controls?
24. List eleven safety rules which must be observed when using paper cutters.
25. What serious injury may be expected if the safety precautions for the paper cutter are not observed?
26. In mixing solutions, why must the acid (chemical) be poured *into* (added to) the water?
27. List the recommendations for personal cleanliness.
28. What danger is there in looking at a lighted arc lamp?

Problems and Projects

1. With the help of the instructor and the school administration, develop a standard procedure in case of an accident in the shop. Have this plan printed up and copies posted in the shop near the first-aid kit, telephone, and near possible sources of accident.
2. Plan and print up lists of safety rules for each machine or area. Post these conspicuously.
3. Working with the school or shop physician, compile a first-aid kit for the shop. Requisition the needed items. Mount the kit and keep it unlocked.
4. Develop first-aid procedures for each kind of accident which might occur in the shop, such as burns, electrical shock, cuts

(bleeding), and poisoning. Work in cooperation with a physician. Print these procedures for distribution, along with a copy at the first-aid kit.
5. Plan a "first-aid day" when you and your classmates demonstrate first-aid procedures for each type of accident possible in your shop. If feasible, invite the school or plant physician to be present.
6. Work up a plan of procedure to follow in case of fire in your shop. Print up the procedure and post copies conspicuously. Discuss this procedure in a class session.
7. Invite the fire marshal to talk to your group on fire-drill procedure, how to report fires, how to prevent them, and the proper use of fire extinguishers.
8. Develop and initiate a *fire and safety patrol system* in which each person is responsible for safe working conditions for a period of time.
9. List items and situations which should be checked daily by the fire and safety patrol.
10. Requisition any items needed to promote fire and personal safety in the shop. Ask for your instructor's advice. Keep a copy of the requisition.
11. Invite the local electrical inspection authority to your shop to inspect the power and lighting wiring, including all appliances and equipment.
12. Prepare a requisition for electrical work to be done that will comply with any recommendations of the electrical inspector. Keep a copy of the requisition.

New Terms

benzene	OSHA
carbon tetrachloride	phosgene
conduit	strategic
cyanide	toluene
depository	toxic
dermatitis	ventilation
grounded	

Legal Restrictions on Copying

As you have learned, photo-lithography utilizes in many cases the photographic copying of existing printed work for the preparation of plates for reproductions. Therefore, it should be understood that there are certain legal restrictions as to what may or may not be reproduced.

It is impossible, in this book, to give an all-inclusive treatment of this legal problem. If there is any doubt as to the legality of copying any matter, it may be best to seek legal advice on the specific problem. Some general observations on the subject of copying are given here.

Copyrighted Materials

A copyright is a form of protection given by the law of the United States to the authors of literary, dramatic, musical, artistic, and other similar works. The owner of the copyright has the exclusive right to copy that work, and to sell or distribute copies of it.

Copyright Notice

As a general rule, the copyright notice should consist of three elements:

1. The word *Copyright*, the abbreviation *Copr.*, or the symbol ©.
2. The name of the copyright owner.
3. The year date of publication.

The above three elements should appear together on the copies as "Copyright John Doe 1979." Normally, for a book, this notice appears on the page following the title page. In other works, the copyright symbol may be accompanied by the owner's initials, monogram, mark, or symbol if the name appears elsewhere on the work.

Items That May be Copyrighted

Among others, the following items may be copyrighted: books, pamphlets, catalogs, leaflets, cards, single pages, tabular matter, newspapers, magazines, bulletins, maps, drawings, paintings, photographs, musical compositions, greeting cards, labels, picture postcards, filmstrips, and motion pictures.

Items That May Not Be Copyrighted

In general, these items are not eligible for copyright: time cards, graph paper, calendars, account books, diaries, height and weight charts, tape measures, rulers, schedules of sporting events, names, titles, slogans, familiar symbols, familiar designs, and mere listing of contents or ingredients.

Duration of Copyright

On January 1, 1978, a new copyright statute went into effect. Known as Title 17 of the United States Code, it makes changes in the length of copyright protection. Under the old law, an original copyright lasted for a first term of 28 years and could be renewed for another 28 years.

• **Note:** The following is a very brief summary of the provisions of Title 17. For more complete information, write to the Copyright

Office, Library of Congress, Washington, D.C. 20559, or seek legal assistance.

Under the new law, works copyrighted before 1978, and in their first term of copyright, are protected now for 75 years. (This includes a first term of 28 years, plus a renewal term of 47 years).

Works originally copyrighted before 1950 and renewed before 1978 are automatically extended to last for a total term of 75 years (a first term of 28 years and a renewal term of 47 years).

Copyrights in their first 28-year term on January 1, 1978 may be renewed at the proper time for an additional term of 47 years.

A work that is created (fixed in tangible form for the first time) after January 1, 1978 is automatically protected from the moment of its creation. It is given a term lasting for the author's lifetime plus 50 years after death.

Common-Law Literary Property

Unpublished maps, books, photographs, and other works are protected by state laws against copying. This protection begins when the works are created and ends when the works are published for sale or distribution (even free distribution).

Permission for Reproduction

If the owner of the copyright can be ascertained, permission in *writing* should be secured from this person before copying is done. This permission should indicate the nature and extent of the proposed copying, the exact title or designation of the work from which the copying is to be done, and the purpose to which the reproduced copies are to be put, such as for sale, schoolroom use, free distribution, or textbook.

If there is any doubt whatsoever as to whether or not a work is copyrighted, the safest and most courteous method of procedure is to write the owner and request the permission outlined above. In most cases the authors of the work involved will make satisfactory arrangements, and are often very happy to cooperate. If permission is granted, the copied work should carry a courtesy or credit line (as specified by the author or copyright owner of the work) so that the source of the material is acknowledged.

Photographs for Advertising

Any photographs that show clearly recognizable faces of persons cannot be used for advertising purposes without first obtaining written consent from the persons involved. If minors are concerned, permission must be obtained from their legal guardians. To do otherwise may result in a claim of invasion of privacy and a demand for reparations from the parties concerned.

Counterfeiting

Any request for printing or photographing, in part or whole, or the supplying of materials for any work which may violate or seem to violate any part or the entirety of any of the regulations quoted below should be reported at once to the Department of the Treasury, United States Secret Service, Washington, D.C. 20223, for clarification and investigation. If the proposed work is legally permissible, you will be so informed. If it is illegal, you will be far better off having had no part of its execution. Never proceed on the assumption that something similar to what is requested has been publicly distributed with permission. Prior violations may have gone unnoticed or unknown, or they may be under investigation at the time.

U.S. Code of Law, Title 18, Sec. 474. Plates or Stones for Counterfeiting U.S. Obligations or Securities

"Whoever, having control, custody or possession of any plate, stone or other thing, or any part thereof, from which has been printed, or which may be prepared by direction of the Secretary of the Treasury for the purpose of printing, any obligation or other security of the United States, uses such plate, stone, or other thing, or any part thereof, or knowingly suffers the same to be used for the purpose of printing any such or similar obligation or other security, or any part thereof, except as may be printed for the use of the United States by order of the proper officer thereof; or

"Whoever makes or executes any plate, stone or other thing in the likeness of any plate designated for the printing of such obligation or other security; or

"Whoever sells any such plate, stone or other thing, or brings into the United States any such plate, stone or other thing, except under the direction of the Secretary of the Treasury or other proper officer, or with any other intent, in either case, that such plate, stone or other thing be used for the printing of the obligations or other securities of the United States; or

"Whoever has in his control, custody, or possession any plate, stone, or other thing in any manner made after or in the similitude of any plate, stone or other thing, from which any such obligation or other security has been printed, with intent to use such plate, stone or other thing, or to suffer the same to be used in forging or counterfeiting any such obligation or other security, or any part thereof; or

"Whoever has in his possession or custody, except under authority from the Secretary of the Treasury or other proper officer, any obligation or other security made or executed, in whole or in part, after the similitude of any obligation or other security issued under the authority of the United States, with intent to sell or otherwise use the same; or

"Whoever prints, photographs or in any other manner makes or executes any engraving, photograph, print or impression in the likeness of any such obligation or other security, or any part thereof, or sells any such engraving, photograph, print or impression, except to the United States or brings into the United States, any such engraving, photograph, print or impression, except by direction of some proper officer of the United States; or

"Whoever has or retains in his control or possession, after a distinctive paper has been adopted by the Secretary of the Treasury for the obligations and other securities of the United States, any similar paper adapted to the making of any such obligation or other security, except under the authority of the Secretary of the Treasury or some other proper officer of the United States —

"Shall be fined not more than $5,000 or imprisoned not more than fifteen years, or both."

U.S. Code of Laws, Title 18, Section 475 (as Amended). Imitating U.S. Obligations or Securities; Advertisements

"Whoever designs, engraves, prints, makes or executes, or utters, issues, distributes, circulates or uses any business or professional card, notice, placard, circular, handbill or advertisement in the likeness or similitude of any obligation or security of the United States issued under or authorized by any Act of Congress or writes, prints or otherwise impresses upon or attaches to any such instrument, obligation or security, or any coin of the United States, any business or professional card, notice or advertise-

ment, or any notice of advertisement whatever, shall be fined not more than $500."

U.S. Code of Laws, Title 18, Section 481. Plates or Stones for Counterfeiting Foreign Obligations or Securities

"Whoever within the United States except by lawful authority, controls, holds, or possesses any plate, stone, or other things, or any part thereof, from which has been printed or may be printed any counterfeit note, bond, obligation, or other security, in whole or in part, of any foreign government, bank, or corporation, or uses such plate, stone, or other thing, or knowingly permits or suffers the same to be used in counterfeiting such foreign obligations, or any part thereof; or

"Whoever, except by lawful authority, makes or engraves any plate, stone, or other thing in the likeness or similitude of any plate, stone, or other thing designated for the printing of the genuine issues of the obligations of any foreign government, bank, or corporation; or

"Whoever, except by lawful authority, prints, photographs, or makes, executes, or sells any engraving, photograph, print, or impression in the likeness of any genuine note, bond, obligation, or other security, or any part thereof, of any foreign government, bank, or corporation; or

"Whoever brings into the United States any counterfeit plate, stone, or other thing, engraving, photograph, print, or other impressions of the notes, bonds, obligations, or other securities of any foreign government, bank, or corporation. —

"Shall be fined not more than $5,000 or imprisoned not more than five years, or both."

U.S. Code of Laws, Title 18, Section 15. Obligation or Other Security of Foreign Government

"The term 'obligation or other security of any foreign government' includes, but is not limited to, uncancelled stamps, whether or not demonetized."

U.S. Savings Bonds

It is permitted to make, dispose of, and use illustrations of savings bonds for publicity purposes in connection with the campaign for the sale of savings bonds: Provided, that all illustrations of savings bonds shall be in black and white and shall be of a size less than three-fourths or more than one and one-half, in linear dimension, of each part of any matter so illustrated, and that the negatives and plates used in making the illustrations shall be destroyed after their final use in accordance with Section 504, Title 18, U.S. Code.

U.S. Coins

Public Law 79, 82nd Congress, approved July 16, 1951, removed the restrictions on photographing and printing illustrations of United States coins. Photographs and illustrations are now permitted.

U.S. Postage Stamps

Black and White Illustrations.   Cancelled and uncancelled United States postage stamps may be illustrated in any size in black and white in articles, books, journals, newspapers, or albums for philatelic, educational, historical, and newsworthy purposes.

No individual facsimiles of United States postage stamps are permitted. No individual photographs are permitted except glossy prints necessary to reproduce the illustrations in publications.

Colored Illustrations.   Cancelled and uncancelled United States postage stamps may be illustrated in color in articles, books, journals, newspapers, or albums for philatelic, educational, historical, and newsworthy purposes. Illustrations in color of uncancelled United States postage stamps must be of a size less than three-fourths or more than one and one-half in linear dimension of each part of the stamps illustrated. Colored illustrations of cancelled United States postage stamps may be in any size. The cancelled stamps illustrated must bear an official cancellation mark. That is, the stamps must have been used for postage.

Foreign Postage Stamps

Black and White Illustrations.   Black and white illustrations of uncancelled foreign postage stamps in any size are permitted for philatelic, educational, historical, and newsworthy purposes in articles, books, journals, newspapers, and albums. Black and white illustrations of cancelled foreign postage stamps are permissible in any size and for any purpose.

As in the case of United States stamps, no individual facsimiles or photographs of foreign postage stamps are permitted, except glossy prints necessary to reproduce the illustrations in publications.

Colored Illustrations.   Uncancelled foreign postage stamps may be illustrated in color in articles, books, journals, newspapers, or albums for philatelic, educational, historical, and newsworthy purposes, provided such illustrations are of a size less than three-fourths or more than one and one-half in linear dimension of each part of the stamps illustrated. Colored illustrations of cancelled foreign postage stamps are permissible in any size and for any purpose. The cancelled foreign postage stamps illustrated must bear an official cancellation mark. That is, the stamps must have been used for postage.

United States and Foreign Revenue Stamps

Printed illustrations of United States revenue stamps are permitted under the same conditions and for the same purposes as illustrations of United States postage stamps, except that colored illustrations of United States revenue stamps are not permitted.

Printed illustrations of foreign revenue stamps are permitted on the same conditions and for the same purposes as illustrations of foreign postage stamps. Colored illustrations, but only of cancelled foreign revenue stamps, are permissible.

Miscellaneous Documents

The following group of items may not be reproduced in photographic or printed form:

1. Drivers' licenses.
2. Amateur radio operators' licenses.
3. Classified government documents, maps, photographs, drawings, and publications.
4. Military registration cards.
5. Badges, identification cards, passes or insignia carried by members of Federal Departments and Bureaus, such as F.B.I., Treasury, Army, or of similar branches of state and local law enforcement officials.

Illegal and Offensive Material

It is wise to seek advice from the proper governmental agencies and from your legal consultants in cases where there may be possible violation or conflict with copyright laws and laws regulating the reproduction of stamps, bonds, currency, or other items controlled by the Treasury and its Secret Service. Advice should also be sought in cases where you are asked to print or otherwise aid in the printing or publication of any literature, drawings, or photographs which may be offensive, immoral, or detrimental to our form of government, its officials, our accepted moral code, or to any group of people because of their race or religious beliefs.

Remember — almost every invention in the graphic arts industry, from its very beginnings, had its inception in the need to further our methods of communication for the cause of religion, education, and liberty.

Questions

1. Can you photograph and reproduce anything you please? Explain.
2. What is a "copyright"?
3. Where does the copyright notice normally appear in a book?
4. What privileges does the copyright owner enjoy?
5. If a work is created in tangible form for the first time after January 1, 1978, how long does its copyright run?
6. What is common-law literary property?
7. When is common-law literary property no longer protected by state law?
8. Tell how you would go about securing permission to reproduce copyrighted material, and how you would credit its source.
9. What are the prohibitions on reproducing paper money?
10. What does "in the similitude" mean in the law (Title 18)?
11. Besides the prohibition on the actual printing of United States money (currency), what finer restrictions are there?
12. What regulations are there concerning the printing of illustrations of U.S. Savings Bonds?
13. Are you allowed to print illustrations of coins? Explain.
14. Tell under what conditions illustrations of United States postage stamps may be printed.
15. List some miscellaneous documents which may not be printed.

Problems and Projects

1. Secure for your shop library a copy of the copyright laws.
2. Secure for your shop library copies of the laws concerning the reproduction of money, coins, stamps, documents.
3. Arrange with your instructor to invite a speaker from the Treasury Department to speak about counterfeiting to the class or to a school assembly.
4. Make up a small display showing permissible forms of reproductions of U.S. postage stamps for philatelic purposes.
5. Make up a small display of forms of copyright notice. Label each to indicate any unusual items. If you can, include an illustration which carries a credit line.
6. List some inventions in the graphic arts which were primarily developed for the dissemination of religious literature.

New Terms

counterfeit	philatelic
custody	placard
duration	reparations
forging	similitude
monogram	tangible

INDEX

Colophon

Since **Photo-Offset Fundamentals** is a product of offset printing, both inside and out, the production details may have special interest.

Typography

Basic Type Face — Mallard (also known as Melior), originally designed by Herman Zapf in 1948.
- 10/12 on 18 picas for straight matter
- 8/9 for footnotes
- 8/9 Bold for figure captions and table numbers

Contrasting Face — Antique Olive designed by Roger Excoffon in 1960's.
- 10/16 Bold for main-main heads
- 10/16 Medium for main heads
- 10/14 Regular for subheads
- 10/10 Medium for folios
- 8/10 Regular for running heads

Featured Face — Antique Olive Compact
- 36 pt. for chapter titles

Composition

Keyboarded on Compugraphic Editwriter 7500 with storage on floppy disc at Gorman's Typesetting, Bradford, Illinois.

Layout

Page mechanicals prepared by publisher using reproduction proofs, stats of line art, and Parapaque® windows for halftones.

Photography

Four-up negatives on Kodalith Ortho Type 3 film, shot on a Robertson 31-inch Jupiter camera with Xenon lighting. Halftones shot on thin-base film with a 133-line gray contact screen having an elliptical dot.

Stripping

Reversal negatives made from working negatives, then contacted to platemaking positives on Kodalith Ortho Type 3 film. Press imposition for 16- and 32-page signatures. Film mounted on Mylar sheets and pin-registered. Byrum screen tints added.

Platemaking

Platemaking positives exposed to Western Litho ball-grain plate using violux by R. R. Donnelley & Sons, Inc. in Willard, Ohio. Plates for four-color case were exposed to Western Litho ball-grain plate at 1/32 of a second, 5000 kilowatts, using Addulux step-and-repeat machine.

Presswork

Body printed on Cottrell four-unit web offset press on 50# Mead Publisher's Matte. 32 pages of four-color and 368 pages of one-color. Case printed on Appleton Ascot Smooth Finish on Miehle four-color sheet-fed press. Color progression: Y-C, M-Bk. Caseside Mylar laminated.

Cover

Photo by Jim Coventry, Coventry Creative Graphics, Peoria, Illinois. Type photoset by Gorman's Typesetting, Bradford, Illinois. Four-color separations made by R. R. Donnelley & Sons Company, Crawfordsville, Indiana.

Binding

Smyth-sewn in 5/16's and 10/32's. Bound by R. R. Donnelley & Sons Company, Willard, Ohio to meet all specifications recommended by NASTA.